JOHN MISTLETOE

John Mistletoe

CHRISTOPHER MORLEY

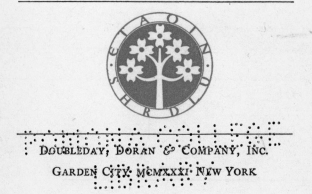

DOUBLEDAY, DORAN & COMPANY, INC.
GARDEN CITY· MCMXXXI· NEW YORK

H. F. M. *knows best how little this tells; but for* T. W. L. *it might not have been told at all; and* J. J. H. *never failed to say the right word, when it was most needed.*

1928–1931

"GOD keep me from ever completing anything. This whole book is but a draught—nay, but the draught of a draught. Oh, Time, Strength, Cash, and Patience!"—MOBY DICK.

"WHAT a strange world, where one has to apologize for loving people."
　　　　—LETTERS FROM WALDEN POND

SHE lifted her exquisite hand in the queerest little shudder of delight and dismay. "But this," she said, "is horrid cultivated stuff."
Presently she looked up again. "I was wrong. I apologize."
　　　　—PORTRAIT OF A LADY OF QUALITY

CONTENTS

"JUVENILE ROBUST"

TO BE deeply rooted in a place that has meaning is perhaps the best gift a child can have. If that place has beauty and a feeling of permanence it may suggest to him unawares that sense of identity with this physical earth which is the humblest and happiest of life's intuitions.

Over the lawns of Haverford in the late '90s there shone the cheery simplicity of an older mode. A college of only a hundred students, which had outgrown some of the anxious problems of its youth, still combined the traditional plainness of its Quaker inheritance with an undergraduate life of busy hilarity and horseplay. "How like an English nobleman's park!" was once the naive exclamation of a British visitor on seeing the college's beautiful domain; and indeed there was a certain agreeable paradox in finding these young Pennsylvania puritans revelling at their ease in a landscaped arcadia worthy of the Duke of Marlborough. Philadelphia Friends have never allowed their ethical "plainness" to interfere with carnal comfort, and a Haverford boyhood's earliest impression was quite likely to be of the rich feastings

3

in front of Founders Hall at Commencement time. Under the bronze glimmer of copper beech trees the long tables were set out. When were there ever such great bowls of strawberries and chicken salad; such largesse of ice cream? On the cricket field were flannels and scarlet blazers; tally-ho parties came driving up the noble avenue of elms; through the long sweetness of a June day would continue the annual match with the University of Pennsylvania, with interval for al fresco lunch. Cricket is not a "game," it is always a "match;" and it is by no means devoid of occasion for hardihood. Perhaps it is not a sport apt for the American temper, but if the day comes when leisurely tourneys no longer pattern Cope Field with white figures, and no connoisseurs sit contentedly smoking on the long weatherstained benches in the shade, something of great charm will have passed away. In the general herd stampede of American life Haverford was always just a little different— not in the least by ostentation or intent; she happened to grow that way.

So it is that the young Mistletoe of whom I write can never be grateful enough for that early glimpse of an arcadian quietness. It is an instructive experience to have grown up astraddle of two epochs. It is interesting to remember the days when there were no taxis at the Haverford station, but old McGurk with his queer-smelling hack; when small

4

boys ran yelling across the campus to see the first horseless carriage; when the Main Line trains were still drawn by those dainty P. R. R. locomotives with the rakish cow-catcher and a slender funnel with a fluted rim; when elderly Friends had their coat collars cut away at the back of the neck, collars and lapels being considered Babylonish. (John Woolman sailed in the steerage of the ship *Mary and Elizabeth*, instead of in the cabin, because he found in the vessel's cabin quarters "sundry sorts of carved work and imagery," which put his mind "under a deep exercise.") It is always the inconsistencies of any doctrine that are most lovable. It gives one pleasure to remember that in the era of Haverford's greatest rigor, when music and fiction were stringently excluded from official countenance, the college built Barclay Hall (1877). For purposes of worldly flourish they abandoned the fine old simplicity of Founders Hall and went in for a vast barrack of clumsy pseudo-Gothic bravado. It even had a spire, the thing which more than anything else caused George Fox epilepsies. This edifice, named for a worthy old Scottish apologist, was so greatly admired that the same architect was later engaged to start the career of Bryn Mawr College with an even more sinister nondescript, Taylor Hall. In course of time Barclay Hall has grown well-loved for its jocund associations, but it exists as a large reminder that

5

even men of immaculate piety are not always delicate in taste.

So much of living is irrelevant, and the phases of it that we learn to have deep dear meaning seem to arrive perilously haphazard. It can hardly be amiss to look inward upon our only sure treasure and try to discern what were the flashes of quintessence. It implies a very profound humility, and an incurable passion for living; but more than that it lays itself upon one by unexplained necessity. In old days of Friends' meeting one sitting in the silence who felt himself moved by some "concern" was supposed to stand and deliver. Just so Mistletoe feels, and has long felt, a concern to explore the memories of thirty years or so and say, This was beautiful; this had a meaning. As he approaches forty (wondering why Thackeray in his ballad represents that age as one of such settled sobriety?) he is acutely aware of the fantastic antinomy between life as it is actually experienced and life as reported to us by the accredited expounders. At that period one should be ready to begin to try to educate himself in the things that matter. No wonder, then, that for his own composure he hankers to set down some hard-won inflexions from his own grammar of surprise. The paradigms that are most beautiful can scarce be discussed in prose. (It is not that poets are granted greater license; it is that they have fewer—and

6

more understanding—readers.) But the time will come when none will be able to put down for you these flairs and furies of your own. Once in the humble little Friends' meetinghouse in Oxford a shy homely girl in a plain tweed suit suddenly got up in the silent sitting. It was a clear spring forenoon, with that moist English savor in the air. Her voice trembled with terror, but she managed to say "I'm thinking of the sky and the trees and the shadows of the trees, and the wind, and the smell of everything." She sat down, subsiding into a shaken privacy of tears; but we understood. Of all the outgivings he heard in his years of Friends' meeting, Mistletoe remembers that one best.

It would be hard to imagine a happier childhood. He did not often in later years allow himself to think back about it, so far from those placid scenes had subsequent preoccupations led him. Save only that there was no salt water near, Haverford was a perfect place for such purposes as his. It is a lively suburb now, but in the 'nineties it was still country. West of the college tall regiments of corn stretched in rustling files toward sunset; all was wood and farmland to the immortal water of Darby Creek. Oh Darby, unspoiled even now, is there none to celebrate you but he?

Haverford was provincial then in the best sense, a social and sectarian integer, drawing its students mostly from a solid (and probably rather unimaginative) swath of Quaker families. One would not, and did not, expect any rare passion for intellectual frenzy in so placid a commune. But in subtle ways one felt influences at work. It was good to come into life in that little world while Isaac Sharpless was its presiding officer. He was a man in somewhat the antique mould, with almost an Abraham Lincoln flavor in his gravity and his humor. It takes one back to excellent simplicities to remember that his first call to the vocation of teaching came to him when he was ploughing in a field near Westtown, where he was waited upon by a committee of Westtown School. Nor does one forget his telling how in the difficult days of his early service at Haverford, for relief from anxieties he would retire at night to the college observatory to study the stars. That little domed retreat, camped in a cluster of confidential pine trees and suggesting a mystic Oriental shrine, was a place of romantic riddle to Mistletoe from earliest days. And somehow he connects Isaac Sharpless's evenings there with a bequest long afterward noted in the college catalogue, "to encourage the ennobling study of the heavens."

Remembered impressions of childhood are under suspicion; it is difficult not to interpolate into them significances we became aware of later. But it is important to reintegrate what one may of the pure

artistic permeability of that prime. I believe all
the little group of urchins who grew together on
the college lawns (the Haverford faculty was always comfortably proliferous) early relished a notion of their sylvestered world as a place apart. In
the Little School (as it was always known), a
yellow cottage by the meeting house, or in over-
heard conversation of their elders, these small fry
gathered a vague idea of the modest but honorable
traditions of their birthplace. James Russell Lowell
had visited there, yes, and even (I think) Matthew Arnold; and the body of Lincoln had passed
by our own grounds on the way to burial in
Illinois. These legends certainly meant less than
the Swarthmore Game; but they were in the back-
ground of one's pride. More important still was the
realization, felt in the passive acceptance of non-
age, that there was beauty on that lawn. Few
places can show such comely sweeps of turf and
shrubbery. To begin life there was to learn later
that almost every bush and tree had unconsciously
become a personal friend. The old mulberry by
the ruined arch, the prostrate mock-orange tree
below the cricket-shed, the tall pines by Chase
Hall, the feathery clumps of pampas grass, the
copper beeches, the fallen flukes of mapleseeds, all
such became part of one's innocence. In spring
there was the constant drowsy whirr of the big
lawnmower, drawn by a horse who wore huge

9

leather slippers on his feet to spare the sod. Nor he, nor the rhododendrons, nor anything else in that perfect picture, were in vain. One had an idea of peace. It would not be until many years later one might divine an almost ominous loveliness in some lights and shades. Under the copper beeches, in Pennsylvania's reckless sun, there is a lustred shimmer that knows no argument, "such tawny shining as gilds the gipsy's knees." The library, brave outwork of austerity, stands on its green terrace; its long lancet windows, fringed with creeper, have the right monastic shape, to admit the maximum of light with the least of worldly view; but the whiff of grassy air comes through to mingle with the savor of old leathers. Rambling in those groves you will sometimes be aware that the woodlands of Penn have never been wholly won back from wilderness. Whatever that visitor may have said, those are not the tame trees of "an English nobleman's park," they are still forest timber, and sometimes the voice they whisper is not of Penn but of Pan.

2

CHIEF necessity for the artist is "imaginative dominion over experience," wrote Pearsall Smith in one of his porcelain essays—that same Pearsall Smith whom Mistletoe always proudly alludes to as a fellow-Haverfordian. Truly only the greatest intuitions, at the full flex of their power, can dominate the spin of private experience as the lumberman foots the twirling log; can steer and drive it home to some perfect niche of art. But perhaps to be brought up from first beginnings in ligature with a settled institution may at least tend toward some awareness of stability. In that childish kosmos there were many subconscious intimations of a mood one can only describe as piety, by which one means a sense of respect. There was Old Caleb, the superannuated college facto-tum. He still performed easy tasks about the grounds, carried up the mail bag from the post-office or drove the baggage wagon. To see that ven-erable figure moving about the lawn on a cane or sitting as still as Buddha under a tree, respected by all and even addressing the president of the col-lege as "Isaac," was to receive some inkling of the dignity of age and the continuity of human effort. So also the extraordinary beauty of old Quaker ladies seen in "First Day Meeting," lovely as pigeons in their grey bonnets, was a thrill to every nerve of admiration. There were never lovelier faces or kinder hearts. Something in that guileless way of life kept the soft color of youth on those radiant features, and surely no costume was ever so perfect to set off woman's tender charm. Must Mistletoe confess that not until many years later, in the "Tarara Boomdeay" chorus of *The Black Crook* (irreverently garbed in Quaker grey) did he find quite the same aesthetic thrill? To watch those countenances in meeting was irresistible. Perhaps they were sometimes devoid of anything legitimately describable as thought, but they were rapt in a demure harmony of innocent benediction.

What a purely delicious selfishness there is in trying to recapture the lucid impressionism of childhood, which was untainted by any of the sophistications of morality or judgment. And how strange it would be to walk, now, through the little wood of chestnut trees, over the bridge, and up the Meeting House lane. It would best be done quite alone, for there is no game more celestially solitary than the hide and seek we play with the child we remember. At least three ingredients of reminiscence would be the alarming white bulldog at the gate just over the bridge, an almost equally disturbing small schoolmate with very liquid brown eyes, and a rambling tramp smitten by a soft apple thrown with good aim—and then wildly fled from. Perhaps it was that path through the woods, strewn in those days with chestnut burrs, that suggested young Mistletoe's first venture in fiction. It was called The Story of a Woodcutter. Whether written by native ambition or at the insistence of teachers no one can now say; but he was called upon to read it aloud, chapter by chapter, in the classroom; a task faced with a mingling of pride and shame such as still occasionally recurs.

It is curious, Mistletoe here bids me interpolate, with what instinctive wariness one treads the rustling path of memory, not to scare up any irreparable secrets—either one's own or those of others. The task I set myself in deciphering the Mistletoe palimpsest requires a difficult double fidelity: fidelity to his own imagination, and equal fidelity to what reason recognizes as fact. Maturity, alas, is so often a parliamentary affair: there are parties and cabals in the mind, majorities and committees and rarely any chairman astute enough to manage the session conclusively. Childhood is more easily unanimous.

When I say that that place, that green and healthy world, gave one a sense of peace, I mean of course that I now perceive it was so. Peace is a condition not often apprehended while it exists. And a sense of peace is not by any means the whole of life. There are some who cannot carry too much peace at a time without growing morbid. One who has been, now for quite a few years, deeply infected with the wild beauty and lunacy of New York and her terrific creative spell, is perhaps an imperfect judge of quietness. I think however that is said largely for manners: Mistletoe believes himself a connoisseur of silence, for which he has, on occasion, an exceptional capacity. The notion I pursue is that it is not easy to work out a differential calculus of what is really important. There are instants when some casual line from Matthew Arnold or Keats will outweigh battleships or look taller than 42nd Street. We carry both new and old money in pocket simultaneously; who is to say which is the more legal tender? Anyone who has watched children knows how in a flash of gesture or expression they often unconsciously suggest whole vistas of feeling; through the low archway of the moment you see deep landscapes of life. I saw it twice by chance this morning: a child's maternal tenderness as she removed from her small pet dog a muzzle that was irking him; and again another child carrying to safety a terrified infant rabbit the dogs had chivied up in the woods. Or a remark when one of the dogs was at the vet's for inoculation during a neighborhood rabies alarm—"Will Frisky be back for his birthday? He never spent a night away from home before, except the two nights he ran away."

In these millennial moments the hour is dazzled round with prism light. It is such moments we pursue, and which the greater part of the time we must be too polite to mention. Happiness is always embarrassing; sometimes gravely annoying to other people.

Peace is not by any means the whole. The joy

14

and justification of the modern spectacle is its furious high voltage. Is there no comedian divine enough to exhibit the bewildering agility of man? Let red-tapesters contrive it as they may and festoon the earth with rigmarole, the dreamer is too subtle for them. The tremulous instancy of his own bliss drives him, his bliss that can shake him like sickness. He lives on stony soil and thrives there; a lacklustre citizen, perhaps, but he has glorious conniptions of his own. Will none admit such irradiance of fire? Perhaps life has outrun print, for the larger part of our writing seems so pale or so sultry. It impends but does not break. In that deep phrase of Coventry Patmore, it squanders the capital of passion instead of living on the interest. "If I believe in immortality," said Mistletoe once (he always found much antiseptic in *If*) "it's because there must somewhere be time to sit down and laugh." But he knew well enough that there are many things too beautiful for laughter.

The life of any fugitive worth pursuing must be partly a pathological memoir, a dissertation in lunacy. When a mind escapes from prison the big siren yells, and the hunt is on.

In the old wing of the Haverford Library there was a little gallery, reached by an iron ladder. It was rarely visited, used for the storage of an

antique collection of classical and theological texts
annotated in German, and some thousands of legal
volumes in scaling and exhalatory calf. Behind the
bookcases, on the outer side of the building, high
up by the tops of the tall windows, ran a dusty
little passage, somewhat tremulous underfoot and
carpeted with rough cocoanut matting. In the days
when the undergraduate literary societies turned
over their private collections to the college library,
certain volumes of juvenile fiction, esteemed too
frivolous for general circulation, were sequestered
in a remote corner of that gallery. Very likely some
of them are still there, as they have been for fifty
or sixty years. They contain the neat bookplates of
those vanished sodalities the Haverford Athenæum
and the Loganian Society—this latter with its excellent motto *Lectio sine stilo somnium*. Across
these bookplates you will sometimes find written
the ominous legend *Rejected, A. C. T.*, those being
the initials of Professor Allen Thomas, a man of
delightfully definite opinions, loving curator of the
library through many years and never known
otherwise than as "Uncle Allen." There, safe from
visit except by some occasional bearded scholar of
Assyrian or Coptic, these innocent scandals lurked
on the bottom shelf, obedient to the doctrine that a
Quaker library had no truck with fiction.

But perhaps, in his mellowing years, Uncle Allen
softened toward these books, mostly by Captain

Mayne Reid; in fact I imagine he must have enjoyed them himself in tender youth. He was a man quite gnomelike in aspect and his quick flitting among the alcoves was awe-inspiring to urchins. At any rate when Mistletoe was perhaps eight years old Uncle Allen, with an air of much mystery, piloted him up the iron ladder, introduced him to the enchanting concealed pathway round the gallery, and then under pledge of secrecy, where the bottom shelf looked out on the old greenhouse arch, disclosed the cache of tattered volumes.

That, I think, was Mistletoe's fullest introduction to the joys of secret reading. Its nearest competition was hearing the *Jungle Book* read aloud when it first appeared in 1894, and being given a paper-bound piracy of *Treasure Island* to read when in bed with an ear-ache, a hot baked onion crackling and stewing under his cheek. (*Treasure Island* still smells faintly of onions in his mind.)

The delights of Mayne Reid's *Plant Hunters, Cliff Climbers, Bush Boy,* etc., read sprawled out on the floor of that illicit gallery, will not be forgotten. Long long afterward, meeting someone from the Transvaal, Mistletoe was able to please himself by creditable allusions to outspanning and voortrekkers and springbok. All Mayne Reid. The

17

small adventurer would steal alone into the old romantic wing of the Library, catching a permissive spark from Uncle Allen's eye. He would climb the ladder, half afraid of some veto, and creep along the creaking runway, peeping down through the slatted floor at the students reading below. Then there was the open end of the gallery, at the bottom of the room, above the fireplace. This, not to attract comment, must be gingerly crossed on tiptoe. Then, just round the corner, in a haze of dust and book-smell, were the outcast juvenilia. They had to be read in situ, they could not be taken away. So they were read as books are best read in youth, prone on the floor. The reader can still recall the rough prickly feel of the cocoanut matting; and Uncle Allen's little pun about the gallery being young Mistletoe's Mayne Reiding Room.

Ten years later, as an undergraduate, he sometimes used to work in that library, accessioning books, as a way of earning pocket money. You may be sure he revisited that corner of the gallery, and some of the old Mayne Reids were still there. Uncle Allen, when reminded of their history, graciously insisted on his taking three of them as a souvenir. Here, as he writes, is THE PLANT HUNTERS, or Adventures Among the Himalaya Mountains, by Captain Mayne Reid. Boston: Ticknor and Fields, 1858. The word *Rejected* is writ large on the bookplate, but it will not be rejected from Mistletoe's library as long as we have a shelf to stand upon. It seems an odd coincidence that when Mistletoe became interested in an ancient foundry in Hoboken there were found in the attic of that abandoned machine shop a large collection of old books; and among them several stalwart Mayne Reids.

3

As VANISHED as the *Just Suits*, a coarse and forgotten tobacco favored in Mistletoe's own coterie of conscientious smokers, are the moods, simplicities, dolors and merriments of the student era. But smile at it as you will, the world we knew then was fairly sane. It was not magnificent, but it was peace.

In the mind of the undergraduate there was always—perhaps still is?—a pervasive awareness of now being a college Man. This implied a serious obligation of Knowing About Life. To be awake after midnight (at which hour the dormitory lights were shut off at the power-house) and finish a card-game by candles, to consume late pannikins of cocoa with olives and crackers and argument about God, to read *Tom Jones* or Boccaccio, to visit the burlesque theatre in Philadelphia, these were recognized forms of philosophical initiation. Going

Fussing, as calling on young women was then always known, was respected as an inevitable concession to destiny, but hardly regarded as Seeing Life.

Mistletoe's class—I speak of the era 1906–1910 —rather enjoyed fancying themselves as a group of hard cases; they blithely imagined that rarely had so lively and virile a posse of humorists been gathered. How weary of their bumpkin antics their enduring dominies might well have been: their senseless japes and horseplay, the parrotings of a thousand generations of students which themselves believed so fresh and new. Yet it is pleasant to think of that green julep of freedom that ran in the young bipeds. Crude as it was, it was better than the dull mannerly conformity into which the mass output of American alumni soon subsides. For the usual youth that short four years is his only period of fantasy. As soon as he leaves college the docile creature yearns for his destined servitude, from which he rarely again emerges. Likely it is better so. The wise man in his time kisses many chains.

"A guarded education in morals and manners" was the statesmanlike phrase always used in the college catalogue to describe its purposes; a thoroughly prudent and liberal Quaker policy. Behind apparent liberty such as dazzled many boys of eighteen to twenty, a shrewd and watchful observation was alert. But in spite of discipline a good deal of cheery exploration was possible.

The bohemianism of college boys is well standardized. Naive souls, how scandalized we would have been to realize that any Dean with plotting paper could have sketched beforehand the exact parabola of our curve of experience and predicted every coördinate of our supposedly unique conduct. In the few cases where zeal carried the young experimenter over the edge of the plotting paper it did not take the authorities long to hear about it; the two-handed engine was at the door. For the most part our sallies were fairly innocuous, resulting in nothing more unseemly than an occasional misdemeanor in the late smoking car from Broad Street. The Red Lion, long a famous tavern in Ardmore—now I believe the cafeteria of a motor-truck factory—was visited for beer. The Casino and Trocadero burlesque houses in Philly were a steady resort for the student of drama. Mistletoe and I were profitable patrons of that rump parliament, but better than any of the ladies of Billy Watson's Beef Trust (not to be confused with William Watson) I remember the bored air of the large paternal man who stood sawing on the bull-fiddle. It amazed us that he could be unimpressed by the elevated proximity of so much haunch of Venus. Mistletoe always contended that the burlesque show was the lineal descendant of the Tudor spirit, and I fear that some of his relish for carnal mirth can be traced to the old show-house on Walnut Street. In that stage-door alley floated the exhilarating odor of grease-paint. Have you ever considered the delightful Seven Ages of Man offered by the various tones of grease-paint? As you find them listed in the make-up box they compose a perfect Shakespearean sequence:

1. Pink
2. Very Pale Juvenile
3. Juvenile Hero-Flesh
4. Juvenile, Robust
5. Sallow Young Man
6. Flesh, Middle Age
7. Robust Old Age

The period I think of now may be described as a moderate blend of Juvenile, Robust, and Sallow Young Man. Sometimes Sallow had the upper hand, as when, after tremulous waiting in the rain outside the stage door to invite some Casino soubrette to a glass of beer, the hobbledehoys fled in sudden panic; otherwhiles Robust prevailed: Mistletoe enjoys remembering a Chinese restaurant on Race Street where these juveniles, in delicious rakehell glamour, sat at table with some rather jetsam madams and listened to professional anecdotes. The zenith of that episode was when one of the ladies, saying "It's a shame to waste it," tucked an unfinished chicken-leg inside her stocking to take home to her dog. Such evenings were as good as Maupassant. Perhaps, in a guarded education in morals and manners, they had their useful contribution. I think it was probably a strong Stevensonian influenza that impressed the sophomore J. M. with the social importance of harlots.

The exceptional thing is the thing unduly remembered; let me not give exaggerated prominence to harmless escapades into the Debatable Land. More in routine, certainly more approvable by the faculty, were the excursions on Ninth Street where the dioscuri of culture were Leary's and Lauber's. To Leary's famous second-hand bookstore I have paid full tribute elsewhere; for three generations it has yeasted the dumpling temperament of Philadelphia. These boys, buying there their first copies of Chaucer, Wordsworth, or Tennyson, would then proceed to Lauber's "German Restaurant and Wine House" a block or so up the street. The 50-cent table d'hôte dinner was plentiful and accompanied by a musical trio which was excellent. But what lifted Lauber's to the status of education was that there Mistletoe ordered his first own bottle of wine. There was a

23

California claret, 35 cents a quart in that dulcet era; I dare say it was meagre and brackish, and I know we secretly disliked it; but it was claret, which we had read about in Tennyson, and nothing else would do. By some miracle of prognosis Mistletoe has saved one of Lauber's menus all these years, and I see that he has put a sentimental tick opposite that claret on the wine list. Lauber also served most of his wines on draught; claret at "10 cents per schoppen" seems a pleasantly German touch. The date on the menu before me is January 29, 1910, and I see that by the time the young bohemians got there from Leary's the Hamburger Rauchfleisch mit Erbsenbrei was all gone, for the waiter has pencilled it out.

The smart set among undergraduates used to visit a renowned café they called tautologically The L'Aiglon, but it was an overdressed Bailey Banks and Biddle sort of place compared to the homely and burgherish old Lauber's. Lauber took wines seriously, and an inquiring youth could learn something. How excellent to make virgin experiment among parsimonious half-pints (at 25 cents) of Liebfraumilch and Assmanshäuser; or India Pale Ale at a nickel a glass. A dollar an hour was what one earned by tutoring indolent classmates in math., and those dollars were scrupulously divided between Lauber and Leary. What the two L's symbolize is certainly as important as the three R's.

To discover the poets for one's self, and to learn to drink decently, with a sense of ritual, are part of a gentleman's education. As you move on from Juvenile, Robust, toward the epoch of Flesh, Middle Age, it is well to avoid the fatuity of rearward praise. The speakeasy of the better sort has many charms, including the paramount one of raising the death rate among numbskulls, but at its best it lacks something of the good human dignity of a place like Lauber's.

(Those who have known sea bathing can never again be wholly content with swimming in fresh water. There is always a subtle taint about it: it stings the eyes and strangles in the nose. Similarly, if you have ever enjoyed the tidal freedom of a community where the necessities of the artist are understood and respected, it is sometimes perplexing to be immersed in the muddy shallows of the United States of Agility. That sounds like a hard saying, but I prefer we should remark it about ourselves.)

Adventure of another sort was the occasional chance to supe in grand opera at the visits of the Metropolitan company in the old Academy of Music. The first of these thrills was a performance of *Faust*. Mistletoe was told off with other earnest young men to play the part of rustic revellers in a beer garden scene. Equipped with peasant costumes and empty leather flagons they stood about

25

behind the scenes waiting for what might happen next. They had no definite idea of what they were to do, but were keenly alive to the novelty and glamour of the situation.

I have not seen *Faust* since that time, so I may be a bit hazy as to details, but as I remember it the first scene is laid in Faust's study, and at one point in the action Faust (Caruso was playing the rôle) goes to the window, throws it open, and addresses impassioned outcry to the moonlit night. These youngsters had been wandering about trying to see as much of everything as possible and finally the irate stage manager bade them in unmistakable terms to make themselves scarce. Mistletoe had taken refuge in an angle behind the flat of canvas forming the back wall of the scene. Just above his head was a casement window with leaded panes played upon by a dazzling shaft of stage moonlight. Here, he thought, he was quite safe and in nobody's way. But he was a little curious about a young Bauerin, very lavishly made up, who came presently and stood beside him holding a large pitcher of shining amber fluid that seemed to be beer. He wondered incredulously whether his void flagon was actually going to be filled before he walked on in the tavern scene.

Suddenly the casement window just above him was violently pushed open and a head, hugely

dark and vivid, with burning eyes glaring in the
spotlight, thrust out almost over his shoulder,
pouring forth that astonishing and (at such close
range) painfully piercing tenor. He dared not stir.
Then the voice paused, and the face, hidden from
the audience, demanded something in a vigorous
whisper. The girl with the pitcher must have been
wool-gathering, so the marvellous voice went on
again in its soaring music. Then the pitcher was
handed up and the liquid dispatched in a manner
that showed the great singer master of more arts
than one. For an instant the glass jug flashed in
the imitation moonlight as he leaned out, apparently (to the audience) drinking in the beauty of
the night. Then he turned back on the stage to
continue his rôle.

Mistletoe suped with Caruso a number of times
after that, and learned that nothing pleased him
so much as to be asked for his autograph. But
the energy and gusto with which he ingurgitated
that surreptitious jug of beer was specially endearing.

By a natural association of words another episode recurs; in *Tannhäuser* I think. These boys,
habited as monks, had to carry on the body of
Elisabeth lying pure, white and dead on a bier.
Her hands were piously folded on her generous
German bosom, the moment strictly solemnized
with melancholy music and proper sorrow. Just

as the bearers came out from the wings into the full glow of the stage, one handle of the bier broke. The litter tilted dangerously, the composed hands of the corpse flew out with instinctive clutch to seize the sides. She cursed us in an enthusiastic whisper, doubtless thinking it an intentional joke. The horrified bearers lowered the stretcher to the floor and trailed it carefully to the appointed spot. The incident itself was nothing; what Mistletoe remembers was narrating it afterward to a tender nymph of Bryn Mawr. How delightfully sensitive were the embarrassments of a boy of that era! Recounting the affair with lively gusto, he accidentally used a plural instead of a singular. He meant to say, "Her hands were crossed over her breast." But what he actually said was "breasts." Stricken by a sense of his unintended immodesty a warm flood of horror carmined every vein. He was appalled by this breach of delicacy, which he thought must have sounded like wanton boorishness. It ruined a happy social call for him, and long remained a hot flush in memory.

But visits to Philadelphia were rare, and I give a falsely Latin Quarter impression of a college life almost entirely rustic. *Non doctior sed meliore doctrina imbutus* is its motto—a quotation whose provenance not even the faculty classicists have ever been able to place for me. Like the Latin mottoes

28

of respected publishing houses, few of the inmates can parse them or even know they exist. But to that good plea against raw sophistication the college has honorably adhered. If I seem to import an irrelevant tavern flavor, that is of my own private sentimentality. We lived mostly without benefit of orgy; no place was ever less bohemian in spirit. It never even occurred to it to want to be; the peccancies of Mistletoe and his cronies were surreptitious and unauthorized. One of the best of memories is of a volume of Ben Jonson bought at Leary's and *The Alchemist* read aloud with a companion (and shouts of laughter) in a field of cornshocks beyond the college.

I have looked back over some of Mistletoe's notebooks, and I find that he has learned very little in twenty years, about literature anyhow, that they didn't tell him then, or try to tell him. I get a twinge of wistful amusement in some of the old memoranda: as for instance when the poor young scholiast, alongside the purplest stanza of the Eve of Saint Agnes, set innocently down the notation that *shielded scutcheon* was an example of "pleonasm." That, entered probably by dictation, was a mere childishness of pedantry, but every child is properly a pedant. The only danger is in his remaining so. You must start him off hunting for rhetorical oddities, which may be just as much fun as parlor games; perhaps eventually among pleonasms or metonymies he may become aware of what lies behind rhetoric, the burning human mind. It would be wrong to suppose that because he jotted down such naivetés on the margin he did not feel the thrill of Keats. In fact a 75-cent Keats bought from John Wanamaker—not from Leary, because he wanted one utterly his own, with no reminiscence of any previous reader—has been one of the most important things that ever happened to him. To this day he remains one of the few who can tell you offhand what day of the year is Saint Agnes' Eve. The very pages of that poem are loose in the book because he used to read it in bed and fall asleep on it. We were lucky at Haverford in having in the Roberts Autograph Collection one of the most beautiful and terrible of Keats's letters to Fanny Brawne. I doubt if many of the boys were enough interested to go and look at it, but I know one who did. He can still call to mind the actual handwriting of those words at the bottom of the sheet, describing his love. "'Tis richer than an Argosy of Pearles."

4

I PLEASE myself by transcribing some of Mistletoe's old notes of college lectures. Perhaps more accurately than much reminiscent musing they give a cross section of the college process at work;

they show that (however little these youths may have profited) at least they were given exposure to wise and candid notions. Of course these memoranda were not original but condensed by the student himself from the spoken word. You might find them with but small variation in the cahiers of many generations of those who sat under the same magistrates.

But how vividly, to the alumnus himself, these random excerpts bring back the personalities involved, the humors of the classroom, the picture of bent heads and pencils busy in pursuit of doctrine. The breathless feeling in Philosophy IV—famous there too as in greater institutions also—that now at last we were on the near vestiges of the Ultimate. Occasional parentheses of local or topical ribaldry one excises; otherwise these fragments are genuine. Perhaps one smiles at the shrewd way some of earth's larger riddles were simplified for green capacity; but very likely all teaching has to proceed by search for Greatest Common Divisor.

English I.   November 28, 1906

Slang, excepting in cases of abbreviation, is an old word or phrase given a new and undignified application. If a new application is intelligent and in good taste it may come to have a literary value. If the application is the result of loose thinking or of questionable taste it is vulgar and execrable. Indulgence in vulgar slang is the sure evidence of a weak, shallow and slovenly mind.

The *denotation* of a word is the idea for which it stands as a symbol. Denotation appeals to the intellect. Its chief virtue is accuracy. Example: a diamond denotes a hard transparent precious stone.

Connotation is the power of calling up associations. It appeals to the imagination and the feelings. Its chief virtue is suggestiveness. Poetry is richer in connotation than prose. It is always, however, a great merit. Example: diamond connotes great value, sparkling rays of light, dark mines, crowns, rings, brooches. Also baseball fields.

Command of the English language is attained, 1st by the study of words in a dictionary; 2nd, by the observation of words in reputable authors; 3rd, by the translation of foreign masterpieces; 4th, by constant practice in writing. Robert Louis Stevenson carried a notebook in his pocket and recorded his impressions of men and nature. Franklin studied Addison's *Spectator* and rewrote passages from memory.

The 3 chief qualities of Style are Clearness, Force, and Ease. Clearness demands ready intelligibility; Force, impressiveness; and Ease, agreeableness. Macaulay writes a clear style; Carlyle a forcible one; and Addison an easy style.

The rule of Clearness is not to write so that the

reader can understand, but so that he cannot possibly misunderstand. Beware of ambiguities and obscurities.

The rule of Force is to write with the Power of Conviction and Enthusiasm. Ernest preparatory thinking will add force to style. Webster's Reply to Hayne was the result of 30 years of Thought. A style gains in force also by the artificial devices of rhetoric. Force is the result and expression of Personality.

The rule of Ease is a paradox, or contradiction. To write an easy style one must make an intentional effort and at the same time appear to make no effort at all. It is the art of concealing the art.

The aim of all good stylists is attained when in addition to clear statement the writer makes an appeal to the reader's sense of beauty.

English XI. October 2, 1908
Hogarth: Rake's Progress, Harlot's Progress.

Typical Queen Anne house (like Anne herself) was plain, dull, regular, and solid. Blenheim Palace, built by the nation and given to Duke of Marlborough after victory at Blenheim is severe, solid, stolid, lack of ornamentation. These qualities were characteristic of the plain merchant.

Mostly roofed by red tiles. Facades severe, staircases narrow—wallpapers just beginning to replace tapestries in cheaper families. Drinking water

33

brought in and kept in cisterns. See Addison on Street Cries. Raree shows.

Not lavishly furnished. Chairs high backed and stiff. Comfortable couches. Much money spent on beds, huge canopies and curtains. Rents cheap—comfortable house and stable for £40 a year. In suburbs a brick or stone house for £5 a yr. Servants plentiful and cheap. A man kept a retinue who went out with him at night. Footmen enter largely into literature; usually formed the gallery gods at the theatre.

Bedrooms never heated—coal expensive. Swift writes to Stella that he goes to bed early to save expense of coals. A good footman, £6 a year.

Daily life of Women and Men of Fashion. The dandy, known as the macaroni (dude). "Yankee Doodle came to town, riding on a pony, They stuck a feather in his hat and called him Macaroni." This was written in derision of the uncouthness of Americans and Colonials. Men wore large hats with feathers (Merry Widow hats) later the women imitated them. Pontack's, the London Delmonico's.

Satirists of XVIII century direct their shafts against the vanity and uselessness of the fashionable women. Swift considers them no better than monkeys. In Bed till Noon. Afternoon, Dressing. Evening, Dining. Cards till midnight. Objects of her affection: a page, a monkey, and a lapdog.

Women received their friends (even men) in bed. Men kissed each other on meeting. When a man entered a room and was introduced he was expected to kiss all the ladies (on the lips!).

The Englishman is insular, intense prejudices. Didn't travel much. Travelling very precarious until merchant class and commercial interests grew. Roads narrow—teamsters would fight for right of way. Impassable in bad weather. Footpads, highwaymen, some would exact tribute for which they would guarantee protection for the rest of the journey. Claude Duval let a lady off with £100 because she consented to dance with him! When sent to prison, romantic ladies sent flowers.

The bright aspect of English travelling was the English inn. Read The Cloister and the Hearth.

The country squire. Cf Squire Western (Tom Jones) with Squire Cass (Silas Marner.) The squire of Queen Anne's time didn't have more education or culture than the coachman today. The companion of his grooms, &c. Collected rents, acted as local magistrate. Home brewed ale. A hard drinker. His wife had the accomplishments of a modern barmaid. Sewing, spinning, making gooseberry wine, working in kitchen. Squire usually a Royalist, knew his genealogy, fought for his king. It was the country squire who fought for King Charles at Edgehill and Naseby. Hated most things he knew nothing about—Frenchmen,

Scotchmen, Jews, neighbors. Important in the agricultural but not in the intellectual life of his country.

Philosophy IV. November 18, 1909
Wordsworth: *Tintern Abbey*.

Plato's Ultimate Reality is not alone a principle of knowledge. In his highest moments his ultimate is a real presence, to be felt. v. *Phaedrus* and *Symposium* (speech of Diotima). In *Timaeus*, this ultimate becomes personal, as any ultimate must be which is to explain knowledge and purpose for ideas are always personal. A person is a unity of ideas and will-purposes.

In the *Symposium* we find Plato's doctrine of love (*Eros*) which has almost no reference to sexual love but is the principle of ecstasy, of being taken out of ourselves by inspiration. In moments of ecstasy Plato finds himself in the presence of the eternal. This doctrine bridges the chasm between the world yonder and this world. The ultimate is no longer off in another world, but is a real presence in the objects of this world. For the passion of love never arises until we discover the eternal (i. e., the absolutely *kaloskagathos*) in the particular. In *beauty* we find the revelation of something that *is as it ought to be*. In the presence of this absolutely good we find ourselves in state of *eros*, love, ecstasy. Read Tintern Abbey carefully.

36

Throws great light on meaning of philosophy and the search to unify subject and object.

In this interpretation the idea of the good becomes the complete unity of knowing and being, the supreme principle in the world and in the mind & so sums up the whole rational universe.

Is the rational universe the whole of the universe? Is there anything in the universe that cannot be brought to rationality?

3.14159 . . . is irrational?

Can anything that is always the same be irrational?

Mind: no matter.

Matter: never mind.

Philosophy V. February 15, 1910

Conscience—the mental faculty for distinguishing R & Wr, and which gives incentive to follow one and avoid other. Varies in different people— active or dormant. It can always be developed & cultivated. We shall consider Conscience as purely a human faculty, not from any supernatural aspect.

Varies in same individual at different times, & varies with the mental constitution of the individual. Kleptomaniacs have no scruples against stealing, &c.

Education has a tremendous influence on conscience. Public sentiment at Univ of Va is overwhelmingly against cheating or deceit of any kind. But not so in case of sobriety.

The community we are in is continually educating us. We want our conscience to be in accordance with the eternal principles of right and wrong. We want to put ourselves in an atmosphere that will develop our conscience in the right way. The education of the conscience either upward or downward is continuous. The intensity of conscience is also impt. People do things they know to be wrong, because c. doesn't reprove very hard. The best way to develop c. is to obey it. To disobey c. weakens it.

A sensitive c. always educates itself. A live c. will not let its owner alone until he finds out what is right and does it. A man with sensitive c. is always open to new views. Such a man cannot be static.

A sensitive c. is then the greatest thing a man can have. Don't ridicule a man because he looks at things differently from ourselves. The feeling that he can't or won't do certain things is a fine thing in a man. A conscientious man is often wrong. But he has a better chance for alignment with the best that is in him than the other man.

Liberty of Conscience: in England, the idea was introduced by exiles returning from Holland ca. 1640. Roger Wms was prominent. "The Bloody Pennant of Persecution for Conscience' Sake."

38

Cromwell: "I beseech you brethren by the bowels of X to think it possible that you are mistaken." Roger Wms book to the effect that everybody had right to think as he pleased was not appreciated in England. He came to R. I. & started a colony. All cranks and fanatics gathered there, & the colony was pointed to with scorn. Wms and Fox had great disputes. Wms said the Quakers were heretics & wd go to hell but gave them their rights anyway.

5

A SWEET and dangerous opiate is Memory; it is well that we are rarely addicted to it. Even the briefest indulgence confuses the sense of present reality. That busy dream-life has no existence save by deliberate will, yet you can instantly create a whole world and ensphere it in empty nothing for a pause of brooding power. Yes, it can be done in the bliss of anxious thought, but to clench it in words is dreadful. I honor words and they come with difficulty. But memory is something subtler than words, of anterior substance; it lives behind the forehead and not in the lips. It floats an instant in the mind like a smoke-ring, then spreads and thins and sifts apart. If mood and moment could be found when people could just sit down, in mutual passiveness, and say "I remember . . ." what matter might come forth. How seldom it happens; what infinite instruction it might contain.

Mistletoe remembers Lake Champlain. Sometimes he wonders if it is still there. It is twenty years since he last saw it; it must be a big lake by now, and very likely too busy to remember. But shame indeed to celebrate the Lake of Geneva or any other fluid—even Long Island Sound—and not ask forgiveness of Champlain. It is not just a body of water: it is an eternity of summer days. Does the old steamer *Vermont* still come past the stony cape of Split Rock, her paddles sounding across the still mirror of the afternoon? (You could hear them best by listening under water.) At least the blue profile of Camel's Hump must be unchanged. There are red lizards on the rocks, and harebells; and pickerel to be trolled for; thunderstorms, porcupines, and chattering red squirrels that dance on birch boughs after rain and shake down a crystal spatter as you pass beneath. Once he shot a red squirrel with a rifle. That, and a bullet through his own finger, cured him of any joy in firearms.

If you make the effort to lift that lake and all its woodland shore out of the abyss of irretrievable distance, poise it tenderly in balance, you can see that the whole scene moved in a charming sentimental rhythm; and below that emerged some-

thing also much more elementary. (We are concerned of course only with the pure egotism of
memory.) Like the steady pound and sway of the
old *Vermont's* pistons, lulling the watcher almost
to a swoon in long passages on the lake, I think I
discern the power of real meanings behind apparently casual recollections.

The superficial rhythms were pretty enough.
The timely routine of the *Vermont* or her sister
Chateaugay was almost a clock. You saw the
steamer's long diagonal across the wide gulf, with
that air of living and working that a walking
beam gives to a boat. Duly her swell came rolling
over the wrinkled water, greeted by bathers and
canoes. On clear northern days the road to the
village was fringed along with crisping blue. It
was still the Sheet Music Era; after supper canoes
set out to follow the moon-path, and the primitive
harmonies known as College Songs consoled the
Large Pickerel who had Got Away. The shores of
Champlain must still bandy in their rocky scarps
some jaded echoes of "I've Been Working on the
Railroad" a million times reiterated. It is pleasant
to imagine, scattered Lord knows where and
busied in the genteel treadmill of the middle
classes, the innocent alumnæ of Lake Champlain
who once flung moondrops from wet paddles and
carolled "I've Got Rings on My Fingers and Bells

on My Toes." Keep up your hearts, sisters: the worst is yet to come.

Holding that green and blue microcosm for study I am aware of huckleberry pastures with a clank of cowbells; glades of underbrush violent with sun; and the feeling of hills. Perhaps more than any other thing physical, one whose childhood knew big hills misses them in a life too level. Men need mountains; those who have never associated with them have missed much of earth's suggestion. Also one could hear the wail of the wildcat on some of those Adirondack spurs; it was often a blow to those who imagined they liked solitude. There was poetry as well as picnic on those unspoiled shores. No one will have forgotten Grog Harbor, or the windings of Otter Creek, where the wake of the launch sways and tosses the reeds as a strong personality draws softer creatures in its suction. There was a sandy jut, even whose name I have forgotten, surmounted by a steep plateau of pines. Quite deserted in those woods above the lake was a colony of mouldering log cabins, once the home of some utopia or other. When sunset kindled every chink of the forest those mournful old huts were as suggestive as the last line of a sonnet.

It is always agreeable to embarrass my friend Mistletoe by trying to pin him down to the essential. It's a favorite jest to ask him (in the phrase of reporters) to Make a Statement. Asked for a Statement about Lake Champlain he would prowl apprehensively about the room (an annoying habit). He knew very well the great difficulty of Statements, which usually conceal more than they convey. A serious critic (as distinguished from a mere romancer) is compelled to simulate some sort of balance sheet, cogitated in reasonable form; and, as every auditor knows, there are a hundred ways of pastrycooking an itemized report. Liars, we are all liars; and worse, timid and ineffectual liars. To deliver the meaning of anything, Mistletoe would mumble, you must remove yourself altogether from the social tissue; must renounce the innocent pleasure of having your intuitions shared, approved, or verified. In any man's memory there are areas so tender, so silly, so vital, they cannot easily be suggested.

There was a road, powdered thick with dust, that ran along the lake shore. At night it was a deep channel through pine trees where a dark ribbon of sky was granulated with stars. The water below it whispered to the stony beach with Tennysonian delicacy. Add to this the balsam savor of Adirondack woods, and all the endearing mischief of our human race. And in those days, or nights, there were no cars on such roads. It was silence.

There was a boy who, for reasons quite irrele-

vant, was supposed to be doing some studying. As
a matter of fact he was reading Huxley, and I don't
mean Aldous. It was Thomas Henry Huxley;
Science and Education, or something of that sort;
good, solid, uplifting stuff, with occasional sortie
(for relief) into the Oxford Book of English Verse,
which was a new book in those days and highly
favored by a Younger Generation that didn't know
it was a Generation. There were other books too
that he was reading, for instance A. C. Benson's
From a College Window, one of the quietest of
sedatives.

He needed a sedative. Past the lakeside cabin
which was the student's pensive citadel ran this
same road—this road dust-powdered and soft to
tread, now brilliant with noonday sun and upland
air, this Road of Loving Hearts Stevenson's
Samoans would have called it. As he sat, pretending to put his mind on Huxley's Idea of a
University he was really alert for a very small and
complicated sound. It only lasted an instant. It
combined a faint hum, a flutter, and sometimes
(in excess of provocation) a small tingling bell.
It was a girl on a bicycle.

Perhaps a dozen times in the half hour preceding
that hoped-for passage he would have peered out
of the door to look along the road. For, if she happened to be in sight, what more natural than that
he should have chanced to come outdoors: the

road was free to all, wasn't it? And it would have
been equally natural for her to dismount and exchange a few words. Or again, with the practical
ingenuity of the young female, it might sometimes
occur that the bicycle did not seem to run well, or
she would weary of riding at just that bend in the
road and walk a bit for a change; idly chirruping
her bell in a noonday abstraction. But many, far
too many, times (the child was a genius of co-
quetry) she spun briskly by. As he sat with eyes
on Huxley but ears cocked toward the road, he
would hear that faint and adorable flutter, the
flickering rustle of tires and spokes, a tiny chink
of the bell. He would rush to the door. Already the
white dress and revolving ankles, the sunburned
nape, the bronze curly hair, were far down the
way. It was odd, undoubtedly, that she always
chose to ride home with the mail just at the hour
she knew he set apart for being there. Or perhaps
it was he who arranged it so: who could remember now?

But to paraphrase the famous words, in Thomas
Henry Huxley he read no more that day.

There were nights of stars on that road. Perhaps you have known roads something like it.
(Strange to think it is still there; is that summer
dust yet so silent underfoot? does a white dress
still shine so white in starlight, visible down the
dark alley of the pines?) There were certain hu-

morous obstacles to easy meeting, to lend sure enchantment. There was a barn dance once, a real one, when the erection of a new barn was celebrated, before the roof was put on, by open-air merriment in the hayloft; there were Chinese lanterns under warm sky, and a harp and a country fiddler. And early in the evening, as happened to be duty, he drove punctually away in the old rustic surrey; but raced secretly back, miles along that same road of dust and stars, for one more caper before the end.

Well indeed if so young and in such harmless subterfuge one may first divine something of woman's immortal power.

There was a porch that overhung the water, where one fell asleep hearing the small syllables of the beach; woke now and then, as one does in open air, to see always a different pattern of planets. Usually the beam from Split Rock lighthouse was the only company in that small bungalow, except Thomas Henry Huxley. Once in a while however a friend camping farther along the shore stopped in to sit late beside the fire, to discuss symptoms in their wounded bosoms. For both were stricken of the universal endemic, and loyally sought to repair their agitation with the Oxford Book and the bottle of rye reserved for snakebite. But mostly he was alone, and turned in on the camp-cot on the porch surrounded by stars and in a happy confusion of ideas, a mixture of T. H. Huxley and the flutter of bicycling skirts.

It is very long ago; perhaps it was only a dream; but one night he woke, and something nearer and dearer than stars or Huxley had been there on the porch. Dazed as he was, he was aware of some thrilling presence; there was a soft step in the brush below the steps, a whispering, a curious radiant sensitiveness on his cheek, a faint suggestion of a sweetness he knew. Does a boy ever forget his first breath of a woman's hair? Dazzled with celestial suspicion he crept out through the cabin into the open. Down the road was a distant laughter.

Only a dream, perhaps; worse, a joke, insisted his indignant crony; but he himself preferred to believe otherwise. Surely it was not just coincidence that for several days Huxley was abandoned for the composition of an Ode on Lake Champlain; which was duly returned by the editor of the Atlantic Monthly with its delightful rejection slip: *The Editor of The Atlantic begs to be excused from the ungracious task of criticism.*

6

I SEE you, Tony, in your blue shirt, in the green and yellow wood. I hear the blows of your axe;

the steady keening of your saw in measured hero couplets. Pure October air is round you, smell of logs and mould, unmitigated sunshine of noon, and you have nothing to think of nor perceive but the split of the axe-blade, the smell of logs, the feel of earth under your bootsoles, the feel of barky wood on your hard brown hands.

It is odd that you are here today, working as lonely as Crusoe only a paragraph from my window. I can see your blue shirtsleeve swinging up and down among that miscellany of green and tawny leaves, and I must catch the charm and power of this moment before it fades. This very morning, before you came, I was sorry because I had not put on *my* blue shirt which I wear for easy hours, a shirt worn and washed until it is soft and fine as an old Medici nightgown—though one imagines the Medicis always going to bed in such a hurry that they didn't bother about nightgowns. That is the shirt I wear for idling and moseying, for sitting on rocks and smelling seaweed. But this was to be a working day, a noble damnable day of pen and ink and typewriter; so by mere habit I forgot the blue shirt.

Then I looked out into this illustrious noon. The line of the meridian, gilded with Now, passed invisible across us; Meaning was not far away. I saw you, swart and faithful Tony, and I thought how lucky you are, dealing only with hard and sa-

vory things like timber. Donny, the old fool sheepdog, lay on the sunny gravel, emeritus and pleased
as a trustee at the Union League Club. He, concerned over so many things, would not even raise
his head as I passed. He was reassured: it was Only
Me. There were faded mauve asters in our little
jungle, and the small tight buds of our jejune
chrysanthemums which have not yet any idea
What It's All About. There was the grey rock that
will still be there long after ourselves have solved
whatever is available for solution. And you, old
Tony, your queer hat abaft your head, with no
notion of your bronze Italian comeliness, were part
of that deep unsearchable world that lies so near
us and which we can never be intuitive enough to
explore. You were the woodcutter in the forest as
we used to read of him in the fairy tales. The white
hens, those lean and spinster fowls who ran away
from home (like ambitious young alumnae) and
took an apartment in a neighbor's dark pinetree,
because they were frightened by rats in the roost,
picked round you undismayed. You were of their
world, world of shine and shower, world of hunger and fear. And I saw that you wore a blue
shirt, man's understood badge of the poetry of
doing.

We lit the furnace together, and now the first
steam of the season (always a miracle and a rite)
is whispering in the radiator; whispering of long

winter nights to come. How much could be said (which I am not fool enough to say) of that first whisper of the steam, its sly teasing suggestions. It suggests green frosty twilights that set the heart crying, when there are a million pale-gold window panes and every tree is black; and there are patterns on paper to be turned into living flesh and ecstasy of men and women. The season comes when ink is proud and the right hand knows its cunning. Avast praise of summer; give me early dusk. Give me, in fact, whatever you please, and I'll make it my own.

You went back into the green cave of leaves where I see you now, Tony; where no telephone can ever call you; where your mind is vacant of all save the pleasure of good labor with air and sweat. Perhaps that is why you seem quite close to all sorts of simple truths. It would not occur to you to accept or deny; merely to endure and continue. You would not ask more of Beauty than she could give you. When work is over you light your pipe, push your hat a little further back, and walk home. Not otherwise maybe, in forest gaps among the rough slopes of Apennine, your far-off cousins bend with axe and saw, and wipe their brows with hairy forearms. And yet I take you Tony, there as you are, now, and fling you across a world. You, unguessing and never to suspect, surpass for an instant both Time and Distance. You, my

better in so much, live here in the sideways slipping of my hand, because, one day of sweet October, you worked in green and yellow woodland
and wore a blue shirt.

For a moment I was somewhere near what I
wanted to think; it trembled away. How may one
keep that thrill of meaning that comes and van-
ishes so suddenly? Sometimes, undeniably, you do
know that everything is part of everything else;
the integrating calculus is perfect; you can guess
how all fits together with yellow light around it
and the trees perforated with bluer blue as the sun
slopes west. Then with equal softness certainty
slips off. Life seems a large idea to hold in your
mind; the disproportion is too severe. It is as in-
equal as a phrase I noticed the other day when an
attorney was reopening a saloon that had been
padlocked. As he relaxed the official vinculum he
handed the owner a legal paper, at which I glanced.
It said, Complainant, The United States of America, vs. Frederick Wogenprall. The antithesis
seemed almost exaggerated.

So I try to keep Tony's blue shirt in mind as an
emblem of decent simplicity. I give his image away
to you as a talisman, and you who will never see
him may think of him as he sawed and chopped
all day under the changing colors of light and
leaves. Perhaps a talisman that is not successful is

dearest of all: if it does not perform what you thought it might, its virtue is still there, unexercised. Once I picked up a blue glass jewel fallen on the stage from some costume in The Black Crook. It did not perform any magic, nor did I really suppose it would; but it serves me as a pocket reminder of a thing I loved much and which had its own fate to pursue. To fortify oneself with small tinsel charms and tokens is a form of innocent savagery; but so is all poetry. To wear such casual amulets a while, then put them away in a ditty-box for occasional study, is to keep a perfect autobiography of one's own pieties. Why should we all be so terrified of being egotists; which is what we were intended to be.

I need no mottled goosebone, while the first steam is whispering, to predict to you that nights will be long this winter; it is the ultimate winter we have had so far. There will be cold and utter silences, when clocks will chime, radiators freeze, and some read Keats. Now, while that steam is brewing, the house is warm again after the pinching days when we made shift to live with electric heaters. Sometimes, if you earn a chill October midnight alone with Keats and an electric heater, in that concentration of stillness the small hum of golden amperes swells like the roar of a train in a tunnel. Then you may remember that the mind of a poet is not different from those orange-hot wires.

Force through them a current too fierce for them, and they grow luminous with joy and pain.

Long nights will be needed; there is much poetry to be written. Be encouraged by the thought how little has yet been done. So many little tin boxes that have fresh new typewriter ribbons in them! Perhaps, my Mistletoe, on one of those small sibylline wheels of tape your own heart may inherit. Not many voices have really come perilously near our secret, to say it without bitterness nor simpering. There are not many that pierce through all tatters of the moment and say ourselves to ourselves with the huge tenderness we deserve. Shakespeare and Whitman were such, yet were only troubled and arrant men. Shakespeare above all, the great laughter from a cloud, distant three centuries of rainswept darkness yet only ten begats away; so much ourself that even at the telephone or in a porcelain bathtub his words invest our very thought. He is our greatest mortgagee; but he will not foreclose, and the loan is worth the swink of our petty cash payments. Neither he nor another can say for you all you knew to be true before earth's mannerly fibs were taught you. You must breathe it for yourself, in the winds of North River, see it on the rising sheers of 42nd Street; even in the coals of the furnace or a Long Island grove where Tony was working in a blue shirt.

53

Bide your own silence then, my Mistletoe, and be aware of your truth, secretly warm and alive, central node of being. And perhaps the oldest dream of your nether mind may come actual, and beauty that abolishes all fear show her brightness unashamed. She has many deceptive sisters but she outshines them all. For such thoughts men need long nights. "Orion does not sleep, and why should I?"

7

I READ in Edith Sitwell's charming Life of Alexander Pope that he sent a parcel of fresh-picked cherries to some ladies, asking them particularly to return the wrapping paper with care. The sheets in which those cherries were bundled were part of his manuscript of the translation of Homer. It pleases me to think that cherries will taste even sweeter henceforward, now I know that pretty episode. They should; so much larger is poetry than the things it touches.

I saw a poet yesterday: my old Endymion. He will not mind my giving him our remindful nickname. He was looking well, handsome, even prosperous; perhaps because he has not been writing much poetry. He looked pinker and plumper than of old, and when I complimented him thereon he said it was Drink. He sat, demure as usual, during

miscellaneous lunch-table palaver; how charmingly, when he was fain to leave, he slid off from
the group, leaving in a quiet ripple, no unnecessary
splash. I God-blessed him in my heart, for I am
happy to be one of those conspirators who know
how great a poet he is. I can prove it to you in a
moment—

But what, I am thinking, does a poet drink;
what must a poet drink? What porridge had John
Keats? Anyone "with the curse in his or her blood
that intensifies experience and makes moments
beautiful or terrible beyond the comprehension of
the cool outside observer," what drug may make
him master of his hour?

What was that comic proposition that someone,
Macaulay or some other vast rhetorician, once de-
bated for our schoolboy task—That as civilization
advances poetry necessarily declines? It is very
likely true in the individual; as he grows established, busied, incumbent upon prosperous fact,
mercifully the flame declines into less troublesome
ember; but who cares gravely to argue so huge a
nonsense. Poetry comes with anger, hunger and
dismay; it does not often visit groups of citizens
sitting down to be literary together, and would
rightly appal them if it did.

What shall a poet drink? For broken hours and
idiot horrors, for beauty seen and unclaimed, for
the hole in the mind that lets loveliness escape, for

sharp edges of Time that cut and bruise, what pharmacist can cater? "Hast thou, O pellucid, medicine for case like mine?" cried Walt Whitman. What savage acids of darkness had he tasted who wrote:

Alas! 'tis true I have gone here and there,
And made myself a motley to the view,
Gored mine own thoughts, sold cheap what is most dear,
Made old offences of affections new;
Most true it is that I have look'd on truth
Askance and strangely. . . .

And then going on to the triumphant conclusion —perhaps the supreme tenderness of intimacy in our language, where the double adverb suggests the double beauty of what it praises—

Even to thy pure and most most loving breast.

Yes, "what's in the brain that ink may character?" What did the poet drink to learn to whisper so? There was a young rhymer once who used the same pretty trick in a madrigal, doubling his bosomy adjective; was he the less pleased with his cleverness because he had to explain it to the gay mammal herself? Or the less proud when he learned that Shakespeare had done it too? What they drink puts them even with Shakespeare; there are more than two gentlemen in Verona.

What must the poet drink? He does not know

and cannot tell. He gazes with amazement on the innocent bravado of editors and critics: think of the incredible perils of conducting a literary magazine, which deals at least part of the time with people trying to feel and say the truth. The word *magazine*, he does not forget, once meant a place that was likely to explode. He lives emotionally beyond his means; in what court of chancery may he petition for receivership? Whatever goblet you bring him, drug it deep with laughter. Some prewar laughter, bartender; He will Say When.

My mature Endymion slipped away; we are all always slipping away. He had work to do; we all always have work to do; sometimes the work does *us*. If Wordsworth thought the world was too much with him in the Lakes, what would he have felt on West 45th Street? The drink the poet must learn to mix for himself needs the ingredient none knows how to name. Shall we call it Wholeness, or Oneness, or Simplicity? Call it what you please, it brings for an instant the drowsy numbness Keats mentioned; and then words neither numb nor drowsy. It brings clean certainty; not the negatives of philosophy but the positives of intuition, the continuous integrality of life. Then he catches up with Time by standing still, and standing so, in an air of dreadful clearness, he knows how simple all is. The philtre scalds in the throat but it goes to the Right Spot. Consciousness is made whole, seeing is believing. A wormhole drilled smooth in dead wood, the fuzz of frost on a mouldered twig, the taste of cold water, an axe-blade going through the billet at one stroke, were one winter morning's suggestions of that feeling. Everything becomes analogy, of which is the Kingdom of Heaven. Then—again quote my old Endymion—he drinks honey from the poisoned lips of life.

What did I have in mind when I said there are still great poets? This:

> O Love, a thousand, thousand voices,
>> From night to dawn, from dawn to night,
> Have cried the passion of their choices
>> To orb your name and keep it bright,
>
> Until, however tides may vary
>> At neap or ebb of life and breath,
> Your influence is planetary
>> Upon this body of our death,
>
> And that dark sea that takes the dying
>> Kindles along its coasts to flame
> For thousand, thousand voices crying
>> The exaltation of your name.

He slipped away, he went about his affairs. I wonder if he knew how much of my love went with him. And he had given me just the drink I needed.

8

It was pleasant to hear again from Mistletoe, who has been silent a long while; though there are worse conditions than Silence. Knowing him as well as I do, I can readily assign at least two reasons for his taciturnity. He was very likely distressed at always being called "whimsical" whenever he blurted any of his suspicions of truth; and he was probably prickled a little by a kind of formula that the reviewers unanimously adopted to describe his occasional outgivings. They used to say that he was a master "within his limitations." To me one of his comic charms was that he had happy enlargements when he did not believe there were any limitations.

It's a pity (I quite agree with you) that he has a habit of being somewhat profane in his private correspondence; and his profanity (if that is the word for it) is not of the kind that is readily excised; it is a humble and reverent sort of profanity that runs throughout the weave of his thinking. If it were just interpolated epithet it could be detached; but no; he is hypodermically profane; as difficult to expurgate as either Shakespeare or Don Marquis. What he has been doing all this while, he tells me, is writing his Will, and he sends me some rough draft of the document. It will cause

pain to his attorney, if he has one, for his bequests
are not too precise and his heirs and assigns very
numerous. In fact he bequeathes "the City of New
York, as I know it" to All and Sundry, and de-
votes twenty pages to those special phenomena and
fantasias of New York which he would have his
usufructuary legatees inherit. Another of his bequests is the constellation Orion, for which he always had a notable regard. Whether this Will can
be proved will be an interesting question. At any
rate he says that composing it has blunted death's
sting, and he regrets that he may not be alive to
see it boblished. (There is some joke about that
word *boblished* that I do not understand. In his
early days he entertained a jocular suspicion of
printing-houses, and got into the habit of calling
them *boblishers*. Perhaps there is something amusing about it that I cannot apprehend. I have heard
him utter the word and then scream with laughter.
I condone anything that made him laugh, because
he did not do nearly enough of it.)

Undoubtedly Mistletoe's Testament will be
alluded to as "whimsical," or else possibly as
"quaint," but he will not turn in his grave because
he insists on cremation (something I myself have
little fancy for). But cremation will be necessary
in his case, for he wishes to be "reduced to readily
portable form." This is so that the funeral cere-

mony can be carried out as per instructions. There are a great many Given Points which he desires the procession to pass, and unless the corpus delicti can be easily transported the whole scheme is impossible. What he wants, he says, is Urn Burial in the New York Manner.

"Just for one day," he says, "viz., the day of my funeral, which must be deferred until a clear transparent weather when two and two are rather better than four, I should like those concerned to concentrate their minds on the insufficiently regarded beauty of this astounding town. With the same exquisite pleasure which I now have in thinking about them, I should like the committee (carrying my cinders in a decent brief case or Boston Bag) to visit certain of those cusps and campaniles that I love; places where coördinates cross. I cannot mention them all, but I give a few suggestions. I am inclined to hope, for reasons of my own (what other reasons are there?) that it will be a windy day when this happens; when the gales of March suggest the daffodil, or when April prepares her green traffic light and the world thinks Go. Then climb the L station at 42nd Street, looking from that windy deck across Bryant Park and over the Tree of Sparrows, and show me the Chrysler Building spiring into the improbable. What is it I hear about a Cloud Club that is to nidify in the upmost twigs of that tall tree of steel? I should have liked to be a member.

"It will be a long day for the committee" (Mistletoe's memoranda for sepulture continue) "and having risen early they will require, toward midday, some warming relaxation. At such a time it would be seemly that they repair, always bearing the Urn, to a favorite hideaway; I suggest the one known to me as the Villa Curiosa because it is in a building owned by a bookseller who specializes in the kind of literature so classified in catalogues. There, ascending in the little private elevator and depositing the Urn on the mantel of the sitting room, they will enjoy (at my expense) a modest tiffin and expound a well-mannered toast. During this day any telephoning that is to be done shall take place in one of those booths in a shoeshining parlor in the Hudson Terminal, where it was my habit to dissolve Space in Time and rearrange my own small zodiac. I remember the extraordinary day when, making for my particular cubicle (I have always found that booth the easiest to talk in) I was horrified to see a truck taking away the whole row of little compartments. I thought with horror that they were gone for good; I remembered all the thousands of anxious electricities I had poured into that poor wooden box (it looked horridly like a coffin, being borne out by lusty engineers) and wanted to climb into it. But in a

day or so it was back again, re-equipped with
the new dial gadget by which you get your number for yourself. I have marked on the chart (ap-
pended to these notes) the exact location of said
booth.

"While in the Hudson Terminal the committee
will not omit to note the place, downstairs, where
cinnamon buns are sold; and it would be an act
of piety to pause a moment in the Prune Exchange
Bank, a place where my modest destinies often
trembled in the balance. Among subterranean
pleasures they should certainly pause at the lavender stall in the 33rd Street terminal of the Hudson
Tubes. There, in that unlikely crypt, small bags
of fresh lavender may be had at two for a quarter.
A dramatist friend of mine, relying on the kindness of the young woman who sells lavender, once
left the script of his play—a melodrama whose
aroma was very different from that of the old-
fashioned herb—at that stall to be called for by
envoy; and so learned that the lavender dealer
was herself also a playwright. What miracles of
impossibility cannot this city of mine offer if you
give it a chance? I would ask the committee, for
one day, to be aware of all such. The broad sunny
plaza in front of the Columbia University Library,
always populous with micro-organisms of culture,
is a good vantage to consider such things.

63

"Nor need the day be entirely urban. Perhaps, in the afternoon, a decent vehicle can be procured to travel certain routes on Long Island (indicated on Chart Number 2, herewith) occasionally repeating the old dashboard incantation. 'I've got Minutes, I've got Amperes, I've got Oil, I've got Gas, I've got Miles.' Among prayers to be uttered should be that for Rich People Who Don't Have Fun. I am fond of this prayer, as it is a delightful illustration of the bourgeois defensive complex which likes to believe that the Rich have a poorer time than the indigent. Of course that is essential bosh; Rich People often have Excellent Fun."

I am extraditing only a few random paragraphs from the testament: and to get any picture of my friend's temper I must not choose only the jovial portions. "I suspect," he writes, "that even this Will is thoroughly dishonest because it seeks to lay emphasis on things that have made me happy. Perhaps it is too much Special Pleading. As the old property man said, getting ready for the stage-hands' ball (his annual splendor) 'I'm going to get myself manicured from head to foot.' This manuscript should not be manicured; it isn't a Balance Sheet for it won't balance. There is a debit unaccounted for: I have received more than I have given, and I am ashamed. What have I done to even up for the trembling color of daffodils, or for the terraces of the French Building on 45th Street in a pink afternoon light? I was always fond of detective stories, and certainly life is the best of them. Even these notes and codiciles have been written in a hurry; a pity, because at least in composing his Will a man should think slowly. But unless I am in a hurry I never do anything, I apologize for having been in a hurry, but I often enjoyed it. A good sleep sometimes makes extraordinary changes in a man's theology. By the time you read this I shall be having it."

Happily that remark was premature. I hope my friend will long continue these prolegomena to a future congé. As the greatest and dearest of all simpletons said of himself, he is an unperfect actor on the stage. When I knew him, he was not wise, not clever, not well-read; not even whimsical; but he had His Own Ideas.

9

CLEANING off a crust of dried ink from this pen I have used so long, it suddenly came to me that its little cloven beak, or hoof, is bright gold. Dipped in jet black ink, the liquid glistens purple, dark as some Burgundy wines or those roses on the south wall of the Physic Garden at Oxford (where the

Cherwell bends round below Magdalen Bridge).
It is a fountain pen. I bought it in Paris in 1924,
but I use it as I always have to use fountain pens,
by dipping. That is the best way to use a pen, it
gives you time in mid-sentence to think, but not
so much time that you know you are thinking. At
the top of the thin split in the nib is a little cavity;
I have just noticed (for the first time in all these
thousands of pages) it is shaped like a heart. From
that small dark ace of hearts the ink drains down
to the point.

There is an inscription on the gold of the pen,
apparently a Russian name. I like to think of that
mysterious Russian who has gone diving for
sunken treasure in my behalf, so many many times.
His name seems to be REGUS PATOFF. He is a
queer fellow; I am smiling just to think about him.
Sometimes he lies idle for days, scaled over with a
scurf of dead ink. He is obstinate and without
shame. When he knows there is something he
should or must do, he cares naught for it. But set
him loose to go ploitering on his own hunch,
there's no such fun in the world. I have to walk
about a bit and think of his pliskies. (I spoke of
him as Russian, but he seems to have had a Scottish wet-nurse.) He has to be watched. He can take
as many shapes as Tam Lin in the old ballad that
prickles your cushes like that wind out of the
north, "a sharp wind and a snell." He can shape

66

himself the snake, the wild deer, the burning iron; but hold him fast, he takes at length his simple being, the mother-naked man. He dives deep, he tells true.

Yes, clean off the crust of dead ink; the pen is pure gold.

Regus Patoff, like so many Russians I suppose, has a touch of dangerous instability in his temperament. I have found him bitterly mocking some fat editorial in a great newspaper, yet on his knees before a plume of swansdown from Hodgson or de la Mare. He is so thrilled by the gallant snouty highstepping look of a locomotive that he would easily forget to board the train. Up through bottomless ink he dredges for me such beaded bubbles as

> I saw with open eyes
> Singing birds sweet
> Sold in the shops
> For the people to eat,
> Sold in the shops of
> Stupidity Street,

and again—equally irrelevant—

> Who said, "All Time's delight
> Hath she for narrow bed,
> Life's troubled bubble broken?"
> That's what I said.

67

Why should he spout me these jets of black rainbow? I who live on Stupidity Street, what am I to do about them? Even the dogs know more than I. Living alone with some dogs for several days (and bedevilled by Regus Patoff) I was walking about and saying aloud Ralph Hodgson's rhyme about singing birds sweet, sold in the shops of Stupidity Street. You know how deep and satisfying a voice can be in an empty house. And poor Frisky, a young dog of many follies but still aware as dogs are, was horrified. He raised his head with dreadful eyes. He understood the tone of my voice. He knew it was true, he was frightened. I let him out to go and bark it off.

We do sell the singing birds; we sell our own children into slavery. Perhaps it is impossible not to: they plead to be sold. Stupidity Street looks often so damned safe and solid. If you try to fight Stupidity Street with its own weapons you are sure to lose. "Let me choose my own weapons and I'll conquer the world" (or as much of it as I need to conquer). Who was it said that? It doesn't matter: nothing is true until you say it to yourself. But I'll put quotation marks around it to make it look less braggart.

I remember once pleading to a taskmaster that a pen was not a jade in harness but a feather lifted on the wind. He forgot it promptly; he was an editor. Now Regus Patoff reminds me that pens are often gold. There is, presumably, some stiffening alloy; pure gold would write too sirupy. "Give me a golden pen," cried Keats, and proceeded to write probably the worst maudlin sonnet; though appropriate to its title, "On Leaving Some Friends at an Early Hour." The gold in Shakespeare's pen was not of metal. There was living goose-quill in the point that wrote the tragic, the almost mumbled epilogue, which some scholars tell us was his last word to his customers:—

> My project fails,
> Which was to please—
> My ending is despair.

So must all projects end that aim to please any but one's self. You write for others, and live in hope to strike home into their gristle, yet you dare not take thought whether or if they shall approve. For this I like my Russian serf. He dives deep, he brings up what he finds, and heeds not my dismay. But enough of Patoff: he is only a phantom anyhow.

I was thinking not of writing but of living, or being. Very little writing at a time is plenty; that is why there are essayists, who are people who are lazy, or frequently interrupted, or both; who pretend to Tell All, but really are making continuous

subtle choices of omission. It is queer that there are
not more women essayists: women have so much
to do. But no, the women all write novels. It
takes courage, because a woman can be very happy
rearranging bureau drawers. I suppose the bureau
drawers of women novelists are very impromptu.

But when you begin to write about actual living,
instead of nice fantastical stuff, you are immediately embarrassed; it all sounds very humble. If
you admit that one evening (you remember that
cool evening in April when there were more stars
than lonely people knew what to do with?) you
sat down in the kitchen with a dog and a plate of
frankfurters and said to yourself, This is unquestionably one of the most beautiful evenings I have
known,—well, it isn't the kind of thing that goes
well in print. A mature dog is excellent for conversation. Anyone who has ever sent the family away
for a holiday, and lived alone with the dog and the
icebox, understands why old virgins soliloquize to
their cats and canaries. No one, moreover, appre-
ciates the very special genius of your conversation
as a dog does. If you chat with him a while, gradually building up the argument and the intonation,
he relishes it so that he will roll all round the floor,
lie on his back kicking, and groan with joyous worship. Very few wives or husbands are so affected.

I fear that our affection for dogs is based on
very low motives. We know that no matter how

paltry we are, we can count on their admiration; and man has a strong craving to be admired.

The furnace fire burns primrose and blue—again, if you wish, you can call on one of Keats's worst sonnets: "Small busy flames play through the fresh-laid coals." It is not to be supposed that a poet's tailings and slag have not their service: very often they are what pleases us most for random combustion. The kitchen clock ticks conscientiously. There is some excellent theology in the fact that kitchen clocks are always kept ahead of time. You wash up (a pipe never tastes better than over the sink). You consider the adventures of the day —how you got weighed on a subway platform: and discovered that the scales not only tell your weight (176 with overcoat on) but Fortune too. "Will I succeed?" was the question the machine put into your mouth, and gave its own answer: "No, you are not a sticker." That statement you had tried to put in French for a hostess in a little gallic restaurant. "Vous ne collez pas," was your version: why did she shriek so with mirth?

Night, the clear night of spring, comes down and surrounds the well-loved house. This evening is not words, it is life. It is the whole world. Going out to put away the car, I am staggered by the brilliance of Orion. He is earlier and earlier now; soon daylight will overtake him and he is gone until next winter. (At least so I think? I never seem to see him in the summer?) He is running, his head stretched forward, his great limbs awkwardly bestriding the dark; running with the ungainly fierceness of a commuter slogging for a train. It is easy to see what he is running for: Diana, the new moon, eddying away through the lacy trees. The frogs are fluting sadly in Gissing Pond: they seem to think he will not catch her. Turning back from the garage, the corner of my eye tingles upon an illusion, and for the freezing of an instant nerves are knotted with a twitch. The lamp in the study with its rounded hood has taken the form of a head bent watchfully over my table. I see a face, looking downward, radiating light. Do we sometimes see more truth than we know out of what we call the corner of the eye? (or is it the cornea of the eye?)

The enormous hours of this evening. It is still younger than eight o'clock and there is no necessity. There is nothing between me and space. I can read, I can think, I can walk to and fro and (if necessary) look at myself in the glass. There is nowhere I have to go, there is nothing I have to do. And even tomorrow the same will be true. Like the nautilus, I build the hours of vacancy around me. I can think the most idiot things: I forgive myself everything. Tonight, I say to myself, I am divine. I put on my old blue slippers.

Who can sit down, deliberately and by day, to

write of Night? The one I want to remember, is gone forever; tonight may never come. Last Night was too precious to try to write about it while it lasted. I lay down on the couch to try to watch it go by, to see what it was made of.

Night, I discovered, has a faintly bitter taste, caused by its large ingredient of Unattained Possibility; which is another word for Memory? It flows more steadily than Day. Perhaps Eternity is the sum total of Nights, Time just the adding up of Days. Perhaps nothing in Night can quite match the proud feeling of the late forenoon hours; but there are large tracts of Day that Night might well take over. For a sensitive observer Sunsets are protracted far beyond decency. They cause pain. Women however approve of sunsets so they will probably remain unchanged. Sunset is the beginning of women's power. There is a phrase about turning night into day: it is nonsense. It cannot be done. You yield yourself to Night as never to the other. Why has no one ever told me what people think about Night? It has been going on a long while, and is no one doing anything about it? I lie here and glory in it and am terrified. Is it because we see so little we are aware of so much more? I do not believe I have taken Night seriously enough.

I began to weaken—I saw a package of books and found myself wondering whether, by any

73

chance, there might be a detective story in it. When I went to look for Orion again—at 10:20— he was vanished. I don't know where he goes, but after he leaves the accustomed place over the garage I can never find him again. And I put on the kettle for a cup of cocoa.

The pen, Regus Patoff, lay untouched on the table, his gold all sooted with stale ink. Tomorrow would do for writing. That night I only lived. I was.

10

WILL you hold me this new moon, this first warm wind of spring, keep it just so, long enough to tell you what I saw? Over the green grass of Central Park, broad meadows of reality on which one might not tread, came the southern breeze heavy with soft threatening magic, foreboding all the dazzling grievance of Manhattan summer. Trees, still only sketchy green memoranda, would soon thicken into full folio, complete publication. Blued in pale haze the great heights of 59th Street stood like Camelot on the sky. Dangerous fairylands, bastions of unbelief! And under those blue citadels, terrifying solids of dominion, I dreamed the small gray outline of an old old city. She was selvaged by clear slow rivers; she gave away her eternity in music every quarter-hour. But there was a time

74

when New College bell tower seemed to reach just as near the top as the gilded pinnacle of Sherry-Netherland.

(How well trained we are; the gods, or the Police Commissioner, must sometimes grin. Such narrow concrete paths and everybody on them; such wide generosities of turf being kept off of. . . . Why not, if you feel like it, use a preposition to end a sentence with? Perhaps life ends like that. Looking at the forbidden grass, I realized better than ever before the extraordinary greatness of Walt Whitman's title for his book. To take as emblem this commonest, humblest, most disregarded and yet most satisfying of all earth's generosities, that I think was genius.)

If the paper were not before him as he writes, I doubt if he could quite believe it—

Oxoniæ, Termino S. Mich. A. D. 1910
    Die XV° Mensis Oct
    Quo die comparuit coram me
Joannes Mistletoe è Coll. Novo, Gen. Fil.
et admonitus est de observandis Statutis hujus Universitatis, et in Matriculam Universitatis relatus est.

C. B. HEBERDEN
Vice-Cancellarius

That took place in the Divinity Schools, behind the Sheldonian, on a Saturday afternoon. Each young freshman, properly wearing his white tie, mortarboard, and the comic little cape dignified as a "gown," was given a large blue copy of *Statuta et Decreta Universitatis Oxoniensis*. Carrying which, and filled with a pleasant sense of important anticipations, they all trooped back to their various colleges. There would be time to study those Statutes while the kettle was boiling for tea. I know that Mistletoe took great pleasure in the section entitled *De Moribus Conformandis*, written in a vigorous dog-Latin of the 17th century, and still happily and humorously perpetuated in the volume. There, while waiting for hot buttered crumpets to come up from the college kitchen, the freshman might learn something of academic etiquette. He might learn (you must allow me the pleasure of writing down the actual captions)

De Reverentia Juniorum erga Seniores,

De coercendis otiosis Scholaribus in Civitate oberrantibus,

De Domibus Oppidanorum non frequentandis,

De Oenopoliis, seu Tabernis vinariis, Popinis et Diversoriis non frequentandis.

("It is decreed that scholars of whatever condition shall abstain from lodging-houses, inns, wine-shops and any houses, whether in the town or the precinct of the university, in which wine, or any other drink, or the nicotian herb known as To-

bacco, is ordinarily sold." This excellent statute, a
student of academic history would ponder, was not
originally devised for moral requirements only,
but also because the various colleges had their own
breweries and cellars, and quite properly intended
to make their own decent revenue on the potations
of their members.)

De Nocturna Vagatione reprimenda—

"It is decreed that all scholars of whatever condition who chance, for whatever reason, to be outside their colleges or halls in the evening, shall be-
take themselves to their own colleges and halls
before the ninth hour (which is wont to be de-
nounced by the pulsation of the great bell of
Christ Church College); and that immediately
on the pulsation of this same great bell, the gates
of the several Colleges and Halls shall be shut and
locked. These having been shut, if occasion requires, the prefects shall explore (by perlustrating
the cubicles of individuals) whether any are per-
noctating or wandering outside their own College
or Hall."

What a language is Latin: the phrase for Big
Tom's 9 p. m. "pulsation" is *quae denunciari solet.*
To denounce, to report downward—yes, perfect.

De Ludis prohibitis—

—"That scholars shall abstain from the hunting of
wild beasts with dogs, traps, nets or guns; from carrying bombards and crossbows; and from the use

of falcons for fowling. Also that within the University of Oxford or its precinct, unless by special grace of the Vice-Chancellor, no tight-rope walkers, actors, nor contests of gladiators are permitted."

De famosis Libellis cohibendis, et de Contumeliis compescendis,

De Armis non gestandis—

"It is decreed that no scholar, or other person, within the ambit of the University, shall carry either offensive or defensive weapons or missiles, by day or by night, except those who for honest recreation carry a bow and arrows."

De Vehiculis—

"It is decreed that all scholars abstain from the use of vehicles in which they are wont to be carried with themselves as charioteers, by whatever name these may be called, unless on account of infirm health or any other rational cause a license has been granted by the Proctors."

I have chosen, and baldly translated, a few of these good old precautions. No one could read them without realizing he had become part of something very ancient; nor without perceiving Oxford's sovereign and typically English sense in keeping these archaic statutes in force. By interpretation, by latitudes and fictions, they cover every contingency of modern life. When an airplane first appeared in Oxford, in 1912, it was by

78

the statute *De Vehiculis* that undergraduates were
forbidden to go flying.

I leave him there for the moment, that young
Mistletoe, with his new copper kettle steaming on
the trivet, and the ugly brown teapot he bought for
himself, and the small silver teaspoons. Already he
had paid his first visit to his tutor, and learned
what were the requirements of the examination *In
Rudimentis Jurisprudentiæ*. Already he had bought
his copy of *Englische Verfassungsgeschichte* by
Gneist, that learned and illegible German; and his
Gaius's Institutes. R. L. Stevenson remarked that
of his own studies in Roman law all he remembered
was that "emphyteusis is not a disease, nor stilli-
cide a crime." It is sad that of the sprightly Gaius
all one is likely to recall offhand is the doctrine that
women were excluded from suffrage *propter levi-
tatem animi*. Mistletoe now regrets having parted
with his copy of Gaius, who would undoubtedly
bear re-reading. Also, as he drinks his first tea as
an Oxford matriculate, he meditates that he is to
undergo an examination in Divinity, viz. in Greek
Testament; but that "those who object on religious grounds to the study of Holy Scripture are
entitled to offer the equivalent." The "equivalent" is stated to be either Plato's *Apology* or
Pascal's *Pensées*. I leave him there, alone with his
tea and very happy. I would not intrude on the

dreams of a boy at such a time. Very likely it was
a soft hazy afternoon, the treetops in New College
garden, seen over the ancient wall, were turning
yellow, and the stroke of those innumerable
chimes beginning to din themselves into his memory.

I rarely speak of Oxford; I do not often think of
her, as I knew her; it is not wise. To think of Oxford, alone and from far, is to be thrilled as one
is thrilled in reading Donne or Milton or Sir
Thomas. I do not think now of the much hilarity
of that life, of its hale frolic and good wine, of its
joy in exercising the mind for the mere pleasure of
it. I think of the unbelievable beauty of those colleges, their fantasy of green and grey, of flowers
and firelight, fit indeed to blast open the mind of
many a young outlander come from the uglier alcoves of education. I was in Oxford, years later,
for a few hours only; it was a rare morning of sunshine and I spent it strolling about, or thinking in
New College garden. No, not even thinking, but
aware of those flowers, the lindens and chestnuts
and the fortressed wall. I was reproached afterward, in all kindness, by an old good friend, for not
having gone to see him. But I was not in Oxford to
see anyone. I was there to recreate a little heaven
of my own, and I would not willingly have crossed
the lawn to meet Walt Whitman or the King.

I speak of what I know. Often the most sociable of creatures, Oxford helped to teach me the bliss of solitude, the power when needed to beget my own world for myself.

To be too near her now, too often, I could not bear. She is a dream, and for some who love her she must remain so. To be too near her would remind one of her delicious snobberies (which I pray God she may never lose; nor will she as long as she has plenty of young Etonians and Wykehamists); of her too comfortable certainties, of her gallant modernizations. I want her, and my heart holds her fast, as she was in the last of the Unquestioning Era, 1910–13, before the war; when I was a boy and supposed there was an answer to everything. There are plenty of beauties in the world besides hers: I can see, on New York streets, miracles of man's bravado such as she never dreamed. But for something quite other I revisit her in thought, humbly and seldom. How else can I say it but that you will find it also in Sir Thomas Browne, in De Quincey. You will hear it in the deep organ, quivering the squares of stone.

I said to Mistletoe that it would be well not to be sentimental about Oxford; to which he replied, What else does she exist for?

In honor of those bells, those gardens, those friendships, those idle evenings by the fire, I make the enormous impossible effort to reach back. How gay, how clear, how naive might the language be, to tell the comedy of that time. But it cannot be just that; man, the noble animal, splendid in ashes and pompous in the grave, has been at work since then with his drums and tramplings. I would not look at that jocund life without thinking what was preparing for it in the hollow of Time. Then, then, in that golden prime, the great world hung in the balance. Anxieties of trouble to come were not lacking, but who, drugged in such benison of charm, could take them seriously? The dear old Spooner toddled about the quad like a wise and innocent white rabbit; the hansom cabs came clashing up the narrow crooked lane; at dinner time the candle-light shone upon silver mugs and Yorkshire pudding and the starched shirts of dons. In the front lodge the whiskered porter, with more presence than an archdeacon, kept guard over the gentility of this strange mixture of cathedral, athletic club, monastery and tavern. New College bumped Magdalen and went Head of the River; the young sportsmen-monks burned the seats of their medieval privy and capped the chapel pinnacles with jordans. A King was crowned, the college ball was held and there was dancing all night long in a huge marquee. All night long those shy or lonely or frugal scholars who did not attend heard the sweet suggestions of the waltz as undertone to their dreams, or lay awake thinking that Life is Very Unfair.

And what dignity she has. Not once, in all these years, has she circularized her alumnus with appeals, requests, inquiries, questionnaires. Only once, officially, has he heard from her: when she sent a list of her members who had fallen in the war. She is doing her job, let him do his. He wishes he could give her a silver mug, for some unsuspecting child to drink her fine bitter beer.

II

THE first things any Oxford freshman bought for himself—at any rate any American youngster who had the sense not to arrive with a lot of outlandish gear—were a corkscrew, tea-apparatus, and one of those china tobacco-jars with his college arms illuminated on it. Then he began to skirmish among the bookshops. Oh Paradise of booksellers —Blackwell, Gadney, Thornton, Parker, Slatter and Rose—and many many others, whose names for the moment I forget. And with these may I also mention the renowned Heffer of Cambridge? For I should like to make plain—what very likely no Oxonian has ever done before—that whatever one says in praise of Oxford is equally true of Cambridge also. They are two valves of one enormous genteel idea. Cambridge in many respects is luckier: less afflicted with cosmopolitanism and tourists; but they need no comparisons.

I remember Mistletoe telling me that he brought to Oxford no books whatever except the Bible and the Oxford Book of English Verse. So the shelves in his sitting-room looked bare enough. The first feature of Oxford bookshops that caught the economical and aspiring eye was the rich assortment and varying color scheme of Everyman's Library —a shilling a volume in that happy time. Everyman attained a considerable footage in his bookcase before his time was up; but two of the very first that he bought were *Tom Jones* and a selection from Hazlitt. *Tom Jones* because he had first read it (with delightful scandalized tremors) as a freshman at Haverford; and Hazlitt, I think, because a set of Hazlitt's Collected Works was specially prominent in the New College library.

Of course it was Stevenson, the passion of his boyhood, who sent him to Hazlitt. Everyone knows the famous "We are mighty fine fellows nowadays but we cannot write like William Hazlitt." Quoting which, Henley asserted that Stevenson "said no more than the truth;" but I feel that Henley was for the moment more anxious to score against R. L. S. than to honor W. H.—He might with greater generosity have said, as he so finely did of Lamb's tribute to Hazlitt, "Thus does one royalty celebrate the kingship and enrich the immortality of another." For surely Stevenson's bonny outburst (in the paper *Walking Tours*) has done much to keep Hazlitt alive. Why did not R. L. S. (or anyone else, so far as I remember) in remarking Hazlitt's "amorous precision" in the details of the bottle of sherry and the cold chicken on April 10, 1798, at the inn of Llangollen (which I hope you will pronounce correctly, but doubt it) realize that the date was Hazlitt's birthday? Hence, undoubtedly, the sherry, for he was generally an abstainer.

Mistletoe's memories of the library at New College—a surprisingly unimpressive thesaurus and not much frequented—always associate with that set of Hazlitt, a modern edition and apparently unread before. For Hazlitt, as for the other Mr. W. H. to whom certain Sonnets were dedicated, we may predict, within due limitation, the right kind of eternity. It would be folly to think that Child Mistletoe was then capable of justly relishing Hazlitt. We can appreciate nothing until we have a chance to measure it against our own powers and our own experience. It was not until years later, when he became a practising journalist himself, that he could get a notion of what sort of journalists were Hazlitt and De Quincey. It was not, for example, until he saw the Dempsey-

85

Carpentier fight in Jersey City that he understood what Hazlitt had done in his account of Neate and the Gas-man's set-to a hundred years earlier. As an education in English literature, working four years on the old *Evening Post* was more valuable than any college course. It is idle to imagine that any college can teach you much about literature; but it can make you sensitive in those regions of the mind that are likely to bear the full impact of literature later on. What the secure young student is unlikely to realize is that writing is not always just a spontaneous flowering; it is also a way of earning a living, and often conducted under conditions of huge irony, farce or fatigue. I had a hearty grin the other day when I picked up a volume of Shakespeare edited by a famous scholar and found him naively observing that "*As You Like It* was in all probability produced under circumstances necessitating great haste on the part of the author." Few plays were ever prepared otherwise.

Whatever voice or instinct pitched him on Hazlitt, it was a sound one. Smatterer then as now, he only dabbled in that great set of books but he got the feeling of the man. The *Liber Amoris* was beyond the scope of undergraduate sensibility; and even to savor the full humor of an essay like *On the Want of Money* requires some various experience in worldly pinches. How exquisite is the comment "of all people, I cannot tell how it is, but players appear to me the best able to do without money." Perhaps Mistletoe was interested in the fact that Hazlitt—like Burns and Shelley—so nearly became an American author; though W. H.'s child years in this country did not give him any special affection for it. Of America he wrote at eight years old "It would have been a great deal better if the white people had not found it out. Let the others have it to themselves." But who that has ever seen it even in photograph can forget the beautiful child-portrait of him done by his older brother: the long inquisitive nose, the anxious eyes, the sensitive uncertain lips. You understand then something of the boy of nineteen who was glorified by meeting Coleridge—

My soul has indeed remained in its original bondage, dark, obscure, with longings infinite and unsatisfied; my heart, shut up in the prison-house of this rude clay, has never found, nor will it ever find, a heart to speak to; but that my understanding also did not remain dumb and brutish, or at length found a language to express itself, I owe to Coleridge.

If you have read that beautiful essay—"My First Acquaintance With Poets"—you will remember that Hazlitt wishes someone would write a sonnet To the Road between Wem and Shrews-

bury, where he walked ten miles in January mud
to have his first sight of Coleridge. Similarly does
De Quincey describe how, after his own youthful
encounter with Coleridge some years later, he was
too excited to wish for sleep, and walked all night
long from Bridgewater to Bristol. Forty miles, he
says it was. The Opium Eater knew how to tell a
good story, but there is plenty of testimony that
they had legs in those days.

"The road between Wem and Shrewsbury . . ."
it is such allusions that stir me. For, now that I
remember it, even before buying a single book the
young collegian bought a bicycle, and on some
thousands of miles of country roads learned something of that sense of place which is so vivid in
English literature. If I love a book I hanker to see
the house where it was written, or the roads and
villages it mentions. Hence the joy of that "amorous precision" of Hazlitt's. Remember too that
the years 1910–13 were the last of the old wayfar-
ing world. Motors had not driven the quiet cyclist
from the main highways, and modest inns were
not hard to find. I believe that the Bicycling Era
touched the high peak of human felicity. Perhaps if
I could live it all over again I should ask to begin
with that breakfast at 8 Banbury Road, on July
16, 1911, the day Mifflin McGill and I set out to
bike from Oxford to Edinburgh. In an old black
note book remaining from that journey I see it said

of the two-mile coast into a town called Glossop,
"we sang, shouted and laughed all the way down."
I approve of that.

A sense of place, a sense of the reality of the
past, these were two of Oxford's special gifts. A
lover of literature, sitting down with a large-scale
map of any part of England, would be sure to find
some village or other he would have a special
reason for wanting to see. I remember one day,
poring idly over a chart of Hertfordshire, a magic
name swam into my ken. Only a country farmhouse, but there was no mistaking its identity.
There, among such hamlets as Hatching Green,
Bowling Alley, Custardwood and Claggybottom,
were the magic words Mackery End. Yes, "Mackery End in Hertfordshire," as in Elia. To get on a
bicycle and go there was the simplest thing in the
world; not less shy than Elia himself the boy did
not intrude where so much explanation would have
been needed, but sat in a haystack just outside
the farmyard, ate the sandwiches he had brought
with him, and memorized the old house with an
eye that can see it still.

"Of Persons One Would Wish To Have Seen"
was one of Hazlitt's themes. Certainly he himself
is among them. I should like to have seen him on
the way back from the famous prize-fight, as he
and "Jack Pigott the sentimentalist" walked the
road from Hungerford to Newbury "now observ-

ing the effect of a brilliant sun on the tawny meads
or moss-coloured cottages, now exulting in the
fight, now digressing to some topic of general and
elegant literature." Pigott himself (Patmore, to
give him his right name) has recorded their
evening—

Snugly housed for the night at one of those most comfortable of all public domiciles, a third-rate country inn;
and here, in a little wainscoted parlor on the ground
floor, we were soon warmly and cosily ensconced by a
blazing fire, with the tea-things on the table, the curtains let down, an early supper ordered of roast fowl
and apple-pudding, a neat-handed Phyllis to wait on
us (which was always a great point of comfort with
Hazlitt) and an interminable evening before us, destined
to engender a volume of Table Talk.

But even more I think one would have chosen to
see him at his wedding, at which Lamb was best
man and was almost turned out of the church for
outbursts of merriment. "Something awful always
makes me laugh" was his apology.

On the road between Hungerford and Newbury
they must have passed within view of that Wilt-
shire hill called Inkpen Beacon. What a theme for
conversation that name might have given our Mr.
W. H. On the same map, not far from Salisbury, I
see written very small the word *Winterslow*, where
Hazlitt used to hide himself to get writing done.

The best textbook of literature is always an atlas.

12

To REMIND you how long ago 1910 was, it was still possible in that year to sail from Philadelphia in a liner (the good old *Friesland*) that had a clipper bow and a bowsprit. And it makes it seem equally remote to remember finding our classmate J. H. under the trees not far from Barclay Hall, preparing himself for the final examinations that spring. He looked up from his notebook with a face of crisis. "It is absolutely impossible to believe in God," he said sadly, "if you take Biology 2." He surrendered God reluctantly, for he was writing much verse at the time, and to tutoyer the Deity is a great resource for young poets; as is also getting the word *harlot* into print. There is a college notebook of R. L. Stevenson's in the library at Haverford, in which he rhymed it with *scarlet;* it delights me to think how pleased he must have been.

But at Haverford, Mistletoe and his cronies thought of literature as something definitely Beyond the Horizon. They had their first great thrill in Keats; and they read, in ecstatic midnight coterie, *Songs from Vagabondia* and *A Shropshire Lad*. (What poet's heart has not responded to

91

Housman's little note in his *Last Poems:* "I can no longer expect to be revisited by the continuous excitement under which in the early months of 1895 I wrote the greater part of my other book.") But actual practitioners of belles lettres were rare in our suburban academe, and we held literature in proportionate veneration. It was something not encountered in being. When we were lectured by famous visitors it was on such safe topics as Browning, or Coleridge, or Eschatology. This last we attended vaguely expecting something about Fish, with lantern slides. There were some lectures by Barrett Wendell, too, but about what I venture no classmate could conceivably retrieve. Perhaps about Cotton Mather? but the young hobblede-hoys were too amused by the good man's Harvard accent to pay much heed to the matter.

At Oxford, on the other hand, Mistletoe found himself under the influence of literature as a pres-ent living reality. I suppose all arts and knowl-edges proceed by their own young contagions and discipleships. To boys at Oxford about 1910–13, Belloc and Chesterton were Dioscuri in Chief who typified the glamour of journalism. Perhaps you have forgotten how those two had the world at their feet in that happy time. Reading *The Path to Rome* it seemed to an Oxford freshman that there never had been such fresh, merry, volatile and humorous writing. And in Chesterton's manly verse, what a blast of beauty and anger—even sending the boy back to his own Whitman, who had troubled him, when G. K. C. trumpeted:

I find again the book we found, I feel the hour that flings
Far out of fish-shaped Paumanok some cry of cleaner
    things;
And the Green Carnation withered, as in forest fires that
    pass,
Roared in the wind of all the world ten million leaves of
    grass.

They were of the great breed of Fleet Street, these two; they incarnated all our vague romantic notions of Dr. Johnson and the Cheshire Cheese and steak-and-kidney pudding. They suggested late hours, burly vigor, and gallant sortie against all things cruel and pettifogging. Certainly their talk about beer increased our orders to the college buttery; how often young collegians are busy sentimentally trying to catch up with the potations of some middle-aged journalist who has by that time been put on a diet.

Let me not speak too lightly. These boyish influenzas are of immense value: later events sometimes temper them, but by those warm flushes of excitement literature passes on her vocation. In the long army of those who live by the pen, we do not forget our loyalty to our former officers. Ah, my Hilaire, do I sometimes see in your later work a touch of bitterness toward this now very different world? Remember there are those, names you never knew, who remember the whiff of your saddleleather as you rode at the head of the troop, whose nerves are stung now as they were twenty years ago, by such as this:

SEPTEMBER

I, from a window where the Meuse is wide,
Looked eastward out to the September night;
The men that in the hopeless battle died
Rose, and deployed, and stationed for the fight;
A brumal army, vague and ordered large
For mile on mile by some pale general;
I saw them lean by companies to the charge,
But no man living heard the bugle-call.

And fading still, and pointing to their scars,
They fled in lessening crowd, where gray and high
Dawn lay along the heaven in misty bars;
But watching from that eastern casement, I
Saw the Republic splendid in the sky,
And round her terrible head the morning stars.

I remember my tutor Mr. Herbert Fisher, then acting as chief editor of the Home University Library (a series of very spirited little books that escaped into print at that time, as exciting to us as

the Modern Library to later youths) showing me
the manuscript of Chesterton's *Victorian Age in
Literature*, which had just reached him. It was all
in G. K. C.'s strong curly hand, and I looked at it
with reverence. I believe it was the first practicable
book manuscript I had ever seen. And yet no omen
was manifest, no tremulation of the shelves, to
warn me how many I was to encounter.

So these two paladins were very real: not
wraiths at all, but visible in print and in flesh. The
Eye-Witness, that lively weekly that G. K. C.
edited, had to be seized in the common room when
you could get it, there were always so many watching for it. When Belloc lectured on Rabelais one
afternoon, the great hall of the Examination
Schools was crowded to the window-sills. Without
a scrap of notes, bundling up the skirts of his gown
behind his squat person, he held us spellbound for
nearly two hours on the doctrine of Exuberance.
Of course there were other figures too. There
was a delicate rumor that Max Beerbohm was an
Oxford man; confirmed by the appearance of
Zuleika Dobson, which we all bought and read at
once, nor could we ever thereafter pass the statued
railings of the Sheldonian without remembering
that perspiration started to the brows of those
Roman emperors when Zuleika came to Oxford.
The picture of Abimelech V. Oover the Rhodes

95

Scholar seemed a little coppery for that silver satirist, and Mistletoe's premature chivalry was perhaps distressed by Max's genial raillery of "The virguncules of Somerville and Lady Margaret Hall" (viz. our Oxford co-eds) whom he had his own reasons for sentimentalizing. He pondered Mr. Oover, who was distressed by "the quaint old English custom of not making public speeches after private dinners," and consoled himself by the reflection that Max had probably never seen a Rhodes Scholar. *Zuleika Dobson*, so highly praised by non-Oxonians, is only half successful. It begins enchantingly, but it dries up. *The Oxford Circus*, by Messrs. Miles and Mortimer, published some years later, seems to me more maliciously amusing, though only the children of Balliol can fully savor all its sinister jabs.

Profiles on the grand scale came over that young horizon too. He saw Henry James and Robert Bridges receive their honorary degrees. The meandering Jacobite style was tenderly parodied, I think, by the Public Orator in his Latin presentation. As for Dr. Bridges, surely one of the poets most truly honored by those capable of honor, it remains strange not that his work is scantly known but that sonnets and lyrics so gravely beautiful should have survived at all.

I wish I could find my old copy of the *English Review* in which Masefield burst upon us. Was it

in the spring of 1912, or 1911? Almost overnight
everyone was reading *The Everlasting Mercy*. Does
a thrill like that come to every undergraduate generation? Somehow I doubt it. Put yourself back
into that setting: spring in those gardens, the
chestnut trees like huge chandeliers, the street-
band playing Gilbert and Sullivan airs in the pink
sunset of the High; white flannels and strawberries
and teabaskets on the Cher—and that blue magazine in which suddenly poetry spoke to us as it
should. We could not know it then, of course, but
one can see now that through all the English-
writing world there was, about 1912, a stirring
and a movement of truth. It was so in America
too, where Vachel Lindsay was beginning to peddle
his Rhymes for Bread. In the too secure and gracious life of Oxford, Masefield came to us with a
glorious twinge. Poetry was still alive, and still
had all its greatest things to say, or say again.
Poor Masefield I suppose paid the penalty: the
undergraduate literary clubs of almost every
college in both Oxford and Cambridge wrote and
asked him to come and speak. Mistletoe still has
Mr. Masefield's very polite little note from Well
Walk, Hampstead—which reminded them that
Keats too was real—regretting he could not accept the kind invitation of the "Shibli Bagarags,"
one of those brief literary sodalities for botanizing
asphodel.

97

13

THERE were three, the Mathematician, the Scandinavian, and young Mistletoe. April was coming in, and they grew weary of the garrets in the rue de la Sorbonne. It had been amusing, even the squalor and the six spirals of corkscrew stairway, the incredibly primitive sanitation and the cooking for themselves. For reasons of romance as well as thrift they insisted on doing their own cuisine, and lived mostly on cocoa, lentils, and porridge. In those days they needed no raw whiskey to make them sing. They sang in the attics, they had one specially lewd and tuneful ditty in which they contrived a gruesome harmony. Scandinavia had a sweet rather thin tenor, Mistletoe could manage a moderate barytone, Mathematics mumbled on an asymptote. It must have been terrible. Even the bearded *patron*, far below, could not endure it. He used to stand at the bottom of the staircase well and scream, "Il ne faut pas chanter comme ça."

But April sunlight began to warm the roofs. Cocottes were leaning out of the courtyard windows washing their hair. Through the thin partitions of adjoining garrets came creakings and ejaculations which were troublesome to youths of spirit. In the little sixth floor corridor the deplorable concierge was discovered misusing the sink where they washed their dishes. They fled to the Forest—yes, the Forest of Fontainebleau.

I should have gone back a little earlier, to the Quai Chanzy, Boulogne, where he first set foot in France. That was the way to arrive, not in a big liner with a mob of prosperous tourists, but in a little cargo steamer that sailed from London Bridge at 1 A. M. It was a brilliant spring afternoon on the Quai Chanzy, and as Mistletoe and Mathematics toted their portmanteaux along the railway siding Mistletoe heard his first French words uttered in their own air. It was a bearded stevedore, a frail and meagre creature (he looked rather like Francis Thompson) who cried out in a sing-song voice "Ce n'est pas la même chose." I can hear him still. Mathematics had been in France before, but his communicative resources were very small. They had several hours to ramble Boulogne before catching the Paris train, and lunched in an agreeable café. Mathematics, a fanatical lover of cocoa, wanted more of it and kept crying to the waiter "Plus de chocolat!" The more he reiterated this unintentional negation, the more the waiter tried to assure him that the chocolate was not compulsory. But Mistletoe's simplicity was not far behind. Rattling toward Paris on the wooden benches of a 3rd-class railway carriage he studied a newspaper. He was somewhat staggered by the number of advertisements of Sages-Femmes, and wondered why France should need so many fortune-tellers, for so he construed them.

Any way of getting to France is a good way, but you will forgive a special affection for that method of sneaking up on her when she didn't know or care whether they were coming. How much, in that spring of 1912, was still in the future; how much always is.

But the scholarly Scandinavian had been living in the rue de la Sorbonne all winter, and was emaciated by hard work and his own cooking. He had discovered that life can be very economically protracted on lentils; by these nourishing but monotonous legumes and the works of the Norse novelist Kielland the energies of his life were recruited. He needed ventilation, and the other two took him off to Fontainebleau.

Not Fontainebleau itself, but to the yonder outskirts of that forest region, to Moret-sur-Loing. I suppose the little main street of Moret, running from one fortified gate to the other, is still the same. Near the western gate, on the right-hand side as you enter the town, was a modest auberge famed for artistic villégiature, where they lunched and dined at the table d'hôte and admired the panels decorated by generations of visiting painters. They bedded in clean, airy but very chill

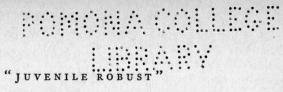
chambers above a laundry, alongside the river.
There, at night, trying to keep warm, they pursued
their various studies. Mathematics was probably
the most conscientious. In his excelsior trudge
upon higher rationality he was approaching the
vegetation-line. After breaking through the thick
forests of algebras and calculus he was beginning
to reach those tilted blueberry pastures from
which the mathematician gets the broadest and
purest view known to the human mind. In spite
of a waistcoat lined with flannel he was not warm,
but his mind was at ease. Mistletoe, supposedly
studying Constitutional History, was neglecting
Bishop Stubbs' *Charters* for the songs of Charles
d'Orléans, Villon, and Ronsard. *Le temps a laissé
son manteau,* said Charles of Orléans, *de vent, de
froidure et de pluie, et s'est vêtu de broderie, de soleil
rayant, clair et beau.* It sounded warm and jolly,
but the attic of the *blanchisseuse* where he tried
to translate it in its own meter was cold enough to
numb the fingers. The meadows along the Loing
were white with fruit-blossoms, which might almost have been snow to judge by temperature.

But it was the problem of Scandinavia that gave
the other two most amazement. What do the
novels of Kielland deal with, that they have so
lively effect on the mind? Or was it just release
from a long winter in a Paris garret that aroused

the mystic Norseman? He decided, first, that his system required fasting; so while the two M's went daily for their hearty viands and white wine at the auberge, the Scandinavian lived on lemon juice and water. Also the gymnosophist that lurks in every Norseman came out and flourished. To escape the chill of their lodgings these boys set off with rugs and books, every fine morning, to a southward-looking lair on the edge of the forest. Arrived there, Scandinavia would strip to his boots, perform a smart routine of setting-up exercise, and then run with fervor along the woodland aisles. That heavenly forest is criss-crossed with grassy paths and alleys, and far down the perspective of these green avenues his anxious companions would see the naked mystic twinkle in a beam of sun. So he would run, singing Norwegian melodies, darting into underbrush if a stranger hove in sight, and startling an occasional woodsman by a flash of his brilliant Scandinavian whiteness. In the ecstasy of this new freedom he laughed to himself continually, particularly when pursued for miles by an excited painter from Barbizon who caught a distant glimpse of that slender flitting pallor and toiled after him with paintbox and easel hoping to transfer it to canvas. Legends that still exist in Barbizon about the White Virgin of Moret, supposed to haunt those forest glades, date back to the Gymnosophist of Stavanger.

Meanwhile Mathematics and Mistletoe, whose wilder sensibilities were allayed by plentiful food and wine, lay on their rugs beneath the walnut tree and did not know what trouble was. Of Bishop Stubbs' collected Charters, those really fascinating documents, the one that seemed there to have most reality was the Forest Charter of Henry III. Surrounded by the green temptation of that old royal domain one could discern some meaning in the severity of the ancient forest laws. Boscage and pannage, venison and vert, began to make sense. There was a pleasure in reading old Henry's concessions to those of high degree:

> Quicunque archiepiscopus, episcopus, comes vel baro transierit per forestam nostram, liceat ei capere unam vel duas bestias . . . sin autem faciat cornari, ne videatur furtive hoc facere.

> "Any archbishop, bishop, count or baron who shall pass through our forest is permitted to take one or two head of game . . . provided a horn is blown, so that it shall not seem to be done furtively."

They could find no clause suggesting that a mystic might run naked in those woods, but at any rate there was nothing furtive about it. They amused themselves by wondering which provision of Henry III's Forest Charter they might appeal to for Scandinavia's defence in case he were run in by the local magistrate. (Henry III believed he had a valid claim to the throne of France as well as England.) The most reasonable defence would have been the claim that their mystic friend was constructively regarded as a domestic animal, for there was a clause allowing free men to take their domestic animals for an airing in the forests of the king.

That sunny forest-edge, looking over clouds of white fruit-petals and the meadows of the Loing—they bathed there once, but only once, for it was icy—seemed a long way from the great turnings of the world. Yet a little sketch still kept of the river-gate at Moret was drawn by a man who was blown to pieces by a shell five years later; and Mistletoe's last drowse under that walnut tree was broken by darkness. It was a fortnight since those young arcadians had seen a newspaper. That morning Mathematics had a strange impulse to walk over to Veneux-Nadon for a journal. The other two were basking on their rugs, listening to the hum of insects when their friend came back with bad news in his face. He threw down the paper and they read of the *Titanic*.

That horror connects in memory with a trivial but curious adventure in Paris the next day. Mistletoe was on the way to Devonshire, and had several hours in Paris. In a barber shop a bad five-franc piece was given him; it had a hole in it which had been plugged with tinfoil. It was an economic necessity to get some service out of the coin: he spent more than he could afford in various shopping to try to pass it. It was always refused in spite of his best stratagems. Discouraged he sat at last on a café terrasse for a humble glass of beer, and then learned that there was to be an eclipse of the Sun. Sure enough, the full beam of April brightness was already growing dim. It was an extraordinary sight, in the midday career of Paris traffic. Life paused, the very taxis stopped in mid-street to watch. The ingenious youth saw his opportunity, and hastily ordered another beer and a sandwich. He ate and drank fast; in the very corona of the eclipse he fled, leaving the imperfect coin as payment, and caught the train for Havre in the penumbra. It was his only triumph over European coinages, and it took the whole solar system to make it possible.

GRUB STREET RUNNERS

THE *Laconia*, sailing from Liverpool to Boston in August 1913, had a level voyage of warm and brilliant blue. How much of it his cabin-mate John Crowe Ransom remembers I cannot surmise, but Mistletoe recalls that they sat one sunny afternoon by the taffrail reading poetry aloud. Proper to unassuming Second Class passengers, it was second-rate poetry; it happened to be one of Francis Thompson's less important things:

> The lover whose soul shaken is
> In some decuman billow of bliss,
> His abashed pulses beating thick
> At the exigent joy and quick,
> Is dumbed, by aiming utterance great
> Up to the miracle of his fate.
>
> The wise girl, such Icarian fall
> Saved by her confidence that she's small,
> Feeling the infinite must be
> Best said by triviality,
> Speaks, where expression bates its wings,
> Just happy, alien, little things—
> And, while she feels the heavens lie bare,
> She only talks about her hair.

There was a moment of pleased young silence; then one of the group, whom he remembers now only as a wise girl from Swarthmore, asked—not unreasonably—"What is a decuman?" Thus originated the nickname Decuman for the deck steward.

Their inside stateroom was hot and crowded; they shared it with a retired blacksmith and a saloonkeeper. The smith, a good old fellow quite worth all Longfellow's homages, had to have his collar buttoned for him every morning. "If it was a wheelbarrow or a sledge," he said, "I could get a holt on it, but these damned little things——" I sympathize with the old man as I look back and try with heavy fingers to fasten together a few intricate memories. Is that what Gertrude Stein meant by Tender Buttons?

The crickets, and all that extraordinary insect obbligato of summer nights, welcomed him back. Coming home after three years abroad, he *felt* America for the first time. Previously I suppose he had taken her for granted, as natives do. August, he has divined since, is a month of special revelation, when the blaze of being comes dangerously near burning through. It is to the year what three o'clock in the afternoon is to the day; what the 1890's were to a great literary generation. The pellucid day of his return he arrived, about sunset, on an island in Narragansett Bay delightfully named Prudence. He smelt those juniper airs of New England seashore, heard again that amazing outcry, the soft yet savage rhythm of our summer evenings. "The crickets shouted, rattled tiny feet of approval like a gallery of young Shelleys." Then first, and by deep immediate choice, he was really an American. One evening of those wide grassy spaces, those August meteors, that shrill demon music, blotted out Oxford bells and all Europe's enchanted sweetness. This was not Francis Thompson, it was Walt Whitman. The strange jocular and terrifying energy of America was evident. Preposterous and damned, no doubt, but he is willing to be damned with it. It offers the tensions of delirium and disgust on which art can build, and the greatest imaginable wealth for literature. It is like rye whiskey, the symbolic national elixir, which for some moods is a nobler drink than any genteel wine; a beverage of godlike violence, a microcosm of American climate. The life of cities also should be savored in small doses, with frequent green escapes.

Any thoughtful man who earns his living round New York has observed in his own régime or that of his friends clear cross-sections of paradox that would give Plato an epilepsy. To live in America in those years, being moderately susceptible to mirth and dismay, and just not to have been run down, deafened, crazed, poisoned, or embittered, requires the agility of a chipmunk. Yet the morning returns, the old Oyster Bay locomotive rounds the curve under Harbor Hill jetting clouds of silver steam, the lunatic spire of Chrysler catches the sun, and who would have things different? It is not the dreamer's job to heckle society for its cruel and spectacular follies, nor suggest remedies for civilized misery. His task, as Anatole France remarked, is to admire life; even love it if possible. "On ne fait une oeuvre d'art qu'avec ses nerfs." In a certain kind of absurdly inconsistent heart why may not irony always cohabit with love, and the two be ambivalent? I seem to have heard a proletarian phrase that expresses, with the wisdom of all popular gnomes, something inherent in the American temper. It might well be written on our coinage instead of the disregarded mottoes still minted there. "It's a great life if you don't weaken." The salt in the aphorism is of course that we *do* weaken.

I am sorry if anyone imagines these groping astigmatisms to be an essay in Biography. Contemplating the comedy of my poor friend's existence, in so far as he allows, I find savory inflexions of the verbs of surprise. These are only a few paradigms from my Grammar of Astonishment. A biographer may be clever or witty; a novelist may lie like a trouper, or even sometimes dare to attempt the beautiful; but here I only try to sketch a few pictures of a youth who is not even dead, though he is ill of a fatal disease. If only it could be written in some other language. A book that deals with personal intuitions should always come from far away, like that exquisite *Journal of My Other Self* (by Rainer Maria Rilke) which reaches us by two saving removes: it is translated from the German, and the author is dead.

There was an abandoned coach-house to which he retired for silence, to think over his plans of campaign. Boards laid across two packing cases served as table, on which he began an intensive study of the New York *Times Book Review*. He had made up his mind to try to get a job in the publishing business; in fact, before leaving England he had even gone and bothered Mr. Walter Page at the U. S. Embassy. Mr. Page, as sagacious in diplomacy as in publishing, had referred him to the office in Garden City. Now there lay before him a statesmanlike letter from that firm (well he remembers the phrase): "Our ranks are full and we contemplate no change." Evidently this was going to be a problem that required assiduity. He studied the *Times Book Review* carefully to see where was the vulnerable heel in the hide of the book business.

The first thing that scandalized him was the

high price of books in America. Oxford bookshops
had taught him that in England most of the books
really worth reading could be had in compact reprint editions for one or two shillings. American
books were bulky and costly in comparison. He observed that English publishers had somehow
learned, better than the Americans, how to use
their older stuff as a backlog for the fire. Perhaps
that impression is still true. But most of his juvenile premonitions of the Trade were gloriously
naive; necessarily so, based upon sentimental rang-
ings in Blackwell's and Gadney's at Oxford, or on
Charing Cross Road. He actually supposed that a
publishing office would be a place buzzing with
bookish passion, with jovial reminiscence of
William Dean Howells or Walter Pater. Fortunately he was soon enlightened. The genial low-
browism of a big publishing plant is part of its
strength. Only a fool will attempt to lay down
dicta on a business which, over and above being a
traffic is also an instinct and a fine art. But probably it is right that literature should have to fight
for its life in the office as it must in the world outside. It is dangerous to make things too easy for
the artist. You destroy him if you do.

When he did presently get employment he was
immediately captivated by the jargon and brou-
haha of the Sales Department, the life of "The
Boys" on the road, the whole interlocking comedy

of that mechanism by which men's printed thoughts are made available. It was vulgar and vivid and had no taint of Literature; it was endlessly amusing. It deals with human hopes and horrors in necessary terms of merchandise; there can hardly be any other trade so gay with anomaly.

But I anticipate. I am thinking of him now as he walked down Madison Avenue to the old boarding house at the corner of 32nd. The first thing he saw in New York (when he came not just to visit but to be a part of her) was the starry ceiling of the Grand Central. And next, Diana, silhouetted in the sky. Ah my Diana—who that knew it will ever forget that tiny figure poised against blue Now. Was she not, though we couldn't have put it into words, secretly an emblem of something that satisfied our hopeful and innocent youth? For we were magnificently young. When a man leaves college and becomes raw apprentice in the world of pay envelopes, how much younger he immediately is.

I hope that youngsters still come to town to look for jobs in the publishing business as naively happy as those boys on the top floor of 149 Madison Avenue. Do you think I would, for any conceivable human blessing, barter away that short sweet taste of pre-War mœurs? We were not clever, not angry about anything, we believed a great deal of what we were told; and really, the world did seem to rest on fairly solid routine. Lizzie Briers, best of land-ladies, now I evoke your substantial phantom. Do you remember how Jack and J. M. shared the fourth-floor back, and you only charged them $7.50 a week each for everything—meals included. And Fred had the Suicide Room as we used to call it; I don't remember why, except that it was unbelievably dark and cheerless, with a ladder leading to a trap in the roof. It reminded us of a certain grim story by O. Henry. Fred, a young man of more social amplitude than ourselves, was rarely there except for sleep; his room was always a litter of dress shirts and invitation cards. Do you remember the two nice girls who shared the big front chamber and worked at an Institute for the Scientific Care of the Hair, and how the Fourth Floor all sat together at the corner table in the dining room, and rather scandalized the Old New Yorkers (Lizzie still had some good Frank Stockton and Bunner types of patron) by their merry palaver.

Under the silhouette of Diana the memory of O. Henry made Madison Square a very thrilling place. He would understand the sincerity, the simplicity, of a boy's first capitulation to the sovereign glamour of Manhattan. In Mistletoe's private thought, certain associations with Sydney Porter moved in those miraculous first days. The man who had encouraged him to think it might be possible to get a job in publishing was Harry Steger, O. Henry's literary executor. Mistletoe had called on Steger at the Caledonia on 26th Street during a brief shining visit to New York the winter before. Poor Steger was actually a dying man when J. M. saw him, in the same apartment which O. Henry had also left to die in hospital. . . .

"The rooms were dark in the winter afternoon; Steger was in bed in an inner chamber and called to me to come in. I felt my way, and gradually saw that he was lying with a towel tied round his head like a turban. Supposing he was ill, I asked if there was anything I could do; he rejected the suggestion vigorously and insisted it was only a bad headache. He asked me to telephone the office for a tray of tea and some ice. We sat in the dark, so I never clearly saw him.

"We had mutual friends to speak of (he was a former Rhodes Scholar) and he talked pungently about the publishing business, which, he said, 'you'll find quite different from what you imagine.' He described his own work, and I remember his saying, after a long catalogue of his occupations, 'also I edit a magazine with my left hind foot.' But he was so restless, throwing the bed-clothes about and putting ice on his head, that I grew anxious and again begged to be useful in some way. He was quite vehement in denial. Remember that I was only a bashful youth, anxious not to offend him and prepared to believe that literary people were eccentric. I concluded that he had had a bohemian evening the night before and needed rest. I was afraid to offer any further sympathy, but as I left I saw a fruit vendor on the street and had some oranges sent up. I sailed the next day to return to Oxford, and did not know of his death until weeks afterward. I believe he was taken to the hospital that same night. I only knew of it by hearsay, but the memory that remains is that he had had a fall from a street-car, and unknown to himself was suffering from concussion or even a fractured skull. He was a brilliant fellow and had made a notable reputation for so young a man."

When, after some ineffectual efforts by the publishers to discourage young Mistletoe's attentions, he finally landed out at Garden City, he was given a desk that had once been used by Steger. In it he found a quantity of forgotten O. Henry manuscript, written on the familiar yellow sheets. I sometimes wish he had bagged just one of them for himself. The pathetic derelicts of the Bagdad-on-the-Subway stories still spent uneasy nights under the portico of Madison Square Garden, and it was partly in O. Henry's memory that these young Grub Street Runners, when they had a few coins to spare on a cold night, would kidnap a vagabond and take him to Childs on 23rd Street for coffee and a stack of wheats. One such I remember, a sensitive old fellow with a face of tarnished refinement who insisted that he was a kinsman of "Rooterford B. Hayes."

ONLY two blocks away from Lizzie Briers' boarding house they were digging the foundations of the
new Altman store. That furious work, going on at
night under pinkish flares, the drills screaming
into solid rock, was a new kind of idea, very
different from Oxford. Also looking for a job gives
a boy a decent anxiety. His job-hunting period
only lasted twelve days, he admits, but it made a
strong impression on him. That ghastly feeling of
uselessness, particularly walking up Fifth Avenue
at dusk past club windows where excellent old
gentlemen sat comfortably looking out, was very
horrible. If I were ever a member of a Fifth Avenue club I should be more prudent, and not sit so
close to the pane.

Mistletoe has often bragged that Elmer Davis,
likewise just back from Oxford, was also hunting a
job at the same time. They met several times in
City Hall Park to compare notes, where the statue
styled Civic Virtue now treads a heavy foot;
though there seems no certainty whether Virtue
is the treader or the trodden. Mr. Davis was also
grieved by a lack of alacrity on the part of employers, but finally discovered an advertisement
uttered by a nabob who wanted his son tutored.
The tutor must be "a Harvard man, a high

churchman, and an athlete." Readers of Mr. Davis's brilliant essays will have suspected that he is not the second of these; as a matter of fact he was none of the three. But his powers of persuasion are irresistible; he obtained the employment.

Of the day when he himself started work as a publisher's devil, Mistletoe best remembers that he suffered a strong dysentery going out in the Long Island train, from sheer nervousness. This was just at Floral Park and he remembers how brilliant the florist's fields of canna were on that September day. The only other literary association I can think of for Floral Park was the Easter blizzard of 1915, when some of Doubleday's editorial staff spent most of the night shivering in a snowdrifted train, and seriously considered making a bonfire of the manuscripts with which their briefcases were plentifully loaded.

Mistletoe's study of the *Times Book Review* had germinated notions, which the impact of New York jarred into premature birth. He was sitting in a barber's chair in the basement of the good old (still regretted) Park Avenue Hotel. A publishing idea struck him, of a desirable series of small and inexpensive manuals on various phases of American life. As he imagined them they should be crisp and inquisitive monographs, damaging to com-

placence and eavesdropping upon Futurity; a kind
of introduction to the American uproar which he
was desperately eager to understand. For even
upon the naivest youth there must have been, in
that autumn of 1913, some sense of a Question
Mark written in the sky. The blaze and glamour
of that Altman excavation, like the new Pennsylvania Station and the Panama Canal and rumors of a new poetry blowing across the latitudes,
gave prickling premonition of all sorts of extraor-
dinaries. Even to the green youth in the barber's
chair this somehow penetrated. His publishing
scheme was an idea which he himself was obviously too callow to develop, but under experienced editorship it might have been something.
(The *Today and Tomorrow* series, ten years later,
was a lively sprouting of a similar germ.) He was
thrilled by his vague vision, and as the shave was
now finished he ordered a face-massage (which he
could ill afford) simply to remain in that warm and
comfortable seat for thinking. It was a momentous
barbering: under the tingle of those hot towels he
decided that though two Pages had already evaded
him he hadn't yet been turned down by any
Doubledays. How many there might be he had
no notion, but he began at the top with the
Effendi himself. The publisher still smiles to remember the agitated aspirant who when asked
"What kind of a job would you like best around

this place?" replied resolutely "Yours." So it was, in the words of the grand old Civil War poem, that he set his battle-flag "Amid the guns of Doubleday." It is not amiss here for the commentator to pay affectionate tribute to one of the greatest personalities of the world of print, who charitably divined some true publisher's passion behind the disorderly excitement of his petitioner. To take a young doctrinaire, with the milk of college still on his upper lip, and laboriously educate him into usefulness, is a slow and even (sometimes) an expensive task for employers. The young Rollo used to grind his teeth at the tardiness of a raise. After two years with only one small advance he went, in a fine frenzy, to assail the boss on this matter. He has not forgotten the skill with which the Effendi turned the tables. Mistletoe remarked that he thought it outrageous to be still working at a weekly figure which I will not specify, to avoid embarrassing them both. Effendi agreed. "You ought to be ashamed," he said, "not to have made yourself worth more than that." However he must have given private orders, for a Raise came through the next day. All this was very likely a benefit in disguise. If his income had been large enough to live on he would not have had to rub his wits against the stone to increase it from the midnight ink-bottle. At any rate by keeping a foot firmly and kindly on his neck for several years the Effendi taught him at least some awareness of realities.

So once again, by good hap, Mistletoe found himself in surroundings of remarkable delight. I cannot, at this distance, be systematic in narrating the charms of that great democratic alma mater known to its alumni as D. P. and Co. There can hardly be any kind of education more stimulating than the life of a big publishing house, which combines the brisk humors of commerce with the sentimental relish of the bibliophile. To one whose instinct moves that way there is endless interest in the whole process. From the mystic exhalation of possibility surrounding an unread manuscript, down to the tall piles of finished books in the huge stock-room, the entire cycle was fascination. The book trade, great as it has been, has hardly yet begun to glimpse its possibilities; still one sees the occasional Tory bookstore sitting still and waiting for customers to come to it, and the embittered bookseller who is too bored with life to read any books himself; still one sees the publisher overloading his list with tripe and uttering dull stereotyped advertising which by mere monotony of method fails to prick blood. It is a business which has its necessary disgusts and wearinesses; times when the whole world seems to wallow and founder in paper, and the dim crowded aisles of the stock room seem Heartbreak House. But it has a pleasant Bohemianism which prevents its young men from dwelling sadly upon irony and paradox. The entertainment of authors—"gruntling" was the excellent phrase invented by Mr. T. S. Stribling—has become more complex than in those simple pre-War days, but even in 1913 and 1914 there were innocent phases of social and convivial doings when young publishers and authors met together to spend an evening. Mistletoe and the colleague I have mentioned as Fred founded an irregular group known as the E. and M. Dining Club; I wish I had kept one of its little invitation cards which bore the emblem of a crossed knife and fork. They used to meet at Moretti's table-d'hôte on 35th Street, next door to the Garrick Theatre. There the Old Reliable Moretti Dinner was 50 cents, *vin compris*. I can still see those battered tureens of strong minestrone, which were to us the new elixir of Bohemia. New York's wintry night glittered outside; above these microscopic creatures leaned the high amazing city blossoming its witch-fires of illusion, and as Fred polished the soup-steam from his goggles these happy youths would discuss the Spring List, or sit down with good old Bouck White to talk about his new book *The Carpenter and the Rich Man* and the possible perishing of our economic fabric. (Perhaps he was not so far wrong.) Thus, thinking (as all men should) that they were doing something utterly new, they entered into the happiest of brotherhoods, that of the Publisher's Young Men. There may be some jobs that a man can leave behind when he closes his desk; but not that one. It touches life at every tangent.

Another place of good memory was the old Yale Club (on 43rd or 44th Street, wasn't it?) of which Fred was a member. It had a shadowy tap-room heavily timbered with dark wood. Moretti's thin wine, or the humble creature small beer, were their wholesome tipple; cocktails and hard liquor were not then in the mode. The other day a very discreet and distinguished Lady Author, who is also the editor of a famous magazine, was to be honored by her publisher. He asked what would amuse her most, and she admitted that in her widely traveled career she had never visited a speakeasy. The publisher thought this should be rectified, and assigned three of his most talented aides to escort her for a ceremonial luncheon. They went first to a haunt of publishers which I will conceal under the name of the Bombay Bicycle Club. It was padlocked. They went to a second house of call; also padlocked; and a third with the same result. By this time they were all extremely hungry, and had a constitutional lunch at the Plaza. "But I mention no names," she said, narrating the adventure; "the publisher wouldn't like it." Considering the reputations involved I agreed it was better not to identify. "The publisher wouldn't like it," she repeated. "He'd hate to have it thought that his Young Men know only three speakeasies."

There is often a dangerous tendency to take the Now, the Now of writing, as an imaginary point of sapience from which we look tenderly down upon simplicities of the past and hopefully upward toward a larger wisdom to come. Not so here. I write sincerely from the bottom. Lately a group of friends amused themselves by drawing graphs of their psychic oscillation during several years. It was odd to see that most of these people, all apparently in the highest spirits, represented their present mood as considerably below the horizontal norm. They hopefully prognosticated an upward slope, but were not unduly confident. I am not inclined to patronize the Past. It was the only Past I'll ever have, and the Future is very uncertain, except that imaginative literature has in store for us triumphs of sensibility we have scarcely dreamed. Virginia Woolf perhaps more brilliantly than any other writer in English has prophesied this, and what she prophesies she herself brings true. We have passed through a decade of rather anxious cynicism; there was plentiful reason for it. You don't bring an era of cynicism to an end by saying it's ended. But I have had occasion recently

to consort a little with young men of undergraduate era, and I seem to see in them the returning
power of that magical naïveté which was the
strength (if we had any strength) of our own pre-
War generation. They are far enough away from
the years of the Teens not to know what extremities of disillusion and sadness the world can go
through. In some respects they are more knowing
than we were, more shrewd, but they seem to have
somewhat the same instinct of regard, or piety,
which you will know I do not use in any religious
sense. They are aware of something more than
easy mockery; they come toward life, as poets
must, with open hands. It is sad to me to think
that there will never be time or space to tell you
how good seemed Mistletoe's entry into the actual.
Is his generation to go past and trickle out into
the sand of cautious maturity without going on
record that it was a thrilling and enormous time?
At Garden City the great press, more college than
factory, stood among lawns and flowers and the
whole building throbbed with the roar of machines
like a ship at sea. The steady grumble of the bindery made a constant monotone beneath our feet.
On the platform of the little Country Life railway
station, at the end of a day's work, one stood high
up as on a boat deck in clean winds. The Long
Island smoker was an editorial annex where one
read manuscripts and argued business schemes

with one's fellows. In those days (1913–14) the house was gathering together all the Conrad books to form them into what publishers like to call a "property," and the younger fry were busy reading *Chance*, perplexing themselves over its 250-page parenthesis, and catching up with the earlier tales. *The Children of the Sea* was taken over from Dodd, Mead and reissued under its original title *The Nigger of the Narcissus*. Mistletoe was reading that book for the first time on the train to Garden City. He was so absorbed that when the huge wave comes out of the mist ("it looked as mischievous as a madman with an axe"; how terrifyingly you perceive that ragged hill of sea towering over the ship) the whole railroad car seemed to rise, lean and roll slowly and sickeningly on its side. In sudden panic he dropped the book and shot out his arms in a scrambling clutch, muttering "God, she's going over." He actually thought for an instant that the train was on its beam ends. His neighbor in the seat must have supposed him crazy.

In the publishing business, as in any other, much time is spent toiling up blind alleys; but to have had a share no matter how small in so notable a work as helping Conrad's magnificent books reach their wider public is to have a secret residue of pride, the pride in the job that makes publishing the happiest of trades. I do not believe adequate credit has ever been paid to Alfred Knopf, then serving an apprenticeship at Garden City, for his early pro-Conrad zeal. Alfred was supposed to be working in the Mail Order department, but the legend was that he spent all his time writing to Conrad and Galsworthy. Knopf was the author of D. P. and Co.'s first little biographical booklet about Conrad, printed about the end of 1913; it is a pleasant item for the Conrad collector, as is also the tiny pamphlet the house issued early in 1914 reprinting (for the first time in America) the long suppressed preface to the *Nigger*. This latter was Mistletoe's own hunch; I see a trace of his earlier manner in the words "Issued by D. P. and Co. for distribution among those interested in English literature." He was then still youthfully concerned about "literature," which strikes me now as amusing, for though frequently damned as "literary" he is probably the least so of anyone I know, and scrupulously ignorant in that field. Unless a man is just a drain for print he is likely to reach a mood when he feels he has read enough books, that it is hardly possible for any new book to come along that can say anything he has not already felt or suspected, and that what he most needs is a chance to digest a few of the old ones and make some sense out of his own intuitions.

129

16

THERE was another barber-shop episode. In those
early days it was a young bachelor's luxury to go
out on bright Sunday mornings for a professional
shave. There was a comfortable sense of grown-up
importance in issuing from one's lodging, walking
down the quiet passage of Madison Avenue and
through the Sabbath pause of Madison Square on
so masculine an errand. Sometimes an elderly
gentleman was feeding the pigeons, who flapped
and nodded about him with bright ungrateful eyes,
like poets about a publisher. There also was the
headquarters of the S.P.C.A. to which these young
idealists once went in grievance to report the sorrows of a huge turtle, painfully bound and in-
verted in the window of a 32nd Street chophouse.
When they appealed to the innkeeper on the
creature's behalf, he insisted that turtles were used
to it and liked it. A special officer from the S. P.
C. A. accompanied them to the relief of the cap-
tive, but probably their interference only hastened
its transformation into soup. By the Farragut
statue was still a file of hansoms; where he sat not
long afterward on a bench, watching the Life In-
surance clock until it should be time to take cab
to the church to be married. There was an airy and
upward and birdlike feeling about the whole

Square in the breezy stir of spring; something like that spacious skyey dream Chaucer had in the *House of Fame;* like that dearest of comedians, the boy afterward found it all "shut in the treasury of his brain." Above, like a happy thought in the back of the mind, one was aware of Diana tightening her arrow toward the bluest void; pleasant symbol of the impossible.

But he was on the way to the barber. Later he discovered the Seville Hotel, and it pleased his fancy to patronize the Barber of Seville, but this particular occasion was in the basement of a tonsor on 23rd Street. The chairs were filled with gentlemen peacefully being shaven, shorn, shined and shampooed, when there was a thunderous deeply booming explosion. The shop quivered, lights went out, there was a raining tinkle of broken glass. Brief silence, then shouts, horns, clamor. Was this the long speculated earthquake which would teach New York her lesson of humility? With one accord barbers, manicurists and customers fled earnestly upstairs to the pavement. From a ragged hole in the street poured a spire of brilliant flame. Men were running, motors and trolley cars anxiously creeping out of danger, a horse was biped with terror. The Gas Company had suffered one of its uterine disorders, there was an unpleasant rumbling underfoot and the feeling that another blast might be imminent. Aproned and lathered as they

131

were, one man bleeding from a slip of the razor, the agitated customers skipped across into the Park. It must have looked like the exhumation of Doomsday, shrouded and fluttering figures bursting from underground, their faces blanched with soap. The first thought was safety, but when the clanging waggoneers had shortly got the better of the emergency came an anxiety for coats and wallets left in the shop. The street was now thronged and guarded; it needed some argument with the cops before these Lazari could win back to the shaken parlor. The barbers' operations were hastily completed by candle-light.

Just so, Mistletoe has sometimes thought afterwards, were a lot of placid Certainties blown from their warm chairs by the explosion of the War. For quite a while they were out in the parks in anxious and unseemly deshabille. A surprising number of them found their way back to the barber shop, but one or two still show a nicked ear where the blade slipped; some others have taken to safety razors.

Like most college boys, Mistletoe had had a vague notion that the desirable job in a publishing house was "editorial," by which he imagined a safe and dignified billet reading manuscripts. He soon outgrew this juvenile idea. His first job, under rigorous tuition, was the compilation of "Literary

Notes," weekly broadsides of press matter sent off
to a large mailing list of newspapers and reviewers.
The first delicacy he had to study, and was not
quick in learning, was the distinction between
Opinion and News. Genuine information about
books and authors the papers are glad to print,
but the attempt to insinuate blurb into unpur-
chased space is vain. The young man's early
attempts to write eloquent press notes must have
caused sharp suffering to the head of the Publicity
Department, an experienced newspaper alumnus.
J. M. could always tell when a call-down was
coming. He turned in his copy for approval, and
from his desk could see his chief examining it. A
look of intense quietness would come over Harry
Maule's face, he would sink back into meditation
and absently begin trimming his nails with a large
pair of office shears. This was a sure sign that
something was wrong. Harry was endlessly considerate, and would often rewrite the offending
piece himself rather than reproach his inexperi-
enced assistant. But his instinct was unerring, and
he never failed (quite rightly) to spring upon
illegitimate editorializing.

The collecting of data about the house's authors
was the pleasantest part of the Publicity job. It
involved all sorts of surprising expeditions. One
was to a remote livery stable in Brooklyn where
by drinking beer with a horse-doctor he secured

domestic reminiscences of a deceased Englishman reputed to have been one of those who wrote the novels of "Bertha M. Clay." But the very first author assigned exclusively to young Mistletoe as laboratory material was our well-loved B. F. Mr. F. then had a workroom on 14th Street where he courteously welcomed the green envoy who gazed in affectionate admiration upon his first Practising Author. There they laid the foundations of one of the happiest friendships of a lifetime. B. F. is a man of exceptional modesty, and I hope he will not resent my recalling Mistletoe's small triumph, which he likes to believe unique. He wrote a biographical sketch of B. F. which he sent to the New York *Evening Post*. It was done with so frolicsome a hand that the austere old *Post* did not realize it was really publisher's press matter and actually sent him a check, at then space rates, for $14. B. F. got even many years later, with his disarming grin, by introducing his friend, in person, into one of his admirable detective stories, *The Mystery of the Folded Paper*. Another pleasant episode of that time was when the quixotic Bouck White, learning that his young friends had been united in the rites of the effete Episcopalian church, averred that they were still living in sin and insisted on reading over them the marriage lines of his Church of the Social Revolution. A sad thing to remember is Bouck White's

prison term of six months (in 1914) when with
almost divine naiveté he attempted to interrupt
a Fifth Avenue church service to suggest the discussion of some social wrongs.

I doubt if any publishing house ever had a
promotion instinct more alert for broad effects,
though in recent years the young firm of Simon
and Schuster has shown extraordinary skill in the
dulcet tallyho. The French publisher's signboard
for De Goncourt's *La Faustin* in 1881—a painted
hoarding 940 feet long and 124 feet high—remains
probably the largest single reclame in the history
of the trade, as I suppose Jonathan Cape's electric
sky-sign for *Babbitt* in London was the most costly.
But in humorous ingenuities Garden City was
always notably inventive. I wish I could remember
who was the astounded employee tricked out in
top hat, cutaway, spats, etc.—"the latest London
mode"—and sent patrolling the financial district
in impersonation of "Colonel Ruggles," the valet-
hero of *Ruggles of Red Gap*. He was supported by
advertisements in the papers announcing that
Colonel Ruggles was in town and would have a
free copy of the book sent to anyone who recognized and accosted him. A time when fortune
played into our hands was when Ex-President
Roosevelt, enthusiastic over Tarkington's *Penrod*,
allowed himself to be photographed reading the

book. By felicitous coincidence, about the same time T. R. had been snapshotted in a railway train, very obviously asleep over another book. This latter photo had appeared in the newspapers. Deleting the title of the rival volume, the two pictures were put side by side on a poster with appropriate legend.

In that democratic and free-for-all outfit there was little time wasted on specialization of functions. The young fuglemen of the Editorial-Advertising-Publicity staff circulated in the mellay, did what they found themselves doing, and did it with their might. They wrote press notes and advertisements, corresponded with reviewers, planned special exhibits for bookstores, touted for MSS and read them until they fell asleep long past midnight, took visitors on tour of inspection through the press and gardens, taught booksellers to play bowls on the lawn when they came out to the annual Peony Party, and collaborated in the preparation of a moving picture film illustrating the processes of book and magazine manufacture. Mistletoe's first experiences as a public lecturer were in taking this film round to high schools in New York City where he spoke while the picture was showing. In remote auditoriums of the Bronx, Staten Island or East New York he would arrive toting his heavy canisters of celluloid, have a bowl of soup in some near-by lunchroom, and then deliver his talk for which the Board of Education paid him $10. He was always glad that these lectures were mostly given in the dark, for those were days of severe frugality and his trousers were not always desirable for public scrutiny. On one such expedition, on the East Side, he discovered Max Maisel's bookstore on Grand Street and bought there a copy of Walt Whitman's Prose. The *Leaves of Grass* he had long been familiar with, but this was his first introduction to the superb *Specimen Days* and *Democratic Vistas* and the 1855 Preface. Walt's prose remains the least appreciated of America's great books, and to see it current in a really legible and inexpensive volume is still one of his earnest ambitions. Once he went as far afield as Sing Sing prison to lecture with the film. By some mistake the reels, sent in advance, had been shown in the mess-hall the night before, so he had the afternoon and evening free to study the life of that tragic place. He met several very interesting men among the inmates, including a notable swindler in the realm of faked de luxe volumes.

When there was nothing else particular on hand, these young men were sent out to sell "jobs," viz. overstocks of laggard titles, and "Special Schemes." Nowadays there is a fat omnibus book that calls itself the Week-End Library, but we had a Week-End Library back in 1913, a quartet of cheap reprints that included Frank Norris's excellent *McTeague* (I forget the other titles) and Mistletoe spent many an instructive hour drumming these among the buyers for chain stores. The big wholesale houses of Butler Brothers and Charles Broadway Rouss remain affectionately in his memory for they actually bought a few. There has been a lot of palaver in recent years about books sold in drug stores; Mistletoe was an unsuccessful pioneer in this line. His efforts to get the pharmacy buyers excited about the Week-End series were feebly rewarded. Mr. Liggett had not yet taken up literature; Mr. Riker was not interested in reading. In the big drugstore at the corner of Broadway and 34th there was a queer little alcove hidden away up a tiny flight of stairs where the apprentice salesman had to wait anxiously until the buyer would condescend to see him. Or, in some of the big jobbers' warehouses, sitting gloomily on a bench while all the salesmen of more likely goods were called in first, was an admirably chastening experience for a young visionary. He had an Order Book, with carbon sheets and everything, and was very proud of it, but he could have wept to see the meagreness of its entries.

Humiliated or not, he saw clearly that it was in the Trade Department—viz. Sales—that the fun

(and emolument) lay, and some natural instinct
gravitated him toward that phase of the business.
One of his early enthusiasms was the invention of
the Booksellers' Blue Book, a little pocket mem-
orandum-diary containing snips of D. P. propaganda hoped to be cathartic and tonic for the
dealer. Then there was the great annual adventure
of going, in the lively season just before Christmas,
to sell books at the famous Old Corner Bookstore
in Boston. There for the first time he learned something of the life of the bookseller; and discovered
that Traveling Men, those luxurious creatures,
actually voyage in Pullman cars. It is a privilege
to have known the Old Corner in its former historic quarters on Bromfield Street, and that antique catacomb cellar stockroom where Tommy
Tolman and other primitive Christians toiled late
into the night. There was a tavern in an adjoining
alley where, after the day's work on the floor,
one recruited with venison chops and ale, then
returned to the shop to arrange a window display
for the next morning. To pull the little handle and
send the money-carrier singing along the wire up
to the cashier was about as much fun as anyone
ever has; it was magnificent. He was there ostensibly as a temporary addition to the bookstore
staff, but actually of course the sport was to see
how many D. P. books he could legitimately sell.
The high percentage of Conrad owners in that

Athenian neighborhood is at least partly due to
the lively efforts of one young salesman through
the Christmas seasons of 1913, 1914, 1915. But
occasionally pure enthusiasm overcame all mercantile affiliation, as when for instance that lovely
lady in black would come in, looking for a Mosher
book. She and Mistletoe would spend I don't know
how long turning out the drawers where the
Mosher stock was kept and confiding their mutual
preferences. Joe Jennings and Dick Fuller, the
humorous chancellors of America's most blue-
stocking bookshop, would sometimes turn a reproachful gaze upon their undisciplined amateur;
for the clerk's job during the Christmas Rush (it
really was a Rush then) is to satisfy customers
promptly; not to encourage them to loiter and
litigate the niceties of belles lettres. How much
can be learned in a bookstore like the Old Corner;
he remembers the tingling thrill with which, early
one morning before business had started, he picked
up Vachel Lindsay's *General William Booth*, just
published by Mitchell Kennerley. That was in
1913. His Old Corner eureka the next year was
Emily Dickinson, whose *The Single Hound* was
brought out in 1914 by Little, Brown. That book
marked the beginning of the rediscovery of the
divine Emily, but it took close to fifteen years for
it to become general. In the book business you can
usually reckon that it takes at least ten years for

work of any really subtle quality to become widely known. That is not as regrettable as you might imagine: ten years is a fair mellowing period, and strong work does not easily evaporate.

Actual bookstore experience is the only way to learn something of the bookseller's depressing problems; of the enormous power exerted by the individual clerk in influencing customers' choices; of the often astounding ignorance in bookseller and customer alike of literature as man's purest passion. Our glorious Thoreau (who probably bought his few books at the Old Corner) remarked truly, "Most men have learned to read to serve a paltry convenience, as they have learned to cipher in order to keep accounts. Of reading as a noble intellectual exercise they know little or nothing." And how little do they know or care of the heat and lustre in which men have written words true enough to last not just one year or ten but a hundred or a thousand. One distinction Mistletoe used to draw between publishing and what he called "boblishing" was this: the boblisher always follows the line of least sales-resistance; but the true publisher makes some attempt to keep alive his author's most genuinely significant work; not necessarily that which has happened to win soft approval.

One of the greatest thrills a Publisher's Young Man can have by serving in a bookshop is that he may find a chance to sell to the ultimate consumer some book that he himself discovered, read in manuscript, wrangled for in editorial council, wrote into a contract, planned the jacket and advertising, wrote about to reviewers and steamed up The Boys to Get Quantities. Actually to sell that book in retail trade, to take the money and wrap up the volume itself, is to make the circuit complete with romantic finality. If you don't get a pleasure out of that, then you are no publisher at heart. Unless you go home with the customer and read the book aloud to him, you can hardly do more.

17

THERE was a morning early in 1914 when the young men on the top floor of Madison Avenue were wakened by snow drifting in on their faces. When Fred and Mistletoe hurried to Penn Station through the storm they found a sign:

ALL TRAIN SERVICE
TO
LONG ISLAND
INDEFINITELY SUSPENDED

They came back to the top floor and spent a happy day catching up with manuscript reading and other odds and ends of work.

Among so many days, somehow that one remains very distinct. The blizzard whistled outside and it was savagely cold, but Lizzie Briers allowed them to borrow the gas stove which belonged in the room of the Hair Culture girls. They sat close and were happy. How many schemes of dominion and enterprise boys can fabricate in one day's busy leisure. Their minds were excited for they had been up late the night before with the proofs of Frank Norris's gruesome lycanthropy novel *Vandover and the Brute*, the posthumous story that was lost in the San Francisco earthquake and lay forgotten for years in a storage warehouse. One of Fred's chores that morning was to finish putting together copy for a circular about Bouck White's *The Carpenter and the Rich Man*. He had a number of excellent quotes, but one more really spirited one was needed to fill the space. He was grunting that he needed just one more blurb, real Grade A, Walker-Gordon quality. Mistletoe had been sitting over the flaming stove reading the book and in combined chill and abstraction had badly singed his breeks. "I'll give you a blurb," he said. He wrote somewhat as follows:

A reader says:—Judge whether the book can absorb. The day of the March blizzard I was sitting in my humble attic room reading it as I cowered over the gas stove. In my excitement over Bouck White's thrilling message to society, I quite forgot myself and my poverty until I sprang up with a yell and found I had burned a large hole in my breeches.

Fred was heartily pleased with this tribute, which was literally accurate and just filled the blank in his "envelope stuffer." But the tragedy was this, that by some error in the job printing department this little vie de boheme testimony, having no signature, accidentally got itself attached to a letter about the book written by a wealthy and prominent New York bluestocking, and appeared with ludicrous effect over her signature. Quite a number of copies of the leaflet had got into circulation before yells of mirth began to arise in the Advertising Department. Fred's face, a mobile visnomy exceptionally adapted for expressions of incredulity and shock, was a Gothic gargoyle of dismay. One of our nicknames for him was Ground Gripper, as he always wore roomy safe and sane footgear with that humorous name. Those large and wholesome pedestals always itinerated with great rapidity, but never more so than then. With one loud and profane cry he disappeared in the direction of the job pressroom to halt the flow of these leaves of infamy.

This impending sequel was unsuspected that snowy morning. They were assiduous at their apparently harmless tasks. Mistletoe's dear ambition

then was to find a chance to do some book review-
ing, and it occurred to him that the best way to
break in would be by offering a weekly column
free to any editor who would print it. He wrote to
John Beffel of the Toledo *Times*, with whom he
had had some friendly correspondence. So it was
that not long afterward the citizens of Toledo,
as a result of a snowstorm in New York, found
themselves faced by an occasional causerie called
Books and Byplay, signed "Andrew McGill." So
far as I have ever learned no one but John Beffel
and the author ever noticed it, but it was written
in a vein of innocent candor and gave Mistletoe
much pleasure.

Instead of commuting to Garden City, a working day in New York, in the muted hush of heavy
snowfall, was something to remember. The pleasant semi-domestic feeling of being in one's own
citadel; the red and yellow Mexican blanket on
the couch; Jack's mandolin; the stuffed bookcase,
which was really a very deep rack of shelves built
for rolls of wallpaper; we had bought it from a
retiring shopkeeper and hoisted it up three flights
with furious toil. I don't know how to suggest the
staggering power of New York's magic upon a boy
to whom everything was new. Oh excellent to receive that dazzling impression upon a totally un-
prepared mind. In clear autumn days of brilliant

light the narrow perpendicular poise of the streets. Fire engines drawn by horses: I can still see a galloping trio of great white beasts bend round from a cross street and go rocketing up the Avenue: silver chimney and boiler with the fire burning underneath, the tolling strokes of the bell; a theme for Walt Whitman. The discovery of old taverns such as McSorley's, one of the most honorably masculine pubs on earth. The little New York office of D. P. and Co. on 32nd Street with its Trade Room at the rear where one sat respectfully listening to the humorous palaver of The Boys, their lively practical joking or interludes of bicker and despondency. By incessant overhearing of such names as Baker-Taylor, American News, Alec Grosset, Harry Burt, Grace Gaige, Marcella Burns, John Kidd, we began to put together a hearsay picture of the business. As a freshman gazes upon the football heroes of the Varsity team so did the young apprentice hearken to these front-line warriors the Salesmen. Into this smoky little den, which in less romantic traffics would be called a Sample Room, came these debonair creatures, fresh from foray against that mystic entity The Trade. The Trade, our means of life and yet which the novice subtly felt (with nascent publishers' instinct) was our Opponent, the other team, cunningly trained and banded against our skill. The Salesmen sat there and talked a lan-

guage of their own which we had to learn by
listening. Richly clad, jocose, sardonic, enchantingly childlike, carrying a subtle aura of adventure
and experience, they telephoned vehement imper-
atives to headquarters, alluded lightly to Mou-
quin's or pinochle parties. We admired and also
were shocked. Why this wasn't dead literature, it
was a fascinating fantastic game, packed with diverse personalities and cunning maneuver. On that
snowy day, when legwork was mostly suspended,
there was much tobacco and talk in the little
Trade Room. They probably had lunch at Moretti's, a place rather too lowly for The Boys, but
esteemed by young litterateurs. There the table
d'hôte lunch was 25 cents and plentiful, with a
glass of vin ordinaire included.

That afternoon he and Fred plowed through the
snow to look in at Brentano's. They wanted to find
out if the Bookseller's Blue Book, on which they
were working together, was really any use to the
trade. There he made the acquaintance of Silas
Howes, the beginning of a delightful relationship.
Quiet, reserved, and faintly saddened by life,
Howes was in those years always on duty just
inside the front door of the old 27th Street shop.
He had learned to wear a gently austere mask for
self-protection, in which mood we used to call him
chaffingly The Deacon; but how his sensitive face

lit up when he saw a trusted friend come through the revolving door. To understand, and gradually to love, this true zealot of the finer seriousness of literature, was an opposite side of the picture from the jovial banter of the Trade Room. Mistletoe always puzzled himself by seeing both sides of the picture and loving both equally. Thereafter, until Silas Howes died five years later (then only fifty-one) the boy rarely went through that part of town without stopping in to see him. It was Howes who introduced him to George Gissing, beginning with *Henry Ryecroft*. There was a good little series called the Wayfarer's Library (published by Dutton) which included some volumes of Gissing; it was sometimes Mistletoe's fancy, when buying a book for which he felt an affinity to ask the book-seller to autograph it for him. This was the only kind of autograph collecting he ever cared much for, and it was always agreeable because some book clerks were so startled, even inclined to suspect a sinister trick. But Silas liked the notion and used to write delightfully prim and sober little inscriptions. Sometimes they dined together at the Constantinople, a Turkish restaurant, and would return to Howes' room on Lexington Avenue where he would brew coffee in a percolator given him by William Marion Reedy. By mysterious ways the secret lovers of literature find each other out. In the pressure of his daily service,

148

at the mercy of customers not always considerate, the little man was guardedly polite with old-fashioned Southern civility, but how his pale face brightened when the coffee urn began to bubble and he would talk of his friendship with Ambrose Bierce or his adventure in the Galveston Flood. Good and valiant gentleman, life had not used him easily. At a time when the trader's notion of books was divertingly plain, it was well for these boys to see the purest dignity and devotion of letters living in this man who had once been a drug clerk in Texas. J. M. mentioned his name in the dedication of a book and was keeping it secret to surprise him. Howes died suddenly while the book was still in proof.

Mistletoe associates this day with one more adventure, though perhaps it was not really the same date. Then, or some afternoon very like it, he first went down to Park Row to see Don Marquis at the *Sun*. Let's forget genteel reticences and speak healthy fact. Of all newly printed words he had seen in New York, Marquis's meant most. He had dreamed of catching literature in the act: here it was in the least anticipated place, an evening newspaper. What matter that it was uneven, sometimes lazy, sometimes slapstick. Here, in arrant fecundity, was that strange and many-splendored thing the comic spirit, pure freak of absurdity, pure freak of stinging lyric. The American press has sometimes much to smart for but it can be forgiven anything when you think of the papers— the *Sun*, and the *Tribune*—that saw Don's quality and gave him free hand.

Marquis's column, the *Sun Dial*, had then been running about two years. It had enormous influence on young Mistletoe. He knew at once that he wanted, and must some day attempt, a job like that. He was not silly enough to imagine any comparisons, but he saw the dangerous relish and opportunity of such work. Like many other youngsters of the time he avowed instant allegiance. They were sealed of the Sons of Don, as Stuart lads three centuries earlier were of the Sons of Ben.

Don's newspaper work was grotesque, chameleon, unpredictable, as all richly temperamental stuff must be. At its best, unsurpassable: it rocked with grave or vulgar mirth, then turned on you with an edge that would cut floating silk. Once he was making merry over some idiot Society's prize offer for the best definition of Poetry, and suddenly said "Poetry is what Milton saw when he went blind." Most beloved newspaper man of his time, probably the most persecuted by the well-meaning snappers-up of unconsidered Time, I should want him to remember there were some who knew him as of Rabelais and Clemens blood. His work, and that of Simeon Strunsky on the old

Evening Post, made it pride to be living in New York. That was the sort of thing to which the young Mistletoes gave their devotion. They would rather be able to write like that, to think like that, than own the Waldorf-Astoria. O rare Don Marquis! Devout and ribald spirit, he also knows the Tavern of Despair. Its fireside bench is well polished by many old customers.

Once, some years later, Mistletoe was writing a notice of one of Marquis's books. He was at home in the country, and to reach the printer before the dead-line the copy had to catch a certain mail. There were only a few minutes, and just at that moment came screams outside the window. The children's kitten had been killed by a dog. After that ghastly interruption, and whatever consolation was possible, he sat down again shaking with nervousness to finish the review. In his agitation he went rather beyond the margin of restraint, exclaiming oddly that the book "comes with a curly tremolo from the midriff" and comparing it to the fierce and tender wisdom of Shakespeare's Fools. Mr. Marquis was not in the least abashed by this affectionate halloo, but more disturbed when he learned that its emotional quality might partly be considered obit for the massacred cat. Therefore I think that Mistletoe would wish, in a calmer moment, to reaffirm the thought.

Mistletoe's young conceptions of literature were

startled when he found Don at the *Sun* clacking
out his column on a typewriter which stood on an
up-ended packing-case. Perhaps it was a grocery
box, for I think it was mysteriously stencilled
1 GROSS TOM CATS. That meant Tomato Cat-
sup, but it may have suggested the career of
Mehitabel. They went across the alley, where
there was an honest dram-shop with alcoves, and
the waiter used to bring round a tray of tiny hot
sausages as relish with one's beer. Each sausage
was impaled with a toothpick for convenience of
dispatch.

18

It MAY have been Joe Jennings' friendly and un-
solicited testimonial to his activity as bookstore
clerk that presently stimulated Mistletoe to suggest to his employer that a new position, Assistant
Sales Manager, be created and himself appointed.
Fortunately this is not a Horatio Alger story: the
powers smiled at the idea. They said he was fertile
in thinking up ideas ("a vivid imagination" was
Effendi's phrase) but not persevering enough in
following them through. That may be so; yet I
still think he might have made a good Assistant
Sales Manager, even eventually worth the $40 a
week he suggested as appropriate remuneration
for such a task. About that time $40 was a sort of

152

mystic figure that bounded his vision in a gilded shimmer. It would be, with the annual $500 or so he could count on making by outside effort, Enough To Live On. Remember that in 1915 you could still buy a decent suit of clothes for $20, shoes for $4, and rent a small house in the country for $28 a month.

Anyhow, checked in this mounting ambition for the lucrative side of the business he became an author almost, as it were, in retaliation. What spare energy there was he bent on the composition of a harmless little tale about an itinerant book-seller. It was a very unpretentious romance and written in appropriately humble surroundings: in the kitchen of a happy cottage on the windy Hempstead Plains. The winter of 1915–16 was a cold one in that small frame dwelling, and to draw the table close to the kitchen stove was the best way to keep warm without unduly squandering the coal hoarded for the furnace. (Coal was then, I think, about $8 a ton?) The little book, though refused by several magazines as a serial, eventually had a modest success, and was followed later by a more ambitious sequel. Both books had a friendly reception in the Trade, so much so that some years afterward when a fiction of quite different flavor was announced, the publisher's salesmen gaily sold it in advance as "Another book about an old bookshop." There was much lamentation when the MS arrived, late as usual, and proved to be some sort of theological fable in which animals and human beings seemed hopelessly confused. Not even any mention of an old bookshop! With a hasty reclassification the anxious travelers now explained it as "a dog-story;" which it was in the same sense that *The Hound of Heaven* is. The more conscientious among them quite properly felt it their duty to warn their customers against buying too heavily, as the book was obviously a sheer uncertainty. Mistletoe enjoys recalling how Effendi, taking him for a walk in the garden, turned upon him in the solitude of the evergreen enclosure and bade him be explicit. "The boys say they can't understand a word of it," he said. "Now come clean, what's it all about?" The embarrassed author said, "Effendi, I couldn't possibly tell you, out here in the sunshine and at midday. But if we could sit down at dusk, by candlelight, or even in the dark, I might be able to give you some idea." "Gosh," said Effendi, "is it as bad as all that?"

So he didn't become Assistant Sales Manager, and now he began to find himself drawn back into the "literary" side of the business. One great excitement in the summer of 1915 was the poems of Rupert Brooke. With what a clear cry of young courage and tragedy those sonnets spoke to us then; it is difficult now to remember. "To turn as swimmers into cleanness leaping"—the lines tingled on scalp and thighs. Under the blaze and doing of those summer days the misery of the War lay beneath everything; one heard it at night in the cry of the crickets in the Hempstead fields, the diapason of human rage and folly. At first it did not seem our affair; to our small concerns, our comic struggles for living, the dear and intimate responsibilities of young providers, the suicidal frenzy of Europe was far away. But it staggered our reason, it cried to our hearts. The England we loved and knew by blood and instinct, the Germany where we had bicycled and bathed in Black Forest waterfalls, the France where we had frolicked in the Latin Quarter and wandered the glades of Fontainebleau, were they not in some queer way all equally dear? Yes, as Walt says, those were "years that trembled and reeled beneath us." None of those young men have forgotten the spring day when Burton Hendrick came past our little platoon of desks in the Advertising Department and said "The *Lusitania* has been sunk by a submarine."

The letter he sent to Rupert Brooke was written, unknowing, on the very day of Brooke's death (April 23, 1915). Presently came a reply from an English publisher, and he was authorized to collect from Macmillan (to whom the book had already been offered, but there had been disagreement about terms) the proofs that had been sent over. I remember the intense reluctance of Harold Latham at Macmillans' to surrender those papers to the eager Mistletoe. Latham's large face was engraved with the twinge of the publisher who sees something really fine going to a rival. He had put up a strong fight for the book, but his principals thought the price asked by London rather steep for a poet unknown—and now also dead. But Mistletoe rode up Fifth Avenue on top of a bus in high spirits. On the same visit he had bought—actually bought—a copy of Edgar Masters' *Spoon River Anthology*, then just published. Gloating on these two so different poets, and anticipating his first triumph as an editorial periscope, he hastened back to Long Island. The elation did not long endure. Garden City thought, as Macmillan had, that the price put on sheets for import from England was too high. Mistletoe succeeded in getting a few pamphlet copies printed to safeguard the American copyright, but after much cabling and heartburning he also was instructed to pass on the script elsewhere. Not less grieved than Latham had been, he laid the book sadly in the hands of Jefferson Jones of the John Lane Company. The book was published that autumn, and ran up to something like 75,000 copies in a few years.

Such trifling memories: I am almost embarrassed to put them down, but their only virtue is their unashamed littleness. There was once a girl who had been brought up in the show business but was now doing clerical work in a big corporation office and heartily sick of it. She heard about some theatrical doings over in Hoboken and wrote to apply for a job there. On sudden impulse, before sealing the envelope, she poured salt into the letter —salt being a traditional good-luck superstition among theatre people. The business manager's secretary, who opened the letter, noticed the grains in the envelope and was interested. She wrote bidding the applicant come to Hoboken for an interview at 11 o'clock on Saturday morning. In order to do so, the girl must leave her current work before closing time. The supervisor refused her permission. She smuggled her coat and hat into the washroom and in that way escaped without notice. It meant the sacrifice of a good $35 a week job, but she trusted the efficacy of her talisman. It worked, and to the very end, the Decline and Fall of the Hoboken Empire, she remained the most devoted of all servants of that queer enterprise. When the Old Rialto was closed for a few weeks in midwinter and the place was desperately cold (they were buying coal a ton at a time) Mildred was found typing scripts down in the furnace room. She believed in her salt, I must believe in mine and try to sprinkle a few granules in these pages. Grains of honest human bitterness sometimes: he struggled hard and was often fantastically inept and inefficient and felt a trap-door trembling beneath his feet. Oh days of mixed joy and drudgery, and of private simplicities and happinesses that have no record here. Days when one dared not spend more than 10 cents for lunch. Hot nights of hay fever in the Hempstead fields (perhaps the most fecund pollen-region known to man) when he gasped and choked and climbed out on the roof of the kitchen stoop to breathe. He sneezed and sneezed and in a world of War there was no "God bless you" that might avail. The dawn began to brighten and he crept in not to be seen by the milk-man.

In the old *Evening Post* building on Vesey Street (now called the Garrison Building) there was at one time a tiny lunch-room at the very top, up a little spiral stair from the Composing Room. There Royal Davis, Jack Kenderdine, Sinclair Lewis and John Mistletoe founded (September 1915) a luncheon group of young writers and publishers which was supposed to include only underlings and beginners. Editors-in-chief and potentates of all sorts were not encouraged as members though welcomed as guests. At that time I think Lewis was still working as George Doran's reader and publicity man. When we used to tell him of the amount of literary work being done on the Garden City trains, he averred briskly that the Port Washington branch also had its Muses. His *The Trail of the Hawk*, published about that time, had been largely written and meditated on the Long Island Railroad. To emphasize the lowly rank of its members we called our club "the small fry" (always written in lower-case) but we were none of us deficient in large dreams. Yet not even the most excitable would have ventured to imagine that one of those Publishers' Young Men was on the way toward a Nobel Prize. Long afterward I met a ticket collector working on the after-theatre trains. In his off-hours he had written a novel about railroading, and was discouraged at the long up-grade on a literary haul. I tried to reassure him by telling him how the L. I. R. R. had at least once proved the direct route to Stockholm.

The small fry grew to large numbers and held many amusing meetings. Sinclair Lewis about that time sold some stories to the *Saturday Evening Post* and slipped away into travel and free-lancing, so we saw him rarely; but among those who attended the cheerful meetings in the big upper room at Browne's Chophouse were several others who have won wide repute in various fields. Richardson Wright, custodian of the minutes, could be more precise, but I think at once of Donn Byrne and Joyce Kilmer; of Fontaine Fox and Edmund Pearson and Gilbert Gabriel; of Elmer Davis and Homer Croy and Heywood Broun; of Frederick S. Greene and Charles G. Norris. Norris was then hunting a publisher for his first and very honest novel *The Amateur*, on which he had worked long and painfully. He had to combat in his mind the unusual handicap of being the younger brother of one famous novelist and the husband of another, a serious perplexity for a sensitive man. One of the most esteemed members of the fry was a quiet reviewer on the staff of the *Times*, a Harvard man of much gentleness and culture who by some oddity of inheritance had found himself part-owner of a high-class saloon on 42nd Street. It was always a pleasure among those who sat latest round the lunch table to persuade our friend that we must adjourn to his bar-room and have one on the house. He begged us to keep the matter dark; if it became known in the *Times* office that he had an interest in a saloon-property . . . Yes, we agreed, it might be thought infra-dig. . . . Not at all, he said; what I mean is that the whole City-Room would be in there looking for free drinks.

The meetings of the small fry continued, with quite a number of distinguished speakers, until they finally faded away after the War. On one occasion Vachel Lindsay was guest of honor and recited to a large meeting and great applause.

Afterward, Lindsay and Mistletoe and some others were going down Broadway. All Vachel's elocutionary glands were well stimulated; like the man in O. Henry's *Gentle Grafter* he could feel millions of synonyms and parts of speech rising in him and he badly needed vent for them. He was genuinely drunk; not with wine, for Vachel is an abstainer, but with the pure excitement of a poet. "Look here," said Mistletoe, when it became apparent that our guest was really suffering from congestion, "we've simply got to find a place where he can spiel some more." We were then near the Childs restaurant at 32nd Street and Sixth Avenue where several of us often had our frugal lunch. The big basement room would be almost empty at that hour (mid-afternoon) so thither we went. A word to the manager, who was puzzled but good-natured. We ordered tea and toast, and in that alabaster cellar, to our own group, a few amazed patrons and a number of white-robed waitresses, Vachel ejaculated the resounding lines of *The Congo*—

Fat black bucks in a wine-barrel room,

he began, and Childs' albino tiling echoed it handsomely. I never heard him do it better, and it was a thrill for us all. "Childs' Garden of Verses," Vachel remarked as we left. He had always a pleasant solemnity of puns. Once, in the *Evening Post* era, Mistletoe took him to a little lunchroom on Vesey Street where several of the editors used to eat together. It was a very masculine place, rarely entered by ladies. This was an agreeable novelty to Vachel, just in from a long tour of women's clubs. He surveyed the thick china, the large bowls of bean soup, the solid slabs of roast beef, the strong atmosphere of smoke and heat and clatter. "This is a regular he-man's place," he observed. Then, tilting back his head and squinting at us in that characteristic pose (not unlike the lions in front of the New York Public Library) "and I don't mean Felicia Hemans."

Another welcome guest of the small fry was Walter de la Mare, whose exquisite verses were much in Mistletoe's mind in 1916. De la Mare paid his first visit to this country that autumn, and the Grub Street Runner was so exercised about the hope of getting the poet's work for his firm that one night he could not sleep. He rose incredibly early and hastened down town to the apartment of Mr. John S. Phillips who was then acting as D. P. and Co.'s literary adviser. He reached there by seven o'clock, forced his way in, and waked Mr. Phillips from slumber to pour out his heart on the subject of De la Mare's genius. J. S. P., still groaning a little with unfinished repose, lay in bed and listened with amiable patience, but nothing came of it as I believe Mr. De la Mare had already made other arrangements. Young Mistletoe and his senior had had many affectionate differences, beginning with Mr. Phillips's adverse vote on *Casuals of the Sea*. J. S. P.'s official report on that book was:

Without form but not void; an able unpleasant shapeless book; of interest, perhaps, to a few people. I would not publish it.

This nearly broke J. M.'s heart at the time, but luckily the book had a majority in its favor. When William McFee saw this memorandum many years later he laughed heartily and said, "I expect he was absolutely right."

So 1916 was a thrilling autumn. *Casuals* was published and was an immediate success. Pearsall Smith's *Trivia* was accepted. The firm took over the authorized editions of Walt Whitman's works; and a son was born. As Mistletoe has told elsewhere, he had made so much uproar in the councils of the firm about McFee's work that he then received a telegram signed by a dozen of his colleagues: *Congratulations. Name him Casuals*.

Chronologically it comes long later, but speaking of Mr. McFee reminds me of Arthur Elder's story of the young admirer of the engineer-novelist who did that very rash thing, made a surprise-pilgrimage to the author's home. He arrived at Mr. McFee's cottage in Connecticut, rang the bell, and got no answer. As he stood, timorous and full of adoring thoughts, he heard a deep vibrating groan from indoors. Nervously he rang again; still no result but another barytone growl of anguish. Heavens, he thought, has a crime been committed? With troubled uncertainty he opened the front door, and heard louder sounds of distress from an adjoining chamber. Convinced that something was tragically amiss, he entered. Apparently tethered to a chain from the ceiling was what seemed to the first horrified gaze a large woolly quadruped grunting savagely. It turned its tortured head and revealed the unfortunate novelist in his underwear, suffering the agonies of a sharp fit of sciatica. The only temporary relief, while his attendant sped for medical help, was by an electric pad on his saddle, the wire being just long enough to reach the light chandelier and allow the sufferer a brief ambit on all fours. Never try to take an author by surprise is good advice to enthusiasts. Better still, never try to take one at all, and preserve your illusions.

A faithful adherent of the small fry, though senior to most members, was Tom Masson, the managing editor of *Life*. His kindness to young Mistletoe was of that good practical sort that is never forgotten. He not only accepted for his magazine innumerable paragraphs, verses, and small jets of satire, but turned over to the struggling journalist a number of minor editorial jobs, such as weeding out the MSS submitted for *Life's* prize competitions. This work was paid on a piece basis, and J. M. got so expert that in some title-contest he once read 3,600 entries in three hours. No one knows how hard he can work until the necessity for it arises. In an old notebook of Mistletoe's I observe that during a month's stay in the city at the time the Urchin was born he sold two poems to *Life*, one to the *Century*, an article and a story to *The Bellman*, a book review to *Everybody's*, two reviews to the *Evening Post*, a skit to the *Smart Set*, an anonymous essay ("The Expectant Father") to *Every Week*, and—not inappropriately—an also anonymous article on "Weariness" to the New York *Sun*. In addition to these little livelinesses he was doing his work for the publisher, occasionally lecturing with the moving picture film at night, and helping sell books at the new Lord and Taylor bookshop by day. As he sardonically noted in a diary about that time, "Getting to be a regular Joyce Kilmer kind of hack;" Joyce having set the record for young men of that era in keeping innumerable balls in air at once. The miseries and dangers of such dispersed vitality are obvious enough. Kilmer fled from it joyously into the lurid single-mindedness of War. The few things he wrote from France were worth everything else he had done. In regard to journalism the shrewd Tom Masson said something once that stuck in Mistletoe's mind; such admirable advice that it deserves repetition. "If you have an idea," he said, "look at it steadily until you think you see in it something that no one else has seen; then it'll be your own, and it'll be something I'll want."

19

I AM ill at ease when I think of the stupidity of these poor memoranda. My friend often gave a convincing exterior of hilarity, but there may have been many a darkness within. I can only transmit such flashes of awareness as he chose to impart. As the Chinese poet asked:

> If every other poet
> Means as much more than he says in his verses
> As I do in mine,
> How shall I read poetry intelligently?

I remember an old newspaper man I once knew in Philadelphia who had heard Abraham Lincoln deliver the Gettysburg Speech; but he was drunk at the time and remembered absolutely nothing of the occasion. He was honest enough not to have fabricated any subsequent recollections. And there may, there must, have been many times when in our simplicity we were near great things, the wind of their passage even blew upon our faces, and we did not know. So I set these notes down not for the wise and confident, not for the gallery Conrad speaks of in a noble passage in *Chance*,[1] but for those like ourselves, ignorant, faulty, and unsure. What was that supremely silly thing a great teacher wrote about seeing life steadily and seeing it whole? To imagine one does is the sure mark of a lunatic. We saw life unsteadily and in very broken bits. But I think of those delicious words of Sir Philip Sidney at the beginning of his *Defense of Poesy:*—

"Self-love is better than any gilding to make that seem gorgeous wherein ourselves be parties."

Oh, is it known or thought (even yet) what a time of stir and experiment that was. The MSS of Sherwood Anderson's first novels came to Eugene Saxton's desk out at Garden City, and he passed

[1] "There are on earth no actors too humble and obscure not to have a gallery; that gallery which envenoms the play by stealthy jeers, counsels of anger, amused comments, or words of perfidious compassion."—*Chance*, chapter 4.

them on to Mistletoe to read. They gazed at each other with a wild surmise, but knew that it was no use, just then, to fight for them in committee. And presently Ben Huebsch published Joyce's extraordinary *Portrait of the Artist* which foreboded so much. As afterwards with Proust, Mistletoe never carefully read more than a little of it, for he was always very canny about what not to read; his ignorance is precious to him. He could see, in a few pages, what Joyce was doing; it was thrilling, but it was something to consider by patient intuition, not to palaver and write to the papers about. There is no harm in reading any number of unimportant things for pastime, but the significant books must be taken cautiously. You don't want them to get in the way of what may perhaps be growing and brooding in yourself, taking its own time.

There was little vacancy, just then, for brooding. He lived on instinct and on action. Perhaps he had not in any real sense begun to think. Perhaps he has not yet. Curse the time when a man begins to experience that lonely and destroying indulgence, tippling in secret the white absinthe of reason. "Hang ideas!" cries Marlow in *Lord Jim*—"They are tramps, vagabonds, knocking at the back door of your mind, each taking a little of your substance, each carrying away some crumb of that belief in a few simple notions you must cling to if you want to live decently and would like to die easy." I can give no easy synthesis of those years. Witty glossarians have been brightly summing up the decade of the Twenties, in which so many sad young men wrung their souls; have offered spirited valuations of the period and its troubled minds. But in the war-time Teens we were too deeply troubled to be articulate about it. Under cover of that enormous regimented clamor young householders clung to simplicity. The morning milk-bottle on the porch, the little paper bag of fresh rolls from the baker, the bean patch, the plumbing, the furnace fire, the baby's bath, the loved and fragrant dark head asleep on the pillow, these were full and sufficient reality. At night there was a wood fire on the hearth, after supper one sprawled weary on the floor and slept beside the blaze. Yes, he should have been working . . . but at least no lights were burning to add to the electric bill. . . . Eagerly he read Lowes Dickinson and Bertrand Russell, but his sentimental pacifism was getting rather shaky. He turned to Walt Whitman; it was Walt who kept some of us alive in those days. Mistletoe had given up his plan of joining a volunteer Naval training cruise in 1916, but in 1917 he was called early in the Draft. Whether to apply for exemption was hard to decide. He took his copy of *Leaves of Grass* and walked out by a little stream to try to think the matter out. In the back of the book, in parallel columns, he set down the arguments pro and con, with full and naive anguish. The temptation to get into the all-atoning uniform was strong, but he could not convince himself and applied for exemption on the plain ground of domestic responsibility. What he really has to reproach himself for is that in the fever of newspaper work during that last year 1918 he was sometimes carried away by the huge frenzy of the time and joined in print in the chorus of journalistic rant. It was a cheap and easy kind of patriotism, the yellow badge of hysteria. Thoreau wouldn't have done it. At the same time, absurdly enough, he was writing a book ("about an old bookshop") which was criticized later both as too warlike and too pacifist. But the intellectual distractions of that time are too painful to remember lightly. He recalls with more pleasure that perhaps the last legal liquor served in American literature was the champagne in the concluding chapter of that story. The book was published June 30, 1919, the day before Prohibition went—as we naively called it—into effect. That same night, in a rowdy tavern kept by a Philadelphia Dame Quickly, his wallet was frisked by a bright-eyed dip. It contained some Liberty Bonds and also a Walt Whitman MS letter that had been given him by old David McKay. It seems pleasant paradox that these two symbolisms should have disappeared together. He never kept a wallet in his hip-pocket afterward.

Perhaps in a long perspective of the future it will be apparent that in those chaotic years the United States entered into civilization. She not only acquired new nationality of her own, but she was forced to think of herself (though slowly and resentfully) as part of a world integer. She was no longer a demi-mondaine. She discovered the world-circulation of the blood. But it was a vast process and a bitter initiation. General Pershing has told us that when we declared war we had only enough large-calibre artillery ammunition for nine hours' firing. The odd thing is that this, suggested as a cause for shame, might also be argued as a reason for pride.

But I am still thinking of the last days before the War. He often tried in clumsy but very honest little rhymes, to commemorate the stress and tenderness of that time. I don't like to use the word "humble" too often, it is likely to have a horrid false sound, but the verses were genuinely so. They were accurate footnotes, or heart-notes, on thought and feeling, as sincere and unabashed as Parson Herrick. I have looked in vain among old memoranda for a little paragraph he once wrote about a tiny bantam rooster that used to crow those sunny mornings. There was infinite merriment, gallantry, pathos in that clear bravado shrill. It had also unusual sweetness of pure tune, a gay unforgotten cadence. C-e-e-g-f-E-D, high in the treble, will give you a notion of it; the notes indicated in small letters are half the time of the capitals. It was as old and simple and artful as an echo from Chaucer or Aesop, yet brilliantly new every morning. The alert little champion of daylight, sure of himself as a cockerel bishop, is long since perished; his martial inheritance distributed eggwise over the suburban meads; but his doomed undaunted cry lives still in the mind; become somehow symbolic of much.

The spring came; the mud on that small byway in Queens Village was deep and wallowy. Flags went up on the schoolhouse where he had cast (for Woodrow Wilson) his first suffrage as a citizen. The overshadowing certainty drew nearer and nearer; yet along the little street where tiny jerrybuilt houses almost touched each other all the elements of the earthly comedy were there already. The old Dutchman who had been a barge captain in New York harbor and believed in neutrality; his Irish-American son-in-law who didn't; the friendly little German a few doors away with a houseful of rolypoly children and his love of beer and plans for a productive garden; another neighbor who read Conrad and whose maidservant was about to have a bastard. There were the ashes to be put out for the garbage man three times a week; the baby carriage to be hoisted up the porch steps; the occasional evening spree to Brooklyn. To take Titania by train to Nostrand Avenue, dine at a rotisserie, buy a long-coveted Latin dictionary in a second-hand bookshop and then go to the movies was as good an adventure as anyone ever had. Can it be that in all the panorama of literature no one has ever celebrated the bright bourgeois gusto of Fulton Street, Brooklyn? And two doves, from no one knew where, nested under the eaves of the little house. I suppose there may have been a lot of doves looking for quarters in that spring of 1917: I remember the outrageously funny cartoon in the *Evening Journal* of Mr. Bryan with the Dove of Peace's eggs nested in the upward-curling thatch of his back hair. At any rate confidential pigeon dialogue could be heard murmuring on the roof in early morning, and two rather argumentative young people took it as a pleasant omen.

He was offered another job. It seemed hardly possible to refuse, the advance in salary was so surprising. Yet he had his private hesitations. The pleasantest job of all, he made secret memorandum, would be to edit the *Atlantic*. (There is no harm, he said to himself gravely, in keeping clearly in mind what the most desirable jobs are.) It was amusing that some years later he was offered a position on the staff of the *Atlantic*. This came almost simultaneously with an invitation to work on the New York *Evening Journal*, certainly a surprising incongruity; a tribute, he tried to make himself believe, to a wide range of interests.

It seemed advisable to make the change, not without grief. Financial necessities were severe, as they always have been. One of life's grotesque paradoxes that had annoyed him was that to his intense surprise he had lately been elected to a famous club of bibliophiles. Practically all the members were elderly and prodigiously wealthy book collectors, and his election as the infant colleague came as a painful shock, for it was utterly impossible, without the most hellish perplexities, to pay the initiation fee. Yet he was too foolishly proud to be honest about it and decline. I think he took the new job partly in the hope of catching up with that fatal initiation. I remember talking with a well-known literary critic of modest means who, on coming to live in New York, was embarrassed by pressing invitations to join several charming clubs. Flattered, and in sheer softness of good nature, he accepted several, more than he could possibly utilize or afford. As the day approached when the initial dues must be paid he was quite desperate, and seriously considered writing anonymous letters to the various committees defaming and blackballing himself. This idea,

174

when I quoted it to Mistletoe, appealed to him keenly as a theme for a very Gissingesque short story. Gissing's *House of Cobwebs* (a book excessively difficult to keep; when you lend it you never get it back) was a volume of stories whose pensive and melancholy tone always appealed to him.

It was hard to leave the Country Life Press, which had grown as familiarly dear as a college does to its students. Among the many smells that make life interesting—the whiff of ships and watersides, the immortal backstage sweetness of theatre make-up, the smell of a loaf of bread, of old rye whiskey, of a baby's head—the ink and glue and paper fragrance of a printing plant must rank high. In all the details of that workmanlike and beautiful place he took a pleasure that was sensual rather than scientific. There were the heat and crash of monotype machines; the bubbling blue acids in the foundry tank where ghosts of men's thoughts passed in electric molecules through the fluid and formed themselves into frail copper shells; the waving arms and little suction fingers of the Miehle presses, the piles of printed sheets, the strong aroma of the bindery, the crisp clean alleys of new books, gay with colored jackets, ready to go out on unpredictable quest. And all their different personalities: some brazenly overdressed, shouting their confident popularity; others quiet but assured of well-earned welcome, decent middle-aged creatures; and still others, frightened and frustrated, with shy awkward charms of their own but who seemed to have no friends at all. Keep away from the stock-room if you are sensitive to books; it may break your heart.

But there is health and life in a process where tangible goods are manufactured, where at the end of the cycle you see a product emerging. The various forms of brokerage and jugglery where a man deals only in quotations, figments, abstract values, sound to me singularly inane. How much more fun to be a grocer or a druggist. It was never less than fairy-tale to think of the adventures of words in that long brick building. Effendi remarked once casually that he would like to know just what kind of dynamite and wildcats live under the hood of a motor-car. There are dynamite and wildcats too in the prenatal life of a book. Any word as you see it here was first dipped up from a bottle of Stafford's Jet Black, then hammered out again through a typewriter ribbon, then punched in type on slivers of hot lead. It lived for a while on long galley sheets and was murmured, for syntax only, not for æsthetic ecstasy, in the patient sing-song of the proofreader. It was rammed into soft wax, went bathing in acid, drew to itself sparkling wraith-atoms of copper, strengthened itself for the world (as any idealist must) with heavy backing of alloy, lay down on the bed of a press, was run over by rollers of ink and crushed by huge sheets of paper. How alive they are, those presses! As you walk through the garden they gesticulate to you. Through the windows you see the white sheets flap to and fro. It is like prisoners waving shirts or kerchiefs to attract attention. Someone's words are there, impatient for life.

One could not work in such a place, well-ordered and strong like a ship, gardened like a Tudor mansion, without some underlying sense of the meaning of our trade. The early printers' symbols were there on the sun-dial; they too had dreamed of sending out their work to stir men's hearts. How much less interesting, he used to think, must a publishing office be that has no printing plant attached. Contact with pressroom realities has its severe problems, but it keeps alive the sense of apostolic succession from Aldus and Plantin. Years later he heard Effendi's story that when that press was built the architects had insisted on some structural additions which he did not approve and felt would spoil the simplicity of the design. But the Effendi could not seem to convince anyone of his dismay so one night, finding the supplementary plans in the construction shanty, he quietly bagged them and buried them deep under bricks and rubble where the front steps were being laid out. There was a hue and cry after the missing papers, but he lay low and as time was urgent the offending schemes were not redrawn. The plans are still there.

It was no wonder that the fry who worked under him adored the clear wisdom and hawklike shrewdness of the man. His integrity, wisdom and humor, his magnificent alertness for business stratagem together with a large idealism for creating big things, made an irresistible combination. There will always be certain phases of publishing in which a large organization has its perils; ever since the time of Shakespeare's Sonnets the fly-by-night or one-man business has often been able to get the things of rarest beauty. Indeed one of Mistletoe's japes in which he took greatest pleasure was having (years afterward, piqued by some harmless dispute with the literary staff) submitted those very sonnets, carefully typed out and under an alias; and received a letter saying they did not seem to be up to the literary standard of the house. But in its own realm the double achievement of Effendi and his partners is surely extraordinary: first on Long Island and then all over again at the Windmill Press in England. Those young men used to wish to themselves that he might have been President of the United States. But more often those romantic youths imagined that bronze clear-eyed profile as it might have been in some earlier era, merchant-adventurer on the Virginian voyage.

ESCAPED INTO PRINT

20

GOING into the kitchen late at night for a glass of milk I often find myself thinking of B. H. in the old office of the *Evening Ledger*. In that office Mistletoe had under his desk a jug of cider someone had given him. Bart twirled himself a drinking horn out of a sheet of copypaper (a knack all newspaper men acquired in those days before little cardboard goblets became universal) and accepted a swig of the rural nectar. He stood for an instant in earnest afterthought. "By gracious, it makes all the strong stuff taste like poison," he said, and went back to the editorial he was writing.

It does indeed. These hours of midnight silence bring a very mute and private plainness. One is content with elemental things, fire and fatigue and bread and milk. Analogy, the oxygen of the mind, is all around you. The old dog, grown uneasy, drums the floor with his shin as he pursues some irritation; then turns and turns and settles himself for sleep. Wise and harmless as Socrates, fine old gentledog, he comes softly toward his end. He has no complaint and nothing to regret. The fire is fallen low on the hearth, just a deep marigold crumble; yet more than once, by some pocketing of soot in the flue that same comfortable chimney has roared with terrorizing flame. In the twilight, in the evening, in the black and dark night (is there any literature greater than our Book of Proverbs?) words of truth come back to you, words wrung out of men and women in the twist of life. Once I heard it said, "But I don't want to do the unusual. I want to do just the commonest things."

I have no idea what Bart was discussing in that editorial, and even the building in which he was writing it has disappeared; but his chance comment on the pleasures of simplicity has remained as durable as fable.

It was probably during one of those interludes of talk that punctuate the afternoon in the editorial rooms of an evening paper. Someone, hard at work, is struck by an idea, but before unloading it on the public he hankers to discuss it a bit. Bart and Jimmy and Mistletoe would find themselves adrift in some badly leaking argument—so uncaulked the very rats instinctively have quit it, but exciting to scull about in. Perhaps it was the paregoric qualities of Woodrow Wilson's prose style, or efficiency at Hog Island, or how soon Pershing would straighten out the St. Mihiel salient. Very likely the latter; a huge map of the battle-fronts was tacked up on the wall near Mistletoe's desk, and Jimmy's first affair every morning was to redraw the lines in accordance with the latest dispatches. Breathing hard, his short plump figure would mount the table to reach the map, and ejaculate "Pop goes the Vesle" as his black pencil included that stream in the regained territory. The argument would go on until the Doc, senior editorial writer, grunting to himself over his leader, would show signs of impatience, probably toward the spittoon. The juniors would remember uneasily that time was flitting and their copy not up yet. Jimmy, solemnly sucking that large curve-stem pipe, waddles back to his encyclopædias to compose the Daily Quiz, a list of questions on general information which was an esteemed feature of our page. Mistletoe bends farther into that cavernous old rolltop hunting for rhymes for his column. And Bart, with a quiet definiteness of purpose which I can see still, strides back to his typewriter. I see his well barbered gray head intent over the keyboard. There was always a grim docility about the way he returned to the task after one of those flurries of conversation.

The best illustration of that disciplined instinct was an innocent but well-remembered occasion when some serious-minded editors took a case of Scotch out to the suburbs for their friend Madrigal. It was a gift from a generous Caliph, to solemnize the End of an Era; on the following day the transport of spirits would become unconstitutional. Madrigal had been laid up at home with a serious flu, so one nicknamed the Soothsayer volunteered to transport the goods in his car. It was a brilliant morning of sunshine on snow, the world glittered in lustres of crystal. Arrived chez Madrigal, and a bottle of the Old Vatted Traymore broached to honor the occasion, the invalid poet began to ettle. The frozen purity of weather tempted him, against cosy domestic counsel. Blanched earth and flashing sun prevailed. Warmly wrapped, and with the bottle in case of relapse, they were to go as far as Jenkintown on some errand connected with an antique chair. This accomplished and the forenoon seeming progressively more radiant, they drove out into open country where the untouched dazzle of snowfields suggested enlargement and caper. There was also a long icy furrow in the road very tempting for tests of equilibrium. They left the car, and there followed an interval of physical rapture which hypocritic memory finds hard to regain and which to the calm eye of Authority would have appeared undignified. It remains one of those lunatic seizures one would least willingly forego. A species of Eskimo saltarello was devised, followed by a game of tag which seemed to involve bursting through ice-spun bramble hedges and rolling in drifts. There was some notion of setting about an igloo, but presently the thought of the Philadelphia public, patiently waiting to be enlightened upon large affairs, became imminent. To turn the car around on that ice-sheathed way was not easy. In doing so they had a skid into the ditch and a severe jolt against a telephone pole. They deposited the antique chair at its destination, where Madrigal handsomely embraced the startled lady of the house, who was much younger than the chair; lunched well at the Bellevue, not realizing until too late that their features were blue with frostbite and scarred with thorns; and returned earnestly to their desks. They set about their jobs. When the copy was finished, and the really noble anaesthesia of the adventure had worn off, one of them remarked a pain in his side. He discovered afterward that he had written his daily stint with a broken rib. As for the ailing poet, instead of dying of pneumonia, his influenza was completely cured.

Every man who has done newspaper work, whatever his rational conclusions, looks back with affection and nostalgia on that life of busy nerves. The pressure of passing time, the sense of anonymous power, a sort of offhand bohemianism and untidyness, a naive conviction of being behind the scenes in the human comedy, are partial elements in a very subtle feeling. Mistletoe's newspaper experience, which he loved to the full, was always anomalous. It would justly be scoffed at by those who have gone in orderly fashion through the customary grades of progress. He began, in sheer hazard, by writing the Leading Editorial on his first day in the office. He got his job when one of those periodical shake-ups had happened, a number of highly skilled journalists had been wafted away in a sudden concussion and a new editor found himself with only a few hours to reorganize his staff. That very day the news of the last great German push toward the Channel was coming through, and J. M. happened to be the one available who knew most about the geography of the terrain. Beginning thus at the top of the profession, by some hasty bombast about military strategy (and leaders in the old *Evening Ledger* really were leaders, set in 10-point blackface so the reader might be certain they were important) he gradually declined through various levels of work, of which occasional sports reporter was undoubtedly his favorite. But he also maintains that there is no fun like writing what they used to call "ears"—editorial paragraphs with an indented blackface head; the nicety of which depends on completing or tilting the innuendo of the paragraph in the three or four brief words allowed for the "ear." The skill of newspaper paragraphing can rise to Baconian dexterity, and it pleases me to think of unsuspected brothers at distant typewriters who may at this very instant be feeling the thrill of a well-turned ear uncoiling from the machine. They have, for the moment, that rare and pure satisfaction of the unthanked artist. They see the anonymous little missile spinning off on a long curve into space. Many many chances are against it; the downward pull of gravity is heavy indeed; but perhaps, somewhere, it will reach the sensitive cheek muscle of the possible reader. Once, in the *Evening Post*, Mistletoe wrote:—

The other evening, riding on the train, we saw a man reading the editorial page of the *Journal*. We couldn't see just what he was reading, because he was sitting opposite. But on his cheek, as he read, there wavered a faint crease, a quiet flitting smile that meant that the writer, whoever he was, had touched his spirit of comprehension. That cheek muscle is what all writers are aiming at. When you are reading something you thoroughly enjoy, something that tickles the sense of quiet appreciation of human ways, that cheek muscle twitches and trembles. It is not a question of laughter; it is far deeper than that. Perhaps that cheek muscle, and not the fabled pineal gland, is the true residence of the soul. Whoever was writing on the *Journal's* editorial page that evening—or perhaps it was the cartoonist—had succeeded in his job, had turned the trick that all writers crave.

187

There was never a pleasanter camaraderie anywhere than in that row of little kennels in the old
Ledger building. Like the officers' cabins in an old
sailing ship they stretched in suite forward from
the skipper's quarters, the Editor's office. Alongside them was the hurrying drama of the City
Room, and under their windows and antique iron
fire-escapes the romantic thoroughfare of one of
America's oldest streets, with Independence Hall
chiming the hours a few yards away. Down that
street came Wilson and Joffre and Pershing and all
the headline figures of the War; and up it, more
troubling to the eyes, brown ranks with the Key-
stone shoulder tab, thankful to be back. Veterans
of an even larger war, too: Louis, the old balloon
peddler, with swaying airy leash of colored globes,
sometimes transfigured by diagonal sunlight into
an Atlas bearing bubble-worlds of soapsud sheen;
and Blind Al, the newsdealer, tapping his stick on
the pavement. Underlings in journalism, however
docile in print, are usually great sea-lawyers after
office hours, irreverent questioners of authority,
iconoclasts of public statuary, rippers of stuffed
shirts, dowsers for hidden well-springs of doctrine.
Sometimes the Soothsayer would drive them out
to his favorite roadhouse along the Schuylkill, and
there the perversity of earth would be well
threshed. One of their favorite theorems was that
the formula for a successful newspaper could

easily be calculated. Yes, said one, quoting Hearst:
Plenty of crime and plenty of underclothes.—It's
like a patent medicine, said another. A chemist
told me that every drug nostrum has three
standard ingredients: a narcotic, a laxative, and a
bitter.—The news is a narcotic, someone cried, and
our editorial stuff is certainly a laxative. But
what's the bitter?—That's the circulation department.—Sometimes the Managing Editor would
join them; dour at first, but warming to his theme
after a glass of wine. Do you remember, he would
exclaim, poor Keats's dream was that his brother's descendants should grow up to be the first
American poets? And what did they grow up to
be? The Managing Editors of newspapers!

That crowded rolltop, which grew gradually
deeper in litter, was Tom Daly's old desk. And
here is Tom himself, singer of Robert Burns charm
and incomparable narrator of comedy, waiting at
the Ben Franklin statue on the broad pavement
outside the post-office. He is rolling a cigarette, his
bright compelling Irish eye has already noted his
young crony hurrying along Chestnut Street. He
puts on a cool don't-know-you air and pretends
to pass by; but he can't keep up the joke, for something has happened that tickles his antic fancy, he
can hardly wait to impart it. How many things
there were that must be told, at once, O instantly,

by or to Tom. Whatever it was, he will unfold it with incorrigible skill, over one of the little tables at Dooner's.

For the best part of three years they must have lunched together three or four times a week, and in all that time Mistletoe never heard Tom tell the same story twice, unless by request. Lifelong habitué of that region, he knew all the best resorts for scrapple, or oyster stew, or any other fine Philadelphia feeding. (I almost hesitate to mention Tom and Jerry, that wintry elixir of eggs, sugar, brandy, rum, hot milk, and nutmeg, not wishing to disgust with life a younger generation that has hardly even heard of it. There was in Green's Hotel a painting of a racehorse which, after two Tom and Jerries, could be seen to cock its ears and whisk its tail.) One day Mistletoe, scouting on his own, discovered a little Italian café on South 9th Street. Knowing Tom's delightful verses in Italo-American he dragged the poet thither in triumph. There, usually the only patrons, they lunched scores of times while Mistletoe revelled in the rich oily gravies, frittura mista, scallopini, spaghetti and ravioli and mushrooms. But meanwhile the poet, not usually slow in announcing his tastes, seemed to be suffering an atrophy. Finally, when the dark-eyed Rosa offered him as special delicacy some pink and very dissecting-room-looking small cuttlefish, he broke down. He was constrained to confess that he did not really care for Italian cooking. They returned to the corned beef and cabbage of Dooner's. But wherever they lunched they managed to get a few minutes for looking over the books at Leary's.

Mistletoe liked to hope that something of Tom Daly's Celtic genius might linger in the pigeon-holes of that old desk. At any rate he was faithful to it, after his fashion. Some of his clearest memories of it are the summer evenings when his family were at the seashore and he sat alone in the dark office, wearing down the point of a pen on schemes of his own. Upstairs in the departments of the morning paper all was blaze and activity, but the afternoon quarters were eerily silent. Hours would go by in that warm enchanted corner, lit only by a green drop-light. Sometimes there was the peaceful companionship of good Charley Sykes, grimly scowling and stretching a lean knotty hand over tomorrow's cartoon, but always there was that strange sense of complete quiet on the edge of uproar. Presently the hum of presses would begin down in the basement, and he would consider dolefully that the men upstairs had covered the news of the whole world while the tyro in his shadowy corner might only have written two or three stanzas. On his way home to a dolefully empty apartment he would read the early edition with coffee and doughnuts.

21

SUDDENLY I draw a deep breath and realize that
no fiction could possibly be as exciting as Mistletoe's frightened and stumbling attempt to convey
to me his remembered glimmerings of essence. He
is specially inarticulate when he tries to tell about
Philadelphia. He used to say, not without humor,
that one of his missions was to try to make New
York and Philadelphia love one another. But he
knew it was unlikely.

Philadelphia, he sometimes thought, is perhaps
the nearest you can find to a locus of the American
identity. New York will never be altogether
Americanized. (Chicago is too fantastic to be representative; Boston too docile; Baltimore too
bohemian and humane.) He had done much commuting in both cities, and was thrilled by the
temperamental dissidence. On Philadelphia's
sacred Main Line, or even on the homely old
Cinder and Bloodshot, how much more settled,
comforted, and sure those people are. The commuter into New York travels farther and uglier,
is more on edge, approaches a fiercer ordeal, is
more rapidly talkative, more on his nerve. Oh how
pleasant it would be to have the gay conscience-
less insouciance of a Strachey, to revel in bright
colors of rhetoric, easy and captivating antitheses.

Perhaps the best and most happily naive thing he did was his amateur attempt to note down the shape and tint of that endlessly lovable town. Those were the last days of the older Philly. Gigantic area of manufacture, she threw herself into War with infernal gusto. The Quaker city loved the war, as manufacturers and editors usually do. They had their midnight horrors, like most men; but locomotive and ship works blazed red in the darkness, and editorials and John Wanamaker's homilies blazed red by day. Editors of the *Ladies' Home Journal* (himself among them) visited training camps to watch the cheery organizers of the Young Men's Christian Association halloo "the boys" into the right martial spirit. Who would not love a world so rich in irony?

The secret thoughts of Philadelphia, if there were any, were as carefully obscure as the private life of old Ben Franklin—which only the very daring have humor to contemplate. New York had sometimes her doubts about the divinity of patriotism, but Philadelphia has few doubts. Her superior classes are too canny, too square in the toe, to be dubious. He used to walk in sunny lunch hours through the gracious area of Independence Square and feel far from independent. Above the humble little State House loomed magnificent monuments of Americanization, and that amazing phenomenon the *Saturday Evening*

Post. Phenomenon so vast, so cleanly managed, so enormously significant to any student of print: so huge that the aesthete would have to remind himself that things are not necessarily unimportant because they are so large. But there were ominous parables in that dear old square. The Liberty Bell itself was cracked and kept in a glass case. It would never ring clear tone again. Would it ever be possible to love life without tramping in regiments; to brood and speculate candid inquiry without being supposed cynic or satiric? How easy, oh how much too easy, is the sardonic vein. He remembered typical intellectualist zanies who would be prejudiced against a story by Joseph Hergesheimer when it appeared in the *Saturday Evening Post*, but would hail the same tale as ripe art when it was reprinted—a year later—in the London *Mercury*. How many private laughters that very great and humorous editor George Horace Lorimer must have had at the expense of the muddle-headed pseudo-literates.

But in those days any second-rate sensitive mind was caught in paradoxes from which there seemed no issue. He consoled himself by disloyally admiring the wine-stains on George Washington's waistcoat, preserved in Independence Hall. On the sunny side of that old building he met Martha, the exceptionally fine State House cat. (Suddenly I remember Don Marquis's remark that the art

194

of newspaper paragraphing is to stroke a platitude until it purrs like an epigram.) Martha was so black that in meridian sunlight her coat gave off an almost purple shimmer. She led him down into the cellar of the Hall where he made friends with old Fred Eckersberg, the engineer of the building. Fred's good comments on a national shrine as seen from the basement often restored his faith in the simple humors of existence. Once when Fred had rheumatism, Mistletoe stoked the Independence Hall furnace for him. How many Sons of the Revolution can say as much? That big firebox in the shadows of the cellar burned with all delicate interchanges of red and white and blue. Even Fred was strongly military, and found Peace a heavy blow. No longer was the Hall a lively oracle of constant pilgrimage, bands and parades and famous visitors.

He liked to escape from the office on long lonely rambles round the city, watching her great humanity. There was more intricate News on any street than the mind could receive or a newspaper print. He loved that city specially for he knew she could never be more than an interlude for him. Philadelphia was nourishing and well-spiced scrapple, but New York was champagne. Philadelphia was sage, but New York was onions. Philadelphia was picturesque and vast, but she could be perceived and even perhaps understood; but New York never.

Philadelphia was self-satisfied; New York was alive with the radiance of the impossible, and will always have the secret inferiority twinge that drives men to fantastic attempts. He loved Philadelphia because he felt he knew her well. He loves New York because she can never be known.

It is odd that so many memories of that arduous time concern excessive practical jokes played on one another by members of the editorial staff. Mostly these are too intricate to describe, but Mistletoe recalls when he was well scored upon in retaliation for some ingenious tricks. He had interviewed and become very friendly with a colored bandmaster who was giving rousing jazz concerts with the military band of a negro regiment. He had talked a good deal to his colleagues about the talent of this vivacious musician; just at that time the news came that the unfortunate fellow had died suddenly in Boston—stabbed in a fight, I think. A telegram with Boston date-line came to Mistletoe's desk, purporting to be sent by the widow, earnestly inviting him to be a pallbearer at an impressive African-Baptist funeral. He was greatly touched by this summons, and in spite of its obvious embarrassments felt it a christian duty to accept. He hastily wired money for flowers, wrote for his column a pensive paragraph about the Great Leveller who abolishes all color-schemes, and was looking up trains for Boston when his

cackling mates mercifully apprised him the message
was a hoax. I suppose it is typical human perversity that those days, thick with the anxieties of a
world on fire, were also the most jocular of a lifetime. I would not have the courage to look up old
files, but I remember that his stuff on the *Evening
Ledger* was often heartily comic. He was even
elected a member of the excellent fraternity of
American Press Humorists, who met in Philadelphia for one of their conventions and planted their
symbolic chestnut tree. There was a blight on
chestnuts about that time, yet it was pleasant to
think himself enrolled, even under false pretences,
in the old boiler-plate trade of Max Adeler and
Petroleum V. Nasby and the Danbury News Man,
of Eugene Field and Opie Read and (his boyhood
favorite) M. Quad. Once at the typewriter he
pushed the dark rider off the rump and gaily waved
his bladder. It was quite safe to do so; as far as the
outside world is concerned writing for a Philadelphia newspaper is the purest form of secrecy.

So these young journalists had their ups and
downs. They loaned and borrowed among themselves, and devised an invocation for hours of
leanness—

Twas the night before pay day, and all through my jeans
I hunted in vain for the price of some beans—
Forward, turn forward, O Time, in thy flight:
Make it tomorrow, just for tonight.

Sometimes, on the old uneven brick pavements of
Pine Street, or in the great arched shed of Broad
Street Station where proud locomotives silhouetted black against the curve, or on the
tomato-scented ferry to Camden, there was a
sudden clarity of feeling, a sense of the reporter's
true passion: his honorable dream of finding on the
common pavement some of those broken fragments of grace men are too hurried to pick up.
The owner, simple and lovable and most tenacious
of dreamers, had a burning vision of making his
Ledger one of the great American journals. One
day in editorial conference there lay on the table
a Chicago paper which carries as a conspicuous
front-page streamer the motto "The World's
Greatest Newspaper." His eye brightened wistfully upon it. "Why didn't we think of that first?"
he asked. He told them charmingly how when
staying at a club in Detroit he used to find the
Ledger in the reading room buried among the other
papers; he always picked it out and put it on top
of the heap. Alas it takes more than a lusty slogan
or preferred position on the pile to create a successful and great-minded paper. It needs also
more than the worthiest intentions. Even the
New York *Evening Post*, under management as
idealistic as the business has ever seen, could not
do it. The *Post* staff were fanatics in the most
zealous tradition. Men like Lawrence Perry and

Dudley Nichols and John Anderson were doing reporting that has never been surpassed. 50,000 was then about as high a circulation as it could reach and hold.[1]

But the memory I summon, typical of so much in the world of newspaper fellowship, is that of Steve O'Grady. I reprint here, without alteration, some items that appeared in the *Evening Post* in July and August 1923. I like to remember that among the rigid and complicated mechanisms of the newspaper linotype there is also a little jet of pure flame. The motto that was printed over this correspondence was a quotation from Paul Bourget: "Il faut vivre comme on pense, sinon, tôt ou tard, on finit par penser comme on a vécu."

23

THE STORY OF STEVE'S SUITCASE

LOS ANGELES, July 3.—Steve O'Grady, veteran newspaper man, who had worked on leading newspapers in many sections of the country and acted as advance agent for traveling theatrical companies, died in the General Hospital yesterday. He was forty-six years old and a native of Kansas City.—New York *Tribune*.

---

[1]And even while these pages were going into type, the New York *World* also gave up its independent ghost.

IT SEEMS to us truly representative of life that a man who never had any enemy but himself while alive should in death find his own words his best friends.

Just a word of explanation. One day in 1918 Steve blew hilariously into the office of the Philadelphia *Evening Ledger* and asked us if he might leave his suitcase under our desk. There it lay for the better part of two years, uncalled for; Steve himself having vanished, as was his way. When we left the *Ledger*, in 1920, we turned the case over to our side-kick Bart Haley, with the remark that some day Steve would turn up to claim it.

In January, 1921, Steve appeared unexpectedly at the kennel of the Bowling Green. "Well, Steve," we said, "did you ever go and get that suitcase in the *Ledger* office?" His face changed and he looked at us sharply. "My God!" he said, "is that where it is?"

A few days later we received the following letter, which we print word for word. This is Steve's memorial.

> *706 South Washington Square,*
> *Phila., Jan. 8, 1921.*
> *After midnight.*

With only a hard pencil between me and success, here I sit in this lovely and quiet spot that you and I love so well. May the ghosts of those great and departed buried in front of me and be-

neath me intercede with the great God of us all to give me the strength to finish this letter as I would!

When I went up to see you on that fateful afternoon and you told me that under Bart's desk lay a suitcase of mine I couldn't believe that it was the same oblong package that contained those precious souvenirs that I had sought by money and prayers for three years. The chase had been given up. That suitcase contained the things that had warmly decorated my little old Washington Square room at 704 South in years gone by.

I continued the celebration in New York, but always with that thought in mind—they're over there—under Bart's desk. I went wild and forgot. I went up to my room in the Roaring Forties and tried to come back. I went down to Park Row only to tumble again. Roving in that ecstasy in which the dreamer roves, at odd moments the thought would pound itself back. Those precious relics, of value to no one but me—still there! After three years. In the recess of a session on William Street I wandered over to the Row. The traffic cop escorted me across in the direction of City Hall Place—near little old St. Andrew's Church. Outside this church stood an Italian with an apple wagon—a pushcart—Beyond a horse, a poor weary horse that had worked all day, and whose head drooped. I said to the Italian: "Did it ever occur to you to feed an apple to a horse? It might improve your luck?"

"He bite me," wildly ejaculated the Italian.

"Bite you!" I demanded. "A horse bite a man who feeds him an apple!"

I continued: "Let me show you—Give me three of your apples. There is the quarter. Now watch the horse bite me."

I took the three apples, patted the horse on the forehead and stood there and held all three apples while he ate them. A crowd gathered. Women who didn't know I was drunk stopped to admire. Men muttered that "horses sure like apples." The Italian was in a trance.

The job of feeding the horse ended, I decided to pray and entered the chapel. It was dark and the pews empty—but as I approached the altar of the Virgin I heard, in one of the clearest coloraturas I have ever heard, the strains of Gounod's "Ave Maria." There was an organ accompaniment. I was afraid to look back. Surely no miracle—But I did look back as the ode ended. Then I realized: A dear old teacher using the organ to train one of his young singers—selecting the most deserted church in town. I didn't dare address them from the chancel; rather I climbed the rickety stairs of the choir loft and asked her to sing it again. They were inclined to regard me as a madman. I assured them I wasn't. I said: "I'm a newspaper man, but

I've been drinking, and I've just fed three apples to a weary horse and now God is rewarding me."

"Go down," said the old teacher. "We'll sing you Gounod's 'Ave,' and anything else you want."

I did go down and got on my knees before the statue group—the Christ Crucified, the Mother at His side, Magdalene on bended knees with her red hair streaming, and St. John the Divine to the extreme left. I prayed. I knelt, and this unknown singer sang perhaps as she will never sing again—For an hour this unusual concert. People came to pray a moment and go—but always the young singer looked down on her kneeling audience during that tremendous and glorious hour—It was the end of the miracle. I got up, bowed my appreciation and left—That night I took a milk train for Philadelphia. The next morning, and it was early, the stars were shining in Washington Square, as I rang the door bell of 704. The house was empty, but in the break of the dawn an old, old lady, dressed for work, clambered down the steps—I called her—"Has Mrs. Smithers quit this house?"

"They've taken it for commercial purposes," said the old lady, "but 706 here is run by a very fine lady, and she has a front room and I know she'll be glad to rent it to a nice young man like you."

"A nice young man?" I queried. "How do you know I'm a nice young man?"

I got the room, and from this great room (Independence Hall strikes 2) I write to you at this witching hour. I am sober and keen and I have the suitcase and its contents—my mother's picture (a rare one), numerous other pictures; autographed books; old books that I loved; a crucifix that I had carried for twenty years; a pair of scapulars that are sacred only to me; a copy of Thomas à Kempis that saved me from damnation; when, tempted in the dark of the night in St. Louis many years ago, I read the pages that I needed by the light of a street lamp. This is a long story, but don't forget the three apples that the horse ate and the greatest "chamber concert" that that coming young coloratura ever will render.

I've stopped here to look out at the sacred ground—all is quiet—Mr. Cyrus H. K. Curtis seems to be staying up late—all the lights in his house are lit—and the old broken tree still stands at the S. W. corner and commercialism not yet has cut down the bushes on our side of the street. Good luck and God bless you! and having delivered this I shall now turn over in my wide bed and see if this January *Bookman* is better than the last.

Faithfully,
STEVE O'GRADY.
P. S.—If you want to use any part of this or all of it in any way go to it. It's all true and I'm in

Washington Square, so a hell of a lot I care as to what the world thinks.

So we have used Steve's letter—as he gave us permission to. He turns over in bed, and cares not what the world thinks.

* * * *

After the above was printed, the following letters arrived.

[from H. T. CRAVEN]
Philadelphia, July 7.

It was altogether right and admirable of you to publish the best obituary of Steve O'Grady that could be printed. But somewhat in the spirit of the boy in *Tom Sawyer* whose claim to glory (on hearing that Tom was reported dead) boasted that "Tom Sawyer licked me once," I am moved to recall the part I played in the replevin of the precious suitcase.

Your introductory facts are wrong. Steve was staying at Green's Hotel. After a characteristic "party" at various bars, including doubtless Green's—the monarch of them all—Steve departed without paying his bill. The suitcase with all its treasures was seized.

Not long afterwards Steve wrote me one of his wonderful letters, which unfortunately I have since lost. It told about some remarkable adventures, including a bewildered visit to some Paulist fathers or something equally ecclesiastical in a kind of semi-monastery on the Hudson. In this environment Steve edited a little religious paper and indulged in all the processes of spiritual regeneration with his characteristic emotional zeal. His letter pleaded with me to rescue the suitcase from Green's and besought me immediately to inform him of the deliverance and he would appear to claim his possessions. My good intentions and performance sagged seriously in the middle. I did explore the baggage cellar of Green's. I found the suitcase and carried it to the *Evening Ledger* and deposited it in Bart's editorial cubicle, where there was slightly more room than in the quarters there occupied by you and Doc Douglas and subsequently by myself and the Doc. How often you said (why did you forget all this?) "Have you written to Steve O'Grady about his suitcase?" How often did I guiltily answer, "No, but I'm going to."

I never did. My good deed did not shine out in a naughty world. It had no publicity. I gave it none. I shamefully neglected Steve after a half performance of his earnest request. From here on your chronicle is correct. Your word to Steve, after three years' inaction on my part, supplied the lacking link of information. I shall not forget the qualms and the feeling of hopeless contrition that filled me when Steve at last entered the office and asked for his suitcase. "There it is by Bart's desk," I replied. I felt disproportionately rewarded for the little I had done and absolved from my blundering. Steve's pleasure, his genuine joy, was not to be matched.

In the following two or three years I saw Steve fairly often, and he never failed to regard me (who had made such a hash of good intentions) as a kind of benevolent magician. To him the adventure of the suitcase constituted a kind of miracle. Once in a moment of typical excitation Steve whirled into town, went over the suitcase chapter again in his mind, entered a florist's shop, purchased a huge potted fern, and dispatched it to my wife (whom he had never seen) with his compliments.

[from G. M. G.]

I inclose my check for a dollar. Please cash it and hand the money to the nearest Catholic priest with the request that he bless a candle and light it in memory of Steve O'Grady. I would also send a dollar to the S. P. C. A. did I not believe that Steve would prefer that I spend it myself for a dozen apples and personally feed them to tired horses. I seem to feel that organized charity and organized good were not in Steve's line.

I never met Steve; never heard of him until I

read his letter in your column last night. Once in the happy days when I was a newspaper man I knew a number of Steve's kinsprits. I knew men who would get drunk one minute and go to church to pray the next. I knew men who loved men as Steve loved horses and who loved horses.

Steve is dead at forty-six. Good church people and prohibitionists will probably use Steve as a text for a sermon on the stricter enforcement of the Volstead act. Dead at forty-six! But in those forty-six years Steve lived twice the life of the average respectable octogenarian. Steve wasn't respectable. He couldn't have been. A traffic cop never escorts a respectable man across any street. And a respectable man never buys a quarter's worth of apples to feed to a tired horse.

I have never been drunk. I am too damned respectable. I never left a suitcase under a desk to forget for three years. I never disappear. I am too regular in my respectable habits. But, oh! to have been drunk as Steve was drunk. What would I not give to feed apples to a horse, to hear Gounod's "Ave" sung by a young coloratura as I knelt in prayer in the process of sobering up. What would I not give to turn over in my wide bed and say "A hell of a lot I care as to what the world thinks." Or to say as you have said, and as George Harvey said before you (in the *North American Review*), "We do not aim to please our readers."

Steve O'Grady lived for me as well as for himself. When I wanted to escape my neighbors, myself, Steve left his grip under your desk and disappeared for me. He and Mr. Gissing. Steve visited saloons and chapels and spent long nights in rooms in Washington Square and Mr. Gissing went cruising for me.

But there are not enough Steves and Mr. Gissings. And so the respectable people who are in the majority keep me respectable and dull and aching and wishing. They make me a member of civic betterment associations; they try to force me to teach morals to adolescent boys and girls. They ask me to contribute to organized charity and they consider me and my kind the backbone of the country. And if I told them that I would rather be the author of Steve's letter than Warren Gamaliel Harding they wouldn't believe me.

[from H. F. Woods]

So you knew old Steve O'Grady, too? He seemed to rise up before me as I read his letter to you, and I saw him again with his shock of red hair, his casual garments and his air of always being on the verge of some intensely interesting adventure.

He generally was, too. There was a night, a good many years ago, when Steve was on the *Republic* in St. Louis, when he was assigned to cover the

Veiled Prophet's Ball. The Veiled Prophet's Ball, by the way, is the récherché event of St. Louis. The old residents and the newcomers mingle with apparent delight, and the ciphers which help make up the population figures flock in droves to look on and be part of the picture.

Steve decided that he would honor this event by attiring himself in a dress suit. So along about 7 o'clock in strode Steve, unspeakably uncomfortable in a somewhat tight spike-tail and a marvellous expanse of white linen on the most conspicuous part of which was the mark of an outspread hand. Steve explained that a friend hadn't believed that the shirt was linen and had to convince himself.

"But," said Steve, "that's all right. I'll get a little artist's gum and some whitening and be the belle of the ball," and he did get both of these commodities and restored the shirt to its former pristine purity. Then he went out, ostensibly to dine, but in half an hour was back in the office, very gay and trailing in his wake a bewildered looking little woman with a great deal of blonde hair and a somewhat worn costume of the frivolous sort.

"Now, you sit down," ordered Steve, kicking a chair over near his desk as he attacked his typewriter and turned in a story that had been due hours before.

This accomplished, Steve handed the lady out with a courtly air and announced that they were going to dinner. They went to the Planters grill, where Steve ordered an elaborate and satisfactory repast. The waiter greeted him as an old friend and the girl, who had met Steve casually and unconventionally, asked curiously:

"Say, who are you, anyhow?"

"Ah," said Steve, "I am Prince Charming," and he bowed again.

"Say, who's that?" the girl asked.

"Oh, that man—that's Governor Francis."

"Ah, quit your kiddin'," scorned the young woman. "Come on back home."

Steve with a weary air beckoned the waiter.

"Sam," said he, "who's that man there?" pointing to his acquaintance.

"That man, boss, sure you know him—'at's Governor Francis."

And Steve, grinning at the girl, bowed again and again to other persons in the room.

"Well, who are they?" she asked, this time in an awed voice. And Steve explained that one man was Tom Randolph, president of the Commonwealth Trust Company; another was Charley Hittig of the Third National Bank, and still another was Bob Hedges. The girl by this time was merely able to whisper devoted acknowledgments. She gazed at Steve and Steve's aureole of red hair as one gazes at a vision, long dreamed of but hopeless of reality.

And Steve plied her with more delicacies and conversation such as Steve only could make at times. Then came that dreadful moment when Sam, the shadowy servitor, slipped the check near Steve's elbow. Steve took one glance at it. It totalled $9.25. Steve at that moment probably possessed two or three dollars. But nothing daunted he wrote an urgent message to "Bill" Walker, then chief clerk at the Planters (and now at the Commodore Hotel). "Bill" obligingly sent out a ten-dollar bill and Steve flipped it to the waiter and departed with his adoring young friend.

He took her to Shubert's Theatre and there called the manager, Harry Buckley.

"Harry," said he, "a very dear friend of mine," and he presented the young woman. By this time the lady of faded finery was barely able to control her addled wits. This sudden effulgence of glory, that had begun an hour or so before with a furtive smile and a wink, was too much for a simple-minded miss from East St. Louis.

"I want you to give her a seat somewhere I can join her later," Steve told Buckley, and Buckley with delight gave her a pass to a centre aisle seat near the front of the house.

And Steve with a cordial farewell left her—left her to cover the Veiled Prophet's Ball—and never went back to get her. He had played his little part and was quite satisfied with its dramatic values. He came in, dictated instead of wrote his story of the ball, and departed. Later a young woman in faded finery, with a plaintive voice, beseeched the Gold Dust Twins who sat outside the city room to locate her young man friend—"A gentleman with red hair who was in a dress suit."

But the Gold Dust Twins shook uncomprehending heads.

"No'm," said they, "we ain't seen no man like that. This is wheah they's repohtehs and none of them ain't got no dress suits."

And the bewildered soul stumbled her way towards the stairs.

[from R. T. EDWARDS]

Steve and I roomed together back in the old days during and after the World's Fair in St. Louis, and a better soul never lived. It was like Steve to tell about feeding the horse the apples and opening a new world to the fruit peddler.

But Steve did not tell of the time he covered the funeral of Archbishop Kendrick and wrote a classic that was pasted on the city room of the old St. Louis *Republic* for years. Steve could hardly sit at the typewriter and some of the boys said he never went near the funeral, but be that as it may.

Steve did not tell of the time he was "ahead of"

Madame Butterfly and arrived in Butte, Montana, to find himself confronted with a printers' strike. This was a situation that would stump almost any press-agent except Steve. He got out a four-page paper with a front page of news, two inside about *Madame Butterfly* coming to town and a page advertisement from a department store on the back. He paid the union's demand and newsboys sold the paper for a dollar a copy, the people were so glad to get something to read. The show "stood 'em up" and Steve broke the strike just by making all hands look foolish. The hand of the master is seen in his calling his one edition paper *The Butterfly*.

Steve had a horror of being "fired" and would do almost anything to sidestep that situation except quit drinking. One day Ledbetter of the *Globe-Democrat* had to let him out after repeated warnings. Steve came in at 1 o'clock for an assignment after being absent for two days. In his box he found the bad news. Steve studied the situation a moment and then shoved a piece of copy paper in a typewriter and wrote:

Mr. Ledbetter: Herewith my resignation to take effect day before yesterday. Steve O'Grady.

This to Steve's mind beat Ledbetter to it by forty-eight hours. A good writer is gone and may his soul rest in peace.

[from the Bowling Green, *The Evening Post*]

In cleaning our desk a bit we have found another old letter from Steve O'Grady. It is undated, but we can tell by a memo we wrote on it that it was sent in November, 1921.

> *706 Washington Square, South,*
> *Philadelphia*
> *On a Saturday afternoon*

When I awoke this morning I received a note, slipped under my door, that Mrs. Sawyer could no longer consider me a roomer in her house. I went down to the rooms of Mrs. Sawyer and she told me this: When you came in at 2 o'clock this morning you slammed the front door, you slammed the second door, and when you got to your room you slammed your own door. Every roomer in the house came to me this morning and said to me that you WILL HAVE TO GET THAT HORRID CREATURE OUT OF THE HOUSE, OTHERWISE WE ALL LEAVE. . . . Mrs. Sawyer, who is just as mellow as Washington Square, placed her old and delicious white hair against my shoulder, and remarked: "Steve, I don't want to put you out of the place, but you must make less noise when you come in at 2 o'clock in the morning."

NOW WILL YOU DO THIS FOR ME AND THE SHADES OF DEAR OLD WASHINGTON SQUARE? WILL YOU

SEND Mrs. Sawyer, first name Annie, a special message, of ten words, and ask her to let Steve remain here for another few days? I have at my left hand as I write these lines *The Barrier* by René Bazin, Thoreau's *Walden*, the Works of Francis Thompson, Prose Volume No. III, AND OF COURSE I have the *New Arabian Nights*, by old dear R. L. S., and I am going to make him rise up out of the ground and make you send that ten-word telegram to Mrs. Sawyer, asking her to give Steve another chance and let him remain here for a few days longer.

STEVE O'GRADY.

N. B.—I have a slice of bread, saved from a dinner at Zeiss's last night, and I am going out and feed the birds.

S. O'G.

We are glad to remember that we did write (or telegraph, we forget which) a testimonial to Mrs. Sawyer, giving Steve a clean bill of health—in so far as that was possible. And she did allow him to stay; though certainly good old Steve was far from an ideal lodger, from a landlady's point of view. (You mustn't overidealize Steve, certainly he wouldn't have relished unnecessary canonization.)

B. J., who says she knew him when he was on the Topeka *Capital*, writes that the famous suit-

216

case which Steve left in Philly belonged to her brother—who had lent it to Steve in Kansas City. That puts the perfect shirt-tail (as the City Room would say) upon the story of Steve's Suitcase.

23

THERE is an embarrassing dream that many people are said to have had: that of finding themselves suddenly exposed naked in a dignified social gathering. Mistletoe never had that dream; he didn't need to, for intellectually he had known the actual experience. To find himself conducting a signed column on the editorial page of the old New York *Evening Post* was an exposure to abash the most hardy. It had its terrifying moments.

Yet he thinks with strong secret pride of his connection with that historic paper. It was an organ of truly civilized and liberal tone. There was pride in coming to it; there was pride in attempting for it, however faultily, what would not have been tolerated in any other newspaper; there was pride in being fired from it when it changed its quality. He perpetrated gruesome errors and fatuities. To older people with their enchanted sadness there must have been much comedy in seeing a young energumen blundering onto sharp corners, barking apparently at random like a

217

puppy, rediscovering with loud halloo so much that his betters had known long before. He had little discretion. His naive speculations on religion often got him into hot water with subscribers. With excess of zeal, when the episcopate of New York was shent by one of its recurring hullabaloos of doctrine, he compiled a creed of his own. It was devoutly sincere and began something like this: "I believe in the Woolworth Building and the flukes of Moby Dick." Taken with a pinch of understanding mysticism it was really rather appealing; published as a free-verse canticle in a magazine it wouldn't have caused a ripple—but appearing in a daily newspaper it burst the blood vessels of several hundred patrons.

His employers granted him surprising latitude. His occasional musings about theophany must have caused twinges, but they were never censored. The only time he was seriously reproached was not for questioning the divinity of God, but that of Lord Northcliffe. Sometimes his superior officers moaned a little, but generally they encouraged him to discuss—even at wearisome length—topics from which profitable newspapers cannily avert themselves. As for his other crotchets, it is really laughable to consider how bored many readers must have been with his palaver about food and drink, or steamships, or the wild fantasia of Downtown, or De Quincey and Mel-

ville and Thomas Fuller and Thoreau and Emily
Dickinson and Santayana and Conrad and C. E.
Montague. It would have been hard to tell from
his outgivings which was the more important—
De Quincey or the Woolworth Building. In fact
he did not know; nor does he now.

The problem of what may or may not be printed
in a newspaper, or how far a personal commentator may depart from official policy, is always delightfully ticklish. The traditional clientele of the
Post, though liberal in politics, was supposed to
be Tory in matters of taste. One highly sensitive
associate of the business staff was so upset by a
little verse Mistletoe printed—he had heard it
from that puckish oldtimer Charles Pike Sawyer
—that he implored J. M. to take it out after the
first press-run. Mistletoe was obstinate enough to
insist that no one, not even at the Harvard Club,
could be seriously offended by it. I ran thus:—

> I used to love my garden
>   But now my love is dead
> For I found a bachelor's button
>   In black-eyed Susan's bed.

Among the humors of the time was the naive
credo of that assistant executive that a newspaper
must if possible be conducted by alumni of the
correcter colleges. When he inquired of a certain
hardboiled and long experienced Real Estate re-

porter, "And what was your university?" the indignant reply was "The University of Park Row."

I wonder who now occupy that tenth floor of the former *Post* building on Vesey Street, where we were so happy? And the little coop of a room with a window opening on the balcony over St. Paul's churchyard? On that balcony was the flagstaff from which the great red and blue and yellow bunting of the Three Hours for Lunch Club was first given to the breeze; and neighboring firms began calling up to ask if it was the flag of the newly established Irish Free State (the *Post's* sympathy with oppressed nationalities was always notorious). Looking upward from the typewriter he saw the golden winged statue on the Telephone and Telegraph building, leaning against sunlight. Oh, if I knew how to make it so, Vesey Street would be legendary: there must be something a little sacred about it, it has been so greatly loved. It has changed much even in the few years since it was Mistletoe's byway of surprise. When he went to work there one still looked out on the remaining half of the Astor House; he found his way into the deserted shell and explored the dusty old rooms. The red box was still on the churchyard railings, the Red Box on Vesey Street that H. C. Bunner had rhymed about, put there to receive magazines and books for shut-ins. Down the brief passage toward the river were old bookstores and hardware shops and bookbinders and restaurants and the ancient spicy groceries of Hamblet and Callanan where big coffee sacks always had their necks turned open like Walt Whitman's shirt. Opposite the graveyard was the surprising signboard of Goodenough and Woglom: *Bibles and Prayerbooks and Interchangeable Church Advertising*. There was even some sort of esoteric magazine called *The Truth Seeker*. At the pavement level was a notice: *The Truth Seeker, One Flight Up*. One day this sign vanished. Mistletoe was disturbed. Don't tell me he's found it? he wondered. But it reappeared on the opposite side of the way, repainted: *The Truth Seeker, 2 Flights Up*. It seemed that we were not even holding our own. In the strong depression of his first days' anxieties (starting a newspaper column from scratch is a painful job) he tried to hearten himself by buying on Vesey Street a copy of the *Religio Medici*. Oddly, it was that book that gave him the impulse for his final causerie four years later. During his very first week he made the mistake of rereading Bacon's essays, and concluded that the platinum and diamonds of My Lord's style might well daunt any dealer in paste pearls. But imagine a creature trying to nerve himself to run a New York newspaper column by reading Bacon and Sir Thomas Browne. Was ever anything more agreeably fantastic?

Now for four years he worked day by day actually in the city of his worship; and in that part of the city that means most to those who have her memories at heart. His job, as he imagined it, was to feel her beauty and terror and try occasionally to bring a small glimpse of it on paper. It would be silly to harp on the fact that she was beautiful then; she was, but she is even more beautiful now, and will be more beautiful and terrible still as time proceeds. All I insist is that just then seemed a brave new world. The war was over; New York suddenly found herself the center and cynosure of human scheming. It was significant to see so many cultivated young Englishmen continually drifting in to have a look at Manhattan. In the old days they would have made their grand tour on the Continent. Now, by the shift in financial balance (I suppose finance is the deep tide that secretly governs the arts) these lads or their parents had waked to the fact that America was thrillingly interesting and must be reckoned with. To Mistletoe the *Evening Post* was the most exciting place to be, in the most fantastic city, in the most extraordinary age.

One did not come to such a paper unmoved by its traditions. He was always sensitive to the dignity of the past. Walking in Riverside Park with a child he recognized dear old Major George Haven Putnam, head of the famous publishing house.

He recalled from the Major's memoirs that Washington Irving had once laid his hand on Putnam's youthful head and wished him luck. There was the Hudson, still flowing down from Irving's hills: why should not the ancient piety also be current? He ventured to address the Major and present the urchin to him. The good old man kindly passed on the blessing to the four-year-old. It meant nothing to the child then, but it pleased Mistletoe to think that only one human touch intervened between that boy and Rip Van Winkle. He could even trace that blessing higher still, for (as the Major remarked) it had been given to Irving by George Washington himself.[1]

In the office of the *Post* was Mr. J. Ranken Towse, the dean of dramatic critics, who had been on the paper fifty active years, had been there under William Cullen Bryant. To see good Mr. Towse with his black velveteen hat coming grimly down the aisle at the opening of some dubious farce, steeled to resent any affront to the higher dignities of the stage, was to perceive something of rugged human honor. One of the blessed absurdities of the office was that once a year Mr. Towse made his young colleague feel immeasurably old. The veteran had preserved, from undergraduate days at Cambridge, a passionate concern about

---

[1] *v.* George Haven Putnam: *Memories of My Youth.*

Oxford and Cambridge rowing; in which he confidently expected even a bastard Oxonian to be equally interested. Every spring, as the contest of Blues approached, Mr. Towse was eager to discuss details of the boats. He had pored over the London *Times's* reports on the training and now was full of doctrine about some powerful Cantab at Number 5, who was an Etonian oar and weighed over 14 stone. Alas, though he had once done some sweating on the Isis, Mistletoe's curiosity in this matter had evaporated; he must have grieved Mr. Towse by his inadequate response. The desks of Mr. Towse and Mr. Finck, the music critic, were back to back in a small sanctum. Nothing was more delightful than to hear these Nestors affectionately bickering together. Mr. Finck had only been on the paper forty years, so Mr. Towse still considered him a mere youngster. (In any argument Mr. Towse had the clinching advantage of being the only one of us who had worked under Bryant.) Mr. Finck's hobbies were anthropology and diet. His discussion whether Romantic Love existed among aborigines was a surprising one in the staid bureaux of the *Post*. In the matter of diet he was an exponent of bran, and frequently insisted to young Mistletoe that the success of his Bowling Green would depend largely upon mild wines and proper aperients. Both Mr. Finck and Mr. Towse in moments of stress would savage their assistant Charley Sawyer. Mr. Sawyer had then served the *Post* only some thirty-five years, and they still visualized him as an impish office-boy.

One of the special phenomena of those years was the rise of an able but peremptory generation of youths who were briskly disregardful of anything that had been suffered, thought or written before 1917. The Young Intellectuals (so they quite gravely called themselves) were of the opinion that American civilization was hostile to the "artist" and that Paris was the only place to live and learn. One might have wondered sometimes whether some of this was not due to subtle propaganda on the part of steamship companies feeling the post-War slack. Anyhow it was evident that many of the rising sort felt themselves immured in a crass world like the boys in the old painting of the Princes in the Tower. Mistletoe, not himself much senior, should have felt humiliated to be finding American life so amazingly fecund. He read Anatole France and De Gourmont and Valéry and André Gide, and he believed Aldous Huxley's *Leda* the most perfect thing of its kind since Keats. But with plentiful enthusiasm for all these, he was not able to discern that any modern had cut much deeper than Swift, or that anyone had yet outdistanced Chaucer.

God knows I am not inclined to taunt the Young

Intellectuals of that era for their megrims. Every man worth salt will have his own purgatories to go through; he cannot always choose just at what period he will meet them. Luckiest those who get through the worst of them early. There is many a darker phase I might dwell on in this free-hand cartoon of an inquisitive mind. I can identify pitiable limitations, incongruities, and that bad feeling that so many know, the anger of sometimes having been dealt with like an ill-managed horse: reined in or overdriven always at the wrong moment. How rarely a man attains the blessing of complete surrender of all powers and instincts in one creative task. There was at least something of that honorable devotion in the *Evening Post* employ. Men loved her and lived for her. No smug self-deception, no skilled pleasantries in prose, can conceal a man's crises from himself. But sometimes the troubled and uneven lives have proved the most contributory. If ink happens to be the trade, the workman has his debt to this very sheet of white paper, a debt as dearly imperious as any other: to set down as best he may some of the unguarded motions of his thought. In a world where almost everyone seems so much cleverer than ourselves, how dangerous it is.

He had opportunity to find it so. One of the greatest and boldest of living authors once said to him: "What a fool you were to write that book;

what a fool! How you will regret it presently. Thank God I always had sense enough not to try to write about the insides of things. Why did you do it?" The younger man, rather startled, could only say: "I had to." The other looked at him penetratingly, his eyes very bright under thick juts of eyebrow. His voice changed. "Was it laid upon you? It was. Don't attempt to deny it!— Then I understand perfectly."

24

PERHAPS there was a special spiritual emanation from old St. Paul's churchyard. Leaving the office in a warm noontime one found chalked on the pavement *One Hour for Lunch and No Time for Jesus*. The bare arms of some vehement street-preacher were raised above the heads of his little congregation of idlers. Keep, Oh keep, the eyes of wonder, Mistletoe used to say to himself, trying to see all these amazements unblurred by any kind of opinion. Those naked arms and clenched hands lifted in monitory gesture deserved the pencil of Leonardo. What a drawing: the ring of listeners with straw hats tilted warmly back on heads; the graves and the brown portico of St. Paul's beyond; those desperate arms rising in threat or supplication.— Or a Salvation Army service by the curb on Columbus Circle one winter night: the piteous choplogic of the preaching wenches imploring passers-by to be saved; asserting their own blessed ransom and preparedness to meet their Maker at any moment. They nearly needed it, for just then a wheeling taxi, poofing blue gasoline fume, backed unawares into their little kneeling semicircle. How they sprang up in mid-prayer, but even honest human terror did not halt their plea.

There were days (perhaps they came best after a full night's sleep) when there was a spell in the air. When wisps of steam drifting softly from the downtown summits were the gay plumes of gallant venture; when every street was Liberty Street. Days when the mind was too slow to trace the trembles of wonder sifted between earth and sky. It was as though someone had tossed a new planet into the level pond of space, and even here the circling ripples were discernible. If his head were thick or vitality low, then into the crowded subway. Faces braver, more humorous, more strangely carved than ever seen before to wake him to joy and pity. There was one, still unforgotten, an old Irishman fantastically modelled and seamed and with one white cataract eye—a face like the drawings in the old German book of Max and Moritz. Faces full of dumb testimony to the reality of life. Lifted corrugations of brows, surly pursings of the nether lip, or sudden smilings, the flesh over the cheekbone tightened upward and outward by pleasure. A negro platform sweeper pushing a long-handled brush with a slow sly ripple of his bandy legs—legs not a bit less comic than Mr. Chaplin's, had that dark unconscious millionaire been aware of his fortune. A girl demonstrating an adding machine in a window on Broadway. Her eyes were fixed on a sheet of figures, but her hand flying merrily over the keys like a white hen picking up corn; so nimble you would imagine it was the hand that was doing the thinking.

The profile of every building in that part of town was an acrostic of its own. At one particular spot on Fulton Street the little brown spire of St. Paul's was relieved against the overtowering pinnacles of Woolworth (then unmarred by a great clumsy cubistry alongside it). This suggested the question whether ten cents in the cash register gets nearer heaven than ten cents put into the collection plate. The Telephone and Telegraph building was always a place of magic: fluted pillars, ceiling of starry tablets, hanging bowls of light, bronze telephone booths with heavy doors so nicely hinged that when suddenly closed the air compressed inside the booth startled the ear-drums. And on the glass counters of the Dey Street side, stacks of fresh clean telegraph blanks just laid out there to receive memoranda for poems. I do not wonder if he grew a bit arrant sometimes, and wrote on one of those telegraph blanks:

> All cities to the seeing eye
> Are beautiful; there you descry
> Men's miseries and competitions,
> Their paradoxes and ambitions,
> Grown to the fullest dreadfulness—
> All passions at their proud excess.
> For students of the troubled heart
> Cities are perfect works of art.

It was part of his job to go up to the Composing Room every morning and consult friendly little Peter Augsberger, who "made up" the editorial page, on the lay-out of his column. There he became aware of the noble fascination of a newspaper composing room. He used to say that the four most intensely living places he had known were a newspaper composing room, the engines of a steamship, the cab of a locomotive, and the stage manager's station near the switchboard of a theatre. To these can be added the small salon d'attente usually set aside in a maternity hospital for expectant fathers. There was one that many New York parents remember, furnished depressingly with golden oak and potted palms and Victorian engravings. Two young fathers were pacing there anxiously, one waiting for news of his second, the other of his fourth. Too nervous to sit, they grimly patrolled parallel lines on opposite sides of the room. In those long horrors one noticed the engraving in the place of honor over the mantel. Sardonically he beckoned his confrere to recognize the appropriate subject. "The Stag at Bay."

The Comp. Room is never happier than when it has a chance to play one of its traditional jokes. Two distinguished men of letters joined the staff of the *Post* to conduct its newly enlarged literary supplement. They were not familiar with old printshop lore about those imaginary parasites "type-lice." The Comp. Room was delighted to collaborate in spoof by setting up a small printed memo which brought consternation to our old Endymion. The literary editors had taken great pains with the artistic format of their supplement, but when Endymion arrived at the office one morning he found on his desk the following:—

MEMO. from Foreman Comp. Room:
I regret very much that the Book Review will have a very ragged appearance this week. A number of type-lice have got into the galleys and eaten away some of the type face. We have taken every precaution to guard against these vermin, but, as you know, this will happen sometimes. We are having our machines fumigated and hope it will not occur again.

Pale with dismay he hastened upstairs to inquire what could be done to discourage "these vermin." Gravely the compositors deplored the matter, but insisted that it was probably because the lice in the *Post's* cases had been underfed for years. "There isn't much chance in a daily newspaper for a type-louse to get a square meal, things move too fast; it's when you put in a weekly supplement, and keep overset matter standing, they're naturally tempted by all those rich long words." Endymion saw he'd been had; but he prorated the twit by assuring his editor-in-chief that they must be careful henceforward not to use anything longer than five syllables.

Among the best pleasures of newspaper writing are its opportunities for pseudonymity. Mistletoe's rediscovery of a certain 17th century eccentric suggested a weekly budget of prattle signed "Kenelm Digby." The composition of these Digbiana was shared for a while by two writers whose allusions were so inconsistent that serious readers were puzzled. One of their favorite amusements was to represent the best-natured of editors as a cruel taskmaster, and to expound Digby's endless difficulties in trying to get a Raise. I admit that when I discovered the following among some old *Literary Review* clippings I had a completely innocent laugh:

THIS wonderful weather makes us anxious to have more money to spend. * * * So we doped out a little scheme. * * * Without our employer (the Editor of this *Litry*) suspecting what was in the back of our mind, we arranged a picnic with him. * * * In his comfortable Detroit-Henry coupé we travelled out to the loveliest parts of Long Island. * * * We, and the Editor, and the Editor's family, had lunch together on a swarded turf hard by a tadpole mere.* * * As the Editor unpacked the lunch basket, and glimmered benignly over parboiled eggs and prawn sandwiches, little did he suspect what was coming. * * * After lunch we wheeled cheerily to Sands Point, one of the loveliest neuks on Paumanok, and (incidentally) the place where Old *Frederick Stuart Greene* lives. * * * Do you know Fred Greene's yarns? we asked the Editor. * * * Rattling good, he said. * * * We thought at first he was alluding to the Detroit-Henry. * * * Well, anyhow, when we got to the placid beach at Sands Point (come unto these yellow sands, and there take hands, etc.) both the Editor and ourself stripped off hose and shoon and went paddling. * * * The Editor seemed very happy: he found a starfish and began to talk about the wonders of science. * * * Now, we said to ourself, is the time to strike while the ivory is white, or whatever the proverb is. * * * Hearken, Doctor, we uttered (a bit nervously), what would you say to a raise in Old Digby's salary? * * * A hideous yell spread across the still waters

233

of Manhasset estuary. * * * Evidently
our remark was ill received. * * * The
Editor seemed to be in agony. * * * A
number of auditors on the beach hurried
up to see what was amiss, and looked at us
very menacingly. * * * Finally the Editor ceased to lash the water into spume.
* * * "I can't talk about that just now,"
he said, "I've walked on a razor-edge clam-
shell, and nearly sliced off my phalanges."
* * * So again we were put off. * * *
It would be nice to have more spending
money this lovely æstivating weather. * * *

So Mistletoe and Endymion had their full share
of the humors of Grub Street. Creatures of con-
trasting physique, one wide and solid, the other
long and wraithlike, a colleague who found them
poring over a bookstall almost purchased them as a
copy of *Sense and Sensibility*. That was probably
at Mendoza's, the famous Ann Street shop to
which downtown critics always hastened in seizures of indigence, with an armful of review copies
for disposal. Such a group, making for Mendoza's
with burden enough to buy a good lunch for the
crowd, were startled by a menacing gesture from
one of the bookstore staff who saw them coming.
Posted at the front door he waved them wildly
away. Wondering whether this meant No Lunch,
they retired into Theatre Alley to consult. There

from the back door of Miller's Restaurant exhaled savory undulations of food. The thought of finnan haddie and the series of beautiful Miller's Daughters (as in Tennyson) who supervised the service became more poignant. Mistletoe and his comrades became uneasy. What, was Ike Mendoza not going to buy any more books? What would become of literary criticism? Then one of the young Mendozas arrived to explain. "Wait a few minutes," he said. "Ike's got a wealthy customer in there who says he's decided to begin collecting Contemporary Firsts. If he sees all you poets coming in here to peddle review copies, the glamour will be gone."

"Never mind glamour," said the poets coarsely. "When do we eat?"

"Go ahead and get your lunch," said the great-hearted merchant, "I'll come up in time to pay the check." So they parked their precious wares at the back door of Miller's and went in.

Another rather different picture from Ann Street. A hot summer morning in 1921. I believe there was at that time an international conference of some sort about building battleships:

We were coming along Ann Street, on our way to the office, when we saw a queer little detachment proceeding ahead of us on the pavement. It interested us, so we slowed down and followed.

235

There were two small boys—aged, we should guess, about twelve and ten. Ten was carrying a baby, perhaps eight months old, one of those typical city infants, pathetic and philosophical, not yet strongly enough anchored to this dubious life to worry much about it. Its white blinking dribbly little face bobbed on the boy's shoulder as the group hastened. Twelve held by the hand a diminutive urchin with astoundingly crooked legs. This tiny creature, as he was urged along (for there seemed to be some pressing errand for the party), twinkled valiantly with heavy shoes much too large for him, and which overlapped in their course, so bowed were his shins. Behind the others, alone, hastened the last member, a boy of say three years, in dirty blue rompers. Under the noses of carthorses and dodging through the rush of Nassau Street this party proceeded. It would take a more skilful writer than the present to explain the curious emotions that this group, unconscious of scrutiny, aroused in any tender-hearted observer.

But we were anxious to know what they were steering for, and when Ten slipped quickly into a small tobacco store on Ann Street, near Broadway, we followed and bought a box of matches.

Twelve and the two other children waited outside, but Ten, the baby still serene on his shoulder, was talking to the man at the counter. He had produced a thick bundle of tobacco coupons and was trying to sell them. "Sorry, old son," said the tobacconist, kindly; "you haven't got enough."

It is queer to think how much the price of one battleship would do for some of these. Battleships get obsolete, we are told, so quickly, and have to be replaced. But so do city children get obsolete, with terrible swiftness.

The Three Hours for Lunch Club frequently passed along Ann Street on the way to admire a secluded courtyard (since built over) where John Jacob Astor's fur warehouse still existed. It was their ambition to convert that old building into a downtown country club. That dream, like the cruises of the ship *Tusitala* and the establishment of a Free State in an ancient machine-shop in Hoboken, eventually came to nothing. Probably the Three Hours for Lunch Club was the kind of airy republic that flourishes best without physical tenures. But the dreams that failed were the dearest of all. As for the *Tusitala*, still a white profile of beauty on open seas, to the little group of lovers who rescued her from decay she was always more than just a ship. If a "vision" is something seen with an eye that is not merely a reticule of nerves, Mistletoe saw one. He was looking from the balcony of the *Post* one of those golden-grained spring evenings when the great burning village smoulders in sunset vintage-red. The mass of the Hudson Terminal crumbled and creamed apart like smoke, cleft by a heroic bow, a vaguely descried figurehead that loomed above. A great ship of sails rippled irresistibly through glowing space.

237

The incessant clatter of typewriters, tickers, telephones, almost a living presence caged within those office walls, fell hushed. In the gilded April air the rondure of her royals was like the tenderest curve the world knows. Through the open gap between Vesey Street and the Hudson Terminal, where thrilling deep voices come up from the river, a wind blew salty, swept and clean. Beauty that has tormented men so long does sometimes give them ease. "Hither to work us weal" were words from the *Ancient Mariner* that came into his head.

New York has given us great moments. Her long narrow hull was anchored in the stream like a ship riding the gale of Time. In that high focsle of the city how the golden wind seemed to whistle past. Time runs so swift, he said to himself, I believe we must be somewhere near the place it comes from. Sometimes when the sun was over the foreyard—their foreyard was the Woolworth Building—they set out for noon inspection of the great vessel. Perhaps it was the Library for the Blind; the Botanic Garden in the Bronx; the little sunned enclosure of Gramercy Park, kept locked and entered by a key of special privilege. Perhaps it was a day spent on a tug in the harbor, shipyards in South Brooklyn, the overlook from Stevens Castle, or the surprising view of the Statue of Liberty seen from behind. They were startled by the trolloping

trudging sag of the goddess's quarters seen from
the yonder shore of Bedloe's Island. Mistletoe was
struck by the implications of the scene, and even
ventured a little essay on The Backside of Liberty.
Those expeditions discovered incredible poetries
in the corridors of their leviathan. A downtown
stockbroker's office where every year an enchanting Shakespeare festival was given, on Shakespeare's birthday, for the friends and customers of
the firm. The actor who for many years played
Nana, the dog-nurse in Peter Pan, running a lunch-
room on Vesey Street. The Keats manuscripts
in the J. P. Morgan library. The observation
gallery on top of the Woolworth during a blizzard
of snow. The golden boy on the Tel and Tel building was their lookout in the crow's nest. The pure
dazzle of noon between his wings seemed to suggest that anything was possible. Daily he cried
"There she blows—and sparm at that!" Once
looking up from the typewriter Mistletoe saw a
steeplejack on top of the statue. The tiny figure,
in crazy bravado, stood on his hands on one of the
zigzag lightnings. He balanced there, clear against
death. It seemed symbolic of a loved and lunatic
city, but Mistletoe was alarmed. That's my favorite statue, he said to himself; the darned fool might
bend one of those lightning bolts and spoil it.

The wandering posse of engineers, architects,
parsons, sculptors, seamen, reporters that called

itself the Club, was almost Elizabethan in its taste for puns, for which more sensitive æsthetes reproached it. But there was one which Mistletoe believed deserved homage. They discovered a little wig-shop on the East Side; its modest window-display consisted only of two small hair-patches each on an upright stand. That seems a quaint display, they remarked, just those two little top-pieces, exactly alike. . . . As like as toupees, they exclaimed in triumph. Of a more subtle reach was Don Marquis's announcement during some theatre argument. "I've got a great idea; I'm going to dramatize some of Bernard Shaw's plays."

Was there, I have often wondered, any integrating idea behind all this pressure of spasmodic detail? I am doubtful about philosophers who can ticket an era too readily. What meanings there may be do not often expose themselves to deliberate search. Sometimes the greatest books have proved to be those written at least partly for the cruel and ignorant wisdom of childhood. The emergence of Woman as a disturbing intelligence was one of the observations of that time. Women are another form of childhood, burdened by Nature with an overhead psychic expense that makes profitable business almost impossible unless they are exceptionally daring. The work done in those years by such bravely enchanted children as

Stella Benson and Elinor Wylie and Katherine Mansfield taught many of us to listen more attentively for whispers. The origins of all arts are mysterious, especially the art of living, but he struggled to learn something of the damned agility necessary to find and seize the soul's nourishment in the huge fury of that city. He learned how the mind feeds on itself with self-destroying flame. "If I had two friends called Food and Hunger," he found himself thinking, "I'd never introduce them to each other." Perhaps a human spirit has to be broken in, like a pipe. It burns hot and sour at first; long patience is needed; bitter juices darken the wood and charred cake collects in the bowl before it mellows. Then he laughed at himself. Yes, as Fool (he soliloquized) he was a museum piece.

ODE TO THE COMP. ROOM

(*Evening Post, 1922*)

I'd like to work in the Composing Room,
For what happens to a poem before it is published
Is far more poetical, usually,
Than the poem itself.
Poor little bundle of words, here you go—
Boy! Shoot this, prithee—
Up the pneumatic tube it flutters
To Jim Henderson, the copy cutter.

I wonder why there are so many Scots
In all printing offices?
Humorous birds, with shrewd, busy eyes.
Jim Henderson is from Glasgow;
Bill Barron, the foreman, is from Aberdeen;
And Jim, if he thinks Bill is near enough to
    hearken,
Will tell you the old story, something like this:
There was a fellow on a ship, in mid-Atlantic,
And way off yonder he sees another ship,
Just a speck on the skyline.
I wonder, says a fellow passenger, what that is?
Why, it's a vessel, he says.
Yes, of course, replies the other, but where's she
    going?
To New York, very likely.
Sure, but I wonder where's she from?
Our friend pretends to scan the horizon carefully.
I think she must be from Aberdeen, for I don't see
    any sea gulls following her.

In the meantime the poem is on the linotype.
I don't savvy the lino very well, but I'm enough of
    a printer
To know how to light my pipe from it
Where the little blue flame lurks among the ma-
    chinery.
See how the matrices come sprinkling fast
Down the slots of their fan-shaped runway,

And then, if you watch, you'll see the strips of
     type,
Hot and shining,
Slide one by one into the brass galley.
—I tell you, when you see that machine,
And the cheerful calmness of the grizzled oper-
     ator,
You want to write something worthy of them
     both,
Words that would come out hot and shining,
Words strong like metal,
Words built cannily together,
Not to be melted again.
So much of what we send up might as well be set
etaoin shrdlu ("A line of Greek," they call it;
Which, since it may have puzzled you, is simply
     the way
The letters lie on the linotype keyboard,
Just as you might write *qwertyuiop* on your
     Underwood.)

I'd like to work in the Composing Room—
Such ingenious bustle, such humorous haste,
And I never weary of the black skull cap
Worn by Harry Martin, the superintendent
(Who is not a Scot—he sprang from Guernsey,
Home of those plush cows with amberlucent eyes).
I esteem the lively clatter of mallets pattering on
     the forms

Before they go rolling to the stereo room
On nice little trucks
("Bogies," says Bill Barron, "we used to call them
     in Aberdeen.
Say, laddie, were you ever in Aberdeen?
Glasgow's a dour black, reeky town.")
I love to watch the veteran Make-Up Editor,
A fine, portly figure of a man,
Brooding over the forms as they fill with type,
Pondering how to fit a six-inch story
Into a stick of space.
"Here," he says, "that'll never go.
Put in a bit of reshershay Real Estate to fill."
In off moments he'll talk to you about George
     Borrow,
And in between times he's Religious Editor.
I love also to see the magazine pages, already made
     up for Saturday,
Marked ALIVE,
(Aye, for if type isn't alive, what is?)
And a fair young lady, concentrated and proud,
     from the editorial department,
Side by side with some inkstained compositor,
Their heads bent charmingly together over a
     correction.

Now, when the page is made up, I see it pass to the
     molding table,
Where it is blanketed under black sheets of felt,

And, when the semi-cylinder plates are made,
Down to the pressroom.
I tell you, it makes me dizzy to think of that poor
    little poem
Revolving down there, round and round and
    round
More than 60,000 times
(That is, on Saturdays,
As sworn to and subscribed before James W.
    Jennings, Notary Public,
Whose commission expires March 30, 1923,
But will doubtless be renewed).

And here is the Circulation Manager,
With his eyes full of yearning,
Appealing to the Production Manager:
"The Home Edition starts at 12:45, but is that
    Absolute?
Something's happened down on Staten Island,
And I've got to catch that 1 o'clock boat.
Can you go in a few minutes early?"
News, news, news. . . .
Some people smile at my old darling.
But I think she prints more Real News
Than any evening paper I know.
Not much poetry up here, the Composing Room
    tells me,
But I can see the Muse hugging herself
Down every roaring aisle.

25

To STUDY New York as a botanist would study a jungle was the only purpose he could assure himself. I have not yet heard of any botanist who can tell us what the jungle means. To examine and savor each day as it came was task sufficient. To be obedient to the suggestions of impulse; to float, mentally, with the current, not struggle too hard against it; to do what you find yourself doing, was his clumsy attempt to phrase the intuition. When they were living one winter in a small furnished apartment on Morningside Heights (fascinating name) he lay on the floor at night writing. The only desk available was a rickety rosewood toy too wabbly for decent penmanship, so he wrote on the floor. Then for once he did not worry about choice of word or comfort of posture. Good or bad the fable leaped from the ink and ran across the paper. That was joy.

There was plenty of despair behind. Readers of Santayana have learned to luxuriate in despair. "Art, so long as it needs to be a dream, will never cease to prove a disappointment. Its facile cruelty, its narcotic abstraction, can never sweeten the evils we return to." Loved as they may be, the necessary conditions of work in a newspaper office are painful to a man with slow and stupid hopes.

How to bridge the gap between the dreams of art and the ruptures of the day? How can they be fused? Probably they can't. More and more he was tormented by the incongruity between the vision glimpsed and the hasty note of it that must be put down in print. "In the faces of plain men in subway or suburban smoker I often see the unmistakable look and lineament of the poet. How many unspoken poets are ground under by the pressure of life, which has its hard hydraulic laws: the farther below the surface you are, the greater the pressure exerted on all sides." Such comments, in a hundred variations of mood, he wrote down in the long series of journals he kept in those days. The prime puzzle was that even men wise and generous of heart were hardly more successful in ordering their lives than the ephemeral paragrapher. Absurdity, like a mongrel cur, ran yapping at their shins. The banana peel was always on the pavement for the heel of the savant. Was the only solution to see life as gigantic farce? He had the practical joker's very special distaste for seeing himself the butt of the jest. "It's because we all lead such unnatural lives," a grizzling faun once said to him in an accent of singular sincerity. This he often pondered. In what respects may modern life be considered unnatural? A theme for a very hardy essayist.

Yet there are phases of that unnaturalness that

are full ecstasy. To spend an evening reading is
very likely unnatural, but hours with Santayana
or Lowes Dickinson were hard to surpass. "His
blue morocco slippers donned, What evenings
then had Toulemonde." There were lunar nights
of clear glassy stillness, white translucence, when
the house was drowned on the floor of an ocean
of clarity. The soft pallid light might have been
transfused through endless leagues of pure un-
moving water. After an evening drugged in reverie,
how strange the unfamiliar patterns of the early
stars. In those happy moments one has no fear of
any truth. One *is* truth; naked, and at the bottom
of a well. Though born sub signo Tauri he had
twinges of Ariel. At such times Ariel wriggles out
of the cloven pine; men come awake for a few hours
before relapsing into the sleepwalk of daily life.
Then they know that there are meanings never
yet guessed, depth on depth of power and hope.
He pleased himself by putting down naive memoranda:

The arts and sciences are distinct from other regions
of life in at least one respect: among their true servants
there is no such thing as envy. A writer may say jocu-
larly to another that he envies him something he has
written; but in the exact meaning it is not so. Where
there is, in the mercantile sense, no competition, there
can be no jealousy. If a poet or a painter or a mathematician does more delicate or more original work than

248

his confrere, the latter does not envy him. He loves him for it.

That, incidentally, is why I love so many contemporary writers.

He was getting prickles of that thought uttered by Anatole France in the dedication of *La Vie Litteraire* (which, incidentally, was written for a newspaper, *Le Temps*): "Nous parlons de nous-mêmes chaque fois que nous n'avons pas la force de nous taire." He put the idea for himself rather neatly:

> This is all we ever say:
> *Ego, mei, mihi, me.*

Comedy will always pursue the dreamer. He is her favorite sport. A young poet was once invited to speak at a gathering of haut-monde ladies at the most genteel women's club in New York. He was gratified by this summons, for it looked to him like what simpletons call Recognition. Nicely clad he made his way thither. But the rascal divinity, utilizing some irrelevant proletarian as her machine, cast on the front steps of the clubhouse a soft pancake of discarded chewing gum. It stuck to the poet's sole. It did not become noticeable until he was sitting on a little raised platform which was richly covered with a crimson rug. He was introduced and rose—carrying the rug with him. His innocent recitations were ruined by

his efforts to stand utterly fixed and conceal the
humiliating adhesion. Or consider the case of the
Distinguished Critic who had to preside at a gala
dinner of the P. E. N. Club—a serious international federation of writers—where the guest of
honor was a famous and newly-landed German
philosopher. The chairman sat uneasily at the
High Table, for the philosopher had not yet arrived at the board. Time passed, the great hotel
ballroom resounded with the merry clatter of well-
dressed litterateurs, but still the seat at his right
was empty. Then appeared the literary agent who
was the philosopher's business factotum in America. "I'm having a terrible time with the Count,"
he said. "I've got him as far as the ante-room, but
he says he absolutely cannot speak unless he has a
glass of champagne. He *never* speaks without a
glass of champagne to fortify him. He positively
refuses to enter the dining room unless you can
promise him a drink of wine."

"But merciful Buddha," faltered the wretched
chairman. . . . "Dinner of ceremony . . . republic
of letters . . . reporters here . . . occasion of dignity
. . . law-abiding artists . . . conscience . . . ethics . . .
damnation . . . I don't carry bottles of champagne
around with me . . . getting late . . . Where's the
nearest speakeasy?"

A messenger was dispatched in haste, while the
literary agent calmed the sage in the ante-room

and the chairman called on a preliminary speaker to make the necessary remarks about international comities of intellect. The envoy was not able to get wine, but returned with a bottle of Tenderloin Scotch. In a corner of the room was a vast grand piano. The agent raised its lid. There was an impressive hush, for the convives supposed there was to be music. But behind the shelter of that mahogany bulwark and a thin bosquet of palms crouched the unhappy Chairman, pouring a beaker of raw spirit for the philosopher. They say he made an excellent speech.

Riding on the see-saw of youthful spirits it was sometimes my friend's pleasure to masquerade in print as an elderly seer of Oriental disillusion. Once, to see what might happen, he inserted a notice in the miscellaneous advertising section. It appeared under the classification ECCEN-TRIC:—

JOHN MISTLETOE, NOW IN THE SERENE twilight of life, is willing to hear from a few discreet booklovers, but will answer only those communications that interest him or offer material for his Dictionary of Deplorable Facts. Address J. MISTLETOE, Box 100, The Literary Review, 20 Vesey St.

The replies received were mostly disappointing, but there was one—probably a jape—that seemed worthy of the Dictionary:

251

For your Deplorable Facts. I am very absent-minded, often find names and telephone numbers written in my notebook and can't remember what they are there for. Well, lately I had a checking-up and found a man's name and address among my memos that meant absolutely nothing to me. Anyhow I wrote to him, asking was I supposed to do something for him. He wrote back a most cordial and affectionate letter saying I had already done it. He was my wife's first husband.

In the comedy of city life there was one thing that men took very seriously: Money. Occasionally in connection with the problems of buying a home his destiny brought him to the quiet bronze and marble fane of a bank in Brooklyn. What monastic peace and quiet reverential feeling! Men in gray seersucker coats tenderly carrying ledgers and big account books like acolytes with holy vessels. The Three Hours for Lunch Club brooded on this, and came to the conclusion that a little hilarity might sometimes be mingled with Finance. So originated the idea of the Disbursing Bank. It was stated in the paper that the Club had observed that people often needed help in spending their money. Many were too busy or severe-minded to get as much fun out of it as they deserved. Therefore if anyone had a small surplus to spare, which he would like to circulate at random in the general cause of humane merriment, he might deposit it with the Club. No sum larger than $10 would be accepted. The Club would admit no responsibility nor even promise any accounting, pledged itself only to put the funds into circulation as rapidly as possible in the cause of Fun. A number of good-natured souls liked this egregious idea of sending out their money on vicarious picnic; about $70 was received in small deposits.

The poetic disbursal of these moneys was the occasion of animated argument in the Club. They were not spent for merely selfish pastime but distributed where they would cause the most irradiating cheer. One of the Bank's depositors, Mr. Jedediah Tingle (a nom de fantaisie under which a well-known real estate magnate conducted many original generosities) was so much interested that he accompanied the committee on some of their disbursing expeditions. One of these was the Adventure of the Wounded Oyster.

Mistletoe had discovered the old second-hand bookshop on his way back to town from the Dempsey-Carpentier prizefight in Jersey City. It was odd that of all those thousands streaming by he was the only one who stopped to explore the place. Never before had so big a crowd gone past it. As he stood trying to see what classification if any existed on the grimy shelves he could hear the strangely sinister scuff-scuff of the crowd tramping past. There had been sixty thousand people at the fight, and rather than fight for places in buses, taxis and trolleys, about half of them walked back to the ferries.

There was pathos in the puzzled look of the old bookseller. He had emerged from his dusty little burrow at the back and stood at the open door watching the crowd press by. I saw on my friend's face that shadow of gravity that troubles men when they feel the same thing but don't quite know how to communicate it. The hot summer afternoon, the impure air of the book-stuffed shop, the feeling of finality when a long-anticipated event is suddenly over, some dim awareness of all the tender troubled secrets hidden in these masses of abandoned volumes, and the contrast of the voices and movement outside, life going by so fierce and random. . . . I could see in his face that he thought we ought to buy something, even if only to encourage the old bookseller. But we had both lost a small wager on the fight and were feeling thrifty. We agreed that the Disbursing Bank would have to be told about this place.

So not long afterward the committee crossed the river at lunch time. Jedediah Tingle, an older man and rather careful in his garb, was startled by the grime. Devotees of old bookstores are not nice, but I've never seen one sootier than that. There must be some secret symbolism in the affinity between books and dust. Second-hand bookshops that are much frequented keep fairly clean because the patrons carry away so much of the dust on their clothes. But I'm afraid this place had few customers. It was well-stocked: we saw at once several things that tempted us. Jedediah was told off to engage the old bookseller in conversation while the rest of us worked deeper into the store to see what we might find.

Glancing at a copy of Emerson's Essays Mistletoe had a sudden inspiration. Unobserved he slipped one of the Disbursing Bank's clean five-dollar bills into the book, at the first page of the essay on Compensation. He put the volume carefully back in its place on the shelf and blew a little dust around it to conceal traces. Farther along the same row I myself found a copy of *Ethics of the Dust* which I thought would be an appropriate souvenir. The other members were still talking with the proprietor, but we gave them the special signal which means "Come along and don't argue; something important is happening."

Every now and then, when the Banking Committee had a chance to lunch together, they used to slip across the river to revisit the bookshop. While one engaged the old man another would peep stealthily between the pages of Emerson. Always the bill was still there. In one or two hard-up spells Mistletoe was almost tempted to replevin it himself. I suppose there's not much demand for

Emerson in that region of docks and factories, but they were a little disappointed that the stratagem had had no effect. He even read the essay on Compensation aloud to Titania one evening; they found it a trifle solemn.

The following autumn, after a considerable interim, we visited the shop again. What a change! It had been painted, the books rearranged, and the old bibliophile showed signs of animation.

"Well," he said, "a mighty queer thing happened. Just before school opened there was a young woman in here, a teacher, looking for a copy of Emerson's Essays. She got it off the shelf, and then she says 'Why, there's some money in it!' Sure enough, there was a five-dollar bill in the book, what do you think of that? She might just as well kept it, I had no idea it was there, but she wouldn't. Said it didn't belong to her. Well, it didn't belong to me neither, but finally we agreed to split it. After she'd gone, I got to thinking. That was one of a lot I bought from an estate in Plainfield, an eccentric old gentleman; maybe there might be more money in some of those books. Besides I was sort of scared, thought it might be some kind of a plant to get me in wrong somehow, or to pass off bad bills on me; you never know who might want to do you dirt. I went through all the shelves on that side of the store, just to see. I didn't find any money, but I like to suffocate with the dust. That started me cleaning up. This place was too dirty to get decent folks to come in. That school teacher was so excited about finding that bill she come in again and bought a lot more, and she sent all her pupils in here to buy their textbooks. Then the local paper got hold of it and wrote it up. Business has been grand. But say, that was a queer thing, hey? I'm going to put up this sign in the window."

He pointed to a placard, which read:

YOU MAY FIND MONEY
IN THESE BOOKS

As we went back in the ferry Mistletoe looked at me with a special gleam. "The wounded oyster," he said, "mends his shell with pearl." That, I ought to explain, is a line from the essay on Compensation.

I really must get around to reading *Ethics of the Dust*. I have a feeling there are messages in it for me.

26

HE HAD been preparing himself to leave the *Post*, though he had not expected to go quite so suddenly. He left with joy and gratitude; with an enormous sense of relief. The first thing he did with his freedom was to buy a translation of Lucretius. Still incorrigible: still hoping, I suppose, that somewhere he might yet learn meanings and come forth upon "bright coasts of light."

He had supposed that was the end of journalizing. But things moved fast on Vesey Street. (Even the type-lice must have noticed the change.) The two Men of Letters soon followed Mistletoe into the open air, and the *Saturday Review of Literature* was founded. By that time Mistletoe and his family were peacefully in Normandy, but he found himself involved in the project. He wrote a strictly private letter to the editor of the new weekly expressing his hopes for it. As the editor was so indiscreet as to print it I also feel at liberty to use an extract:

In short, my ideal for the *S. R. L.* is a completely *civilized* paper: with all the vices and virtues of civilization: its nostalgia for the old simplicity, its full and generous toleration, its troubled and self-scrutinizing doubt, its divinely useless mirth, its high intellectual boiling-point, its cheerful disregard of things not really worth discussing among tenderly disillusioned philosophers. These, I suppose, are the pangs by which a "civilization" goes round the great sweeping curve toward a rediscovery of Loveliness. We must be of our own era or we are nothing: we must sit in it like frogs in a pond, but with eyes bulging just a little bit over the scum. The mistake we all make is to try to explain things we know to be true: as soon as you begin to do that, they seem doubtful. I have seen pine trees, with ferns under them, that swore that war is inconceivable.

How far the subsequent years have shown a re-discovery of Loveliness we do not now discuss. Lucretius compared philosophy to a cup of worm-wood with a little honey greased round the rim. There have been opportunities to taste some of both.

Escape from newspaper work gave him a chance not only to rediscover France and Britain, but (more important still) to see wider glimpses of his own country. Nothing anywhere has given him more deep satisfaction than raising the blind in a sleeper berth and viewing for the first time the brown fields of the Middle West.

A DOGWOOD TREE

DOGWOOD TREE

FOUNTAIN of snow. Beyond, the shallow blue,
    Elastic envelope thoughts can't break through.
I roll my thought up in a tight round word
And fling it far. It whistles, falls near you.
Perhaps you pick it up and throw it farther still
With your particular projectile skill.
It falls again. And still there's blue beyond.
Every chink is packed with needless blue.

Fountain of snow, tossed up in morning light.
Light brims those tilted vanes of bloom,
Sheets of petalled spindrift, poising spouts
Burst like the creamed explosion of a sea,
A spume of argent, geysered up in sway
On the warm slope of sunny air.
Light meets its equal wave-length there
And rests in clotted crisps and gouts
Upon my reveillé of snow.
Thought, the shrill mongrel with a curly scut
Runs wild with clamor in the thorny scrub.
Tie him, for silence, to the dogwood tree.

The trunk, the bole, a single spring
Of upwardness, rounded in stiff desire and crackled
    bark.
Then parted, spread, sweet groins and forks of
    living,
Comings together and divisions dear
And from the health of all those mimic loins
Flashing a dazzled outburst of relief.
All the other fifty weeks a year
The dumb and level Tuesdays, Thursdays, Sundays
For this one crest of rapture,
Quaternions of snow!
Snow's too white a thought, silver is too shiny:
Love-child of gold and silver, or the tone
Of summer's thighs by summer sunlight kissed
And then in moonlight seen. Or the tender glow
Of a child's clear forehead near the hair.
I dare not, dare not look upon you long
I dare not with too intricate a choice
Ponder the words and prosody I need.
Thought must rise leaping from the central earth
Spray out and ramify in chance design,
Green over with its close-text shelves of shade
The lonely question gazing up the stem.
How can I testify? In verse or prose?
There's more subconsciousness in verse
Living the rush and stupor of the mind:
Words can darkly climb and foliate
And earthy unawares still cling to them.

None learn your glory by just looking at you:
You sprang in fierceness from the searching sting
Where seed fell in the ovary of earth,
And now you pour on many-colored air
Your tilted platitudes of light,
Platonics of cool blaze.

I could not, dare not look upon you long.
You have a meaning and a truth for me—
"Casting the body's vest aside
My soul into the boughs does glide:
There, like a bird, it sits and sings". . . .
Joy that a man might spend his life upon
To plant a Tree of words and let it grow
(Fed by the slow suffusion of his blood)
For fifty weeks of green and shady meaning
If on a quintessential bliss of May
Light broke within, without,
And hung in glittering shifts and rames of foam.
Men almost fear to look against that brightness
Seeing the transitive so seeming passive
And Time grown instant. The immortal Nonce!
Is that what life is like?
Two weeks in fifty-two is good proportion.
They coursed the whole world over, up and side-
        ways,
And found you shine abaft the old garage.

In the defeat and comedy of days,
Along a blazing street, or warmed with whiskey

In vast and whilom certainties of joy,
In sullen clenches of quotidian death,
I held you in the backward of my mind.
It was the taller trees that had no peace
Toiling and shaking in a stress of wind.
But you were quiet, you my tree of dream.

I write not just for Me: I write for you,
You will translate it into your own meanings:
It doesn't have to be a dogwood tree.
There's as much truth in one thing as another:
A pebble, button, or a sheet of music.
Montaigne said almost everything already,
But men still write and publish—as they should.

It's easy to assert: the dogwood tree
Is so successful as a dogwood tree
Because it never tries to be anything else.
That settles nothing: you and I must be
All things to every thought; yes, stone to stone,
Cellar-door to cellar-door; and in a glass of ale
Guess what sunlight feels like to the hops.
You walked in vain in Chartres or in St. Patrick's
Unless you know the thoughts that bishops think.

Consider printers of old famous books,
Tough old books like Kenelm Digby's Treatise
Of Bodies and Man's Soul

266

(Printed for John Williams, 1658)
Or the *Religio*, 1642.
The inkstained printer fumbling in the case
Felt long words grow heavy in his hand,
Smeared the sour ink and saw the black palaver
Square dark and even on the linen page
Nor cared (I guess) what it was all about,
No more than I who see my dogwood spreading
Like the crystal shatter of a wave. . . .

Whiteness crept up through the woody veins
   And spread all sudden on the unknowing air—
That should have cured stupidities and pains?
   I could not watch it long. It's rude to stare.

And you made nothing of it, ere it vanished?
   That naked beauty of your own dear Day,
Life's whitest body—
   I was grateful and astonished,
But what was there to say?

A toss of foaming like the crystal shatter
   Of a bursting wave, in magic pause—
And was that all you thought about the matter?
   I wanted to tell *you* how beautiful it was.

Fountain of snow is gone,
Sodden and yellow, shaken on the grass;
Dazzle that hung over the roof of the garage
Is gone

Leaving only a leak in the shingles
An oily puddle on the concrete floor.
Help me, she said, to be a little Irish about it.
In the golden blast of afternoon
Poets mock themselves, sing Yiddish folk-songs:
If Christ was born in a stable
Then my tree of snow can sanctify a garage.
Come dark, come dark,
I cannot trust these endless afternoons.

Spreadeagle Beauty on the dogwood tree,
Nail down her feet and hands till she is dead;
What is the difference to me
If Space devours Time, as Einstein said.

The fountain of snow is gone, melted, strewn,
May is lost in June.
A gray-green morning, trees toiling and tumbling
    in the high aloft.
I said that I had words of truth to utter,
Where are they now?
Gone the cream-and-gipsy shining,
The tender lustre of a drizzling day,
The silken bloom of gray and yellow light,
"Your bugle eyeballs and your cheeks of cream."
I walked quietly home in the quiet rain.

Temptation always is to say
There will not, cannot, be another day

So fair and sunshot, warm-in-the-blood with life
As this Today, this now; but there will be
Millenniums and millwheels of such Nows,
Such urgencies; and we and all our seed
Gristed and boltered in the turning drum.

Clear pillar of the bole, close leafage of dark green,
I have carried you with me, to and fro
In steepest city and in casual talk;
In the rough comedy of commuters' trains
Or on Jamaica platform
Seeing the locomotive waiting there,
Radiant with heat, animal with power,
Lift its rocking shanks and stroll away
(Grumble, sneeze a little with excitement,
Stroll definitely, consciously away).
Something so masculine about a locomotive
If I were a woman I'd be troubled by it.

Sleep intervened, and sometimes day and night,
The names of rivers, winds and months
(Also masculine).
When the burning moment comes, be grateful.
I saw roses, curled like petticoats
Conceal-revealing in their skirted coil
The velvet softness of their warm wet lips.
And I walked quietly home in the quiet rain.
You are not forgotten, fountain of snow.

WITH ink, which is a dark and acid liquor, you must dare forlorn transfusions the painter would be too sober to attempt. Painters, one hears by gossip, are frolic burly fellows, filled with merriment, late hours, and drink. But in their wildest freak they are old New Haven dominies compared to the rough recklessness of the penman. Consider, with the blunt instrument of scrivening to catch the surface tensions of one human day. For that the tenderest camel's hair would be as thick as cornstubble.

I will tell you one picture, among many, I should ask to paint. The brush would need to be dipped in sand and in gray half-light; in liquid midnight and in curlicues of silver.

You are swimming in the dark, in Long Island Sound. It is the pure dregs of night: not the clear and spacy vault illustrious with stars, but dull heavy close night, midsummer and drizzling. Black water merges with black air, still, sombre, foreboding as pre-Genesis. Wounding your feet on stones and slates you feel your way into the low tide. There, if it were possible, the painting would begin.

This tepid sea is veined with lucifer. Wherever the flat calm is broken it rings and ripples in pale glow. White arms and thighs silver in ghostly radiance. Black water receives you and lustres in circling shimmer; the curve of a shoulder is wet platinum; the stroke of knee and leg is spiraled with glow-worm green. Lines and vortices of phosphorus twirl beneath your hands. Open your eyes under water, gleaming motes dazzle on your very eyeballs. As you wade on sandy bottom a tiny startled fish tickles up beneath your instep, flashes across the sea-floor in a beam of pallid light, grooved on darkness like a small wet comet. You swim in fluid argentine; every motion is pyrography; yet, looking up frightened from this sorcery of spangles you are consoled by soft all-comprehending black. So is all darkness grained with latent radiation? In the depth of all secrecy does brilliance stream from underfoot? Perhaps Adam was faintly luminous, groping in the prime obscure, for the body itself, in mere darkness, has its own dim shine. You should, and will, feel frightened; you tremble with a sudden chill, and the dawn comes gray.

How put all that on canvas, jovial painter? There is too much there that no crystal humor of the eye ever caught. The visual purple of the retina is pale beside the royal purple of memory, purple so imperial it is undistinguished from black. That purple humor of the soul carries its infinite burden of anxious joy, the low midsummer night, the douce and oaken air, grains of sand on wet flesh, black fathoms streaked with cream.

What brush, what dear childish pigments, can be pointed sharp enough for that? Oils and paints and colors are only a medium—something in between. A haze, a web, a shadow between us and the dark sea of words in which the mind must live. We swim black shoreless waters where every stroke is sluiced with goblin fire.

28

A MAN came and said that I ought to have the trees and shrubs sprayed; he said the canker worms were very bad this year, and if I didn't look out I wouldn't have any trees left. I put up a plea for the worms, saying that they also had to have their fun; an insincere plea, I was endeavoring to avert any possible expense, and had learned once before how costly it is to let loose an expert among your foliage. He climbs very high up a tall tree, and riding from the topgallant in a bosun's chair he discovers a nest of weevils that will be fatal to that tree unless something is done pronto. He offers to ride you aloft yourself (in the bosun's chair) to look at it; but I don't care for bosuns' chairs.

Besides in my simple symbolic fashion I had

272

thought that all those cheerful caterpillars were simply measuring worms, a sign that someone in the family was going to have a lot of new clothes.

He said he would do the job for $55, and though I tried to suggest $50 he was quite firm. He said the mixture he used was very costly; I asked what it was, and he said it blended whale-oil, arsenic, and nicotine. I capitulated at once. A mixture so romantic, so suggestive, yes, so symbolic, could not be resisted. If that was a good formula for ver-micide, I said to myself, it was equally good as a formula for literature. Besides, the coincidence was too perfect. The day the tree-man made his proposal happened to be Walt Whitman's birth-day, and if there ever was a book that compounded those particular ingredients it was *Leaves of Grass*. (Though I don't remember that Walt did much smoking? But just as nicotine, a poison, is the "ac-tive principle" of tobacco, and yet smoking is help-ful to the spirit, so Walt was able to take some of the morbid anxieties of life and show us their health and honor.) Moreover the $55 began to seem a rhyme of destiny. For *Leaves of Grass* was published in '55, and I was going to celebrate that very afternoon (a day of blue void and golden breeze) by taking to Walt's birthplace at West Hills a friend who had never seen it and who had been Walt's publisher; indeed perhaps the only publisher who ever appreciated that amazing book the *Complete Prose*. And by one of the incomparable felicities of life, destiny had decanted into the possession of this friend 3 bottles of the very rarest and noblest distillation of America, Overholt 1855. Of this choice, this unique, this coeval elixir of Xanadu, born from the grain and juice of Walt's own pinnacle year, we were to drink (tenderly, austerely, sparingly, as befits men of feeling) at the very farmhouse of his birth.

My $55 were already devoted. The mention of whale-oil (thoughts of *Moby Dick*) and the numerical coincidence were too strong for me. Thousands of canker-worms (the larvæ of geometrid moths) perished the following Monday for the sake of a literary sentimentalism. The cheerful woodsmen, climbing about and spraying their pallid poison in the green eyries above, would have been scandalized to know that I was thinking as much of Walt as of the trees. And the droning rumbumble of their gasoline pump, shooting a tall shower of liquid, was not unlike the spout of the white whale. I hope there really was whale-oil in the mixture.

We found Walt's birthplace divinely solitary. The road was being repaired, and approach was not easy; our only fear—that of finding some other devotees also doing piety—was happily unwarranted. The friendly occupant of the house was away on holiday, and the day's milk-bottle sat demurely unopened on the little porch. In that, and in the disrupted roadway, placarded DANGER, perhaps we also discerned some possible symbolism; but we were too pleased with ourselves and with Walt to analyze intuitions. The wide unspoiled heaven burned with blue glamour, and sitting on the highwaymen's Danger sign, opposite the memorial boulder, we drank the potion of 1855. In its thin silver flask it was just delicately tepid by carriage on a publisher's hip. Of the pious, the nourishing, the harmonic qualities of that famous rye I shall not adequately speak; it is not my duty to sadden you. Few, in these hazard times, have been exterior to such syrup. Syrup is the word: it has the soft benison of cream, a circumflex accent, an unguent property; a meal rather than just a drink. The warmth and sorrow of 75 years was in that rye; it was (as Webster confides) a hardy perennial cereal with a flowering glume. The virtue of Pennsylvania earth had passed into it, for I think it was at Broad Ford in the Alleghanies that Overholt began distilling in 1810. Who will do me a memoir of old man Overholt? Do the genteel of Pittsburgh ever make pilgrimage to Broad Ford? M. K. and I remembered that our own Caliph, who was from those same Alleghany hills and was connoisseur of such matters, had estimated Overholt 1855 as the finest rye whiskey ever begotten. Broad Ford on the

Youghiogheny (I hope for the honor of Pennsylvania that I spell the stream correctly)—what a place to visit. And at the same time I should like to see that other environ of Pittsburgh that has always lured me—Congruity, Pa.

The same ember of inwardness was bright in that precious minim that was alive in Walt's mind as he hopeful-hopelessly set up the type for the *Leaves*. The oneness of everything was apparent. The little farmhouse, neatly closed and blinded for the holiday, kept its secrets to itself. At the side-door the lilac still grows; the old silvered shingles on barn and outhouses are, very likely, the same as they were in 1819. We left a clean copy of *Leaves of Grass* under the milk-bottle, as an offering of courtesy.

Is it not time, by the way, that something should be done about the fine striding open-air statue of Whitman that Jo Davidson made several years ago? It is a noble and thrilling conception of the open-road Walt, hat off, vest open, beard blowing, "afoot and light-hearted." There were plans for putting it on a rocky outcrop in Central Park, also at the Battery, but whatever commissioners preside over such choices seemingly could not agree. I think that Prospect Park in Brooklyn is the happy place for it. One of the loveliest experiences in the world is to see the surprise of human beings when they discover what Prospect

Park is like. Brooklyn, always wisely secretive of her own treasures, says very little about it. Jo Davidson's Walt would be happy there. I wish the editor-in-chief of Prospect Park would give the statue a site; Brooklyn deserves it; Manhattan has had a plentiful chance and neglected it.

Another thing Manhattan has neglected is a tablet to O. Henry on the old Caledonia, 28 West 26. Yesterday on secret impulse I rambled along 26th Street to think about him. The Caledonia is still there, in that drab region contested by the wholesale florists and the garment trades. *Southern Wild Smilax* says one sign, and *Broadway Legging Corp.*, says another; both would have had special meaning for O. Henry. The Vanity Brassiere Company, the Ben Hur Blouse Co., the Amber Lantern tea-room and *As-Sayeh*, the Syrian Daily, would be in his daily purview if he were there now, and he would see stories in them all. I notice that there's an apartment for rent in the Caledonia; I wonder if by any chance it's his?

Just across the street there are plenty of trim little tablets marking the offices of Vincent Astor and the Astor Estate. John Jacob Astor, deceased 1848, is commemorated in a shining brass plate. In his own very different way, O. Henry created holdings in New York not less valuable than the old fur merchant's. It would be a gracious handsome

277

gesture if the Astor Estate would offer to put up a tablet on its neighbor the Caledonia, in memory of the undying unreal estate O. Henry created in the imagination of the city he loved. Realtor of the impalpable! Who is there who does not think of him with love and gratefulness, and with amazement at that extraordinary spendthrift power. On such a tablet perhaps one would write that line of his own that so often strangely recurs to mind— "He saw no longer a rabble, but his brothers seeking the ideal."—As a boy, he was freckled even to his feet, a Greensboro companion has told us. So were his stories, sprinkled with "contagion of the sun," mottled with the bewildering uncertainties of genius.

Speaking of places he lived, does the old Iron Front Hotel in Pittsburgh still exist? There, when he came from prison, he secreted himself to write before making his pilgrimage to New York. An Iron Front, bless his heart! He had it—and how he needed it.

29

WHO would set down the history of those two imperial months July and August? Was there not some curious gallantry in the golden air? Day after day the unblemished sun, until lawns were yellow and leaves fell singed as in October; night after

night the stars and crickets. Was there not, in that
sunburned summer, something of the old Roman
bravado? Great ships ablaze with lights and was-
sail ran white stripes of trigonometry across the
empty dark; glasses of whiskey and soda tingled
with turbine vibration and the smokeroom groups
sat about until the little sandwiches began to curl
up at the edges. Even as I write another vessel,
more uncanny than the rest, slips like a bubble
through the hollows of the wind. Most divinely
reckless of all men's miracles she tilts her huge
frailty against the fluid channels of the air; she has
red wall-paper in her saloon and special racks for
the wine goblets. As Nero undoubtedly said, if you
fiddle well enough it will put out the fire.

Days were so brilliant, dry, and clear, the mint
by the kitchen steps smelt like real julep. Dogs
were hosed twice a day to keep them sane. Grass
dried into a sort of pale excelsior; moles abandoned
their varicose rugations on the kiln-baked lawn;
the suburban gardener, studying his turf more
closely than ever before, found a white quartz Indian arrow-head—still razor sharp—right in front
of his peaceable shack. Was it the enormous candor
of that summer's feminine modes that kept
Apollo's gaze so persistent upon humanity? I am
the last to blame him. Along all sandy fringes of
the eastern seaboard glowed the unending afternoons of stupefying brilliance, gilding fine bronze

bodies bare to the stinging dazzle. Donny, the Emeritus Sheepdog, was shaven to the hide to relieve him of his mothy overcoat in which he lived like a Shakespearean actor of the Charles M. Barras era. He was more embarrassed by his nakedness than a Sunday School teacher.

Filling stations, the wayside temples of American life, looked more and more like Shinto shrines or little Greek arcades. There, making obeisance to their idols and totems, the American folk paid their offerings to the god they understood. They stepped on it: they drove headlong against locomotives at grade crossings; intersections guarded by traffic lights became the most dangerous of all because everyone tried to get across before the green turned red. At street corners sounded the moaning croon of the radio, the Koran of the community, the muezzin of the multitude, trying to keep up with the gait of affairs. The radio began putting children to bed with fables at 6 p. m. Vain hope! The proletarian urchin goes to bed at eleven. Everyone agreed that No Turn on Red was a sound idea, but not to be taken too literally.

Those who were wise rejoiced in all this fecund folly and found it good. America's subtlest artists, the newspaper cartoonists, turned the endearing foibles of their fellows to excellent account. America's most effective poets, the architects and builders, continued to do the incredible. The simple-minded persisted in believing that irony means bad temper. Vitamins seemed to be losing ground; no one had ever been quite sure about them anyway. All the ginger ales became as pale and dry as possible; the real problem was, what to do with the empty bottles. And hailstones as big as hen's eggs fell on Hartford, Connecticut; on just and unjust both.

In the long succession of amazements we call living, it was uncertain which were the greater miracles. Something bumped onto a page of writing; Mistletoe, without averting his eyes from the pen, tossed it into the waste basket. Then he looked and saw it was a firefly—pulsating, in the shadow of the table, with indignant glow. A dead moth on the porch lay there foundered like a little brown-sailed sloop; his great eyes were dull, his tongue curled like a watch-spring. Aphids continued to believe that rose-bushes should be made safe for lice; the Japanese beetle was officially excommunicated by the Department of Agriculture but made marvellous needle-point lace out of linden leaves. Some humble assessors of valuation believed themselves to discern a certain sense of Reality in visits to the midnight ice-box. There is (they asserted) an undeniability about the moon-map of a slab of Swiss cheese, or the smell of bread, or the sharpness of currant jam. Gooseberry jam, however, the best of all such, remained difficult to procure. This was as it should be; few bookstores keep "Marius the Epicurean" in stock. Things that are of high merit should always be crooked in access.

But which indeed *is* the greater miracle—the Zeppelin slipping between star and star, or the fact that for a few cents you can buy an English translation of The Koran and have laid before you for lamplit study the naive and noble dogmatisms of the Moslem prophet? What man in his decent senses does not respond to such promises as Mohammed makes to his hundred million faithful? Is it not excellent to know that to Islam all blue-eyed people are considered sinners and destined "to broil on the great fire"? But if you are a good Moslem, "in gardens and springs you shall be clad in satin, and wed to bright and large-eyed maids." "And were the trees that are in the earth pens, and the sea ink with seven more seas to swell its tide, the words of Allah would not be spent; verily, Allah is mighty."

How long then is an August afternoon? Rash indeed the experimenter who will endure the vacancy of thinking. Has not every theologian anxiously remarked the peril of idleness? Virtue abhors a vacuum, for in a devoted hour of thinking the whole savory earth may wabble in her bearings. You feel the dreadful texture of Time, the warm

sweet air is subtle in the tree-tops, the horror of the
Day is on you. They speak of 2 o'clock in the
morning courage; but 3 o'clock in the afternoon requires greater daring. The world will come to an
end (if ever) at about 3.15 some August afternoon
when reality is at last too vital and all men and
women cry together, This cannot be. Then, over-
trained by these billion years of apprehension, we
shall surrender our civilization to less anxious
creatures—the noisy and naive dogs, the military
and conniving rats, the prolific and gossipping
chickens. Or I myself would bequeath it to the
spiders, who would carry on the pretty puzzles of
geometry and spread their gauze mouchoirs on
every prickly hedge. On every side we hear brute
creation uttering its applause, and—like foreigners
in a theatre—we wonder what they're laughing at.
So how shall men avert themselves from the dangers of thought, against which Allah (the merciful,
the compassionate) and all his prophets honorably
tried to warn them? How may he glut himself with
trifles and never watch too closely the wheel that
spins and spins? In the flicker of rotation emerges
the phantom of stillness or the delusive image of a
backward turn.

It was the Age of Consent, when men agreed to
anything. Everywhere the beacons were eloquent,
No Turn on Red; and everywhere men hoped to
disregard them. In July and August they were

true to their calendar; they were emperors of Rome.

30

THERE was a lady called Leonora—"formerly a celebrated beauty, and still a very lovely woman" —who was immortally and tenderly chaffed by Mr. Addison more than 200 years ago—in 1711, to be exact—for the books he found in her library. If you turn back to your *Spectator* papers—there's no turning that will give you more fun—you'll find the graceful little essay, "A Lady's Library." Addison pretends that his friend Sir Roger de Coverley had asked him to deliver a letter to this agreeable blue-stocking, and while he was waiting for her to finish her toilet he had a chance to make a list of her books. What an enchanting list it is, full of affection for Leonora herself and yet with a dainty satire in the catalogue of the things she was reading. To appreciate to the full all the little jokes lurking in that list requires some knowledge of eighteenth and seventeenth century literature; but no one can miss the pleasant innuendo of some of the items—"*Locke on the Human Understanding*; with a paper of patches in it," and "*Clelia:* which opened of itself in the place that describes two lovers in a bower." Mistletoe often thought what fun it would be to compile a similar list for a twen-

tieth century Leonora, setting side by side with
each of Addison's titles the correlative book for our
present mode. Instead of Locke, it would of course
be Will Durant, or even—dare I hope so high?—
George Santayana. Instead of *Clelia*, probably Mr.
Arlen or Mr. Hemingway. Instead of Culpepper's
Midwifery it would be perhaps something by Mrs.
Sanger; and the corresponding item for the *Instructions for Country Dances* would be, undoubtedly, a Crossword Puzzle Book.

But I refrain. There is no greater fun than making up lists of books, yet whether by caution or by
selfishness, one tends to grow more secret in such
matters. For there are—one might as well admit
it—some books one is so fond of that one almost re-
sents anyone else except a very few intimates finding them out. And it is never fair to deprive people of the joy of discovering things for themselves.

But the importance of Addison's little causerie
about Leonora lies in this: we can see that the
reading done by persons of quality in 1711 tended
to be just as much a matter of fashion and reclame
as it does to-day. Addison remarks of Leonora's
books that "there were some few which the lady
had bought for her own use, but that most of them
had been got together either because she had heard
them praised or because she had seen the authors
of them."—Surely this latter seems an almost morbid reason.—And if I were writing a letter to

Leonora of to-day, I should urge her to be a little more of an explorer; to be a little less fashionable; to buy more of the books of which fewer people have heard.

Did it ever occur to you how complex the bookseller's task is? He must be ready to supply you with all the newest things, but also—unlike almost every other vendor—he must make a stand for the old. One customer will be indignant if he cannot obtain the latest Anita Loos; another even more so if there is not available a volume of Walter Pater or Landor. So the bookseller has to combine the functions of the bar-room and the bodega. He must be able to serve, on demand, not only the cocktail of the moment but also the scarcest of old vintages. How rare is the publican who understands the merits of both.

The particular privilege of the bookseller lies in the fact that the people who find their way into his shop are inevitably interesting. Even the most ill-humored visitor seeking the most banal book is at least in some inchoate mood of enlargement, of curiosity, of hope to extend the boundaries of experience and surmise. Reading is perhaps the supreme egotism, for it is done mostly alone and for the purpose of comparing our own secret life with that of others. So you may feel assured that no one ever entered a bookstore without having in his soul some fertilizable granule of human possibility.

If I were writing to Leonora I would not speak sentimentally about books, for she could easily find in a hundred or a thousand charming volumes the tender spirit of the ink-amorist's passion. What is on my mind at the moment is the fact that the bookstore is one of humanity's great engines, and one that we use very imperfectly. It is a queer fact that whereas most of us have learned the secret of going to libraries not so much in search of some particular book, but just to look round and see what happens to be there, we still have the primitive habit of visiting bookshops chiefly to ask for some definite title. Aren't we ever going to leave anything to destiny, or to good luck, or to the happy suggestion of some wise bookseller? Too many of our dealings with bookstores remind me, in their innocent ineffectiveness, of children learning to play the piano. I hear their happy ploiterings among the keys, their little tunes and exercises ring in my head in times of softened mood reminding me of all the lovely unfinished melodies of life. But it isn't what a connoisseur would call music. And similarly we all have ready to our access, in the bookshop, one of the greatest instruments of civilization; and yet none of us—neither publishers, booksellers, nor customers—have yet learned more than an inkling of what that place can accomplish.

Booksellers, and rightly, are always shy of being

too forward with their patrons. Every bookseller knows that his customers are usually of two kinds: those who need help, and those who prefer—or insist on—being left alone. When Mistletoe was very green and worked in a bookstore during several Christmas seasons, he was hell-bent to persuade customers toward things that had excited *him*. Two of the distinguished and regular customers of that store were Josiah Royce, the philosopher, and Miss Amy Lowell. I well remember the air of pain with which they regarded him when he ventured to tell them about some book or other. I think it was Vachel Lindsay's *General William Booth*, then just published. Professor Royce's anxious and peering evasion, Miss Lowell's heartily arrogant "Thank you, I don't need *your* assistance," were undoubtedly quite justified. It was an impertinence. Yet even they, philosopher and poet, might conceivably have learned something from the enthusiastic young salesman. For the true book lover preserves his humility: among those full shelves there will always be much to remind us of our minority. So with more affection he recalls a gracious damsel in black who used to come in every year and ask him to suggest her Christmas presents for her. And the dear old lady who agreed to read some special favorite of his— I forgot what—if he in turn would read May Sinclair's *Divine Fire*, which she bought and gave

288

him. Do you realize, I wonder, what good soil for rich human relationships a bookstore is? I should like Leonora to have the feeling that in entering a bookstore she is entering a place where almost anything can happen—and has. She must keep an eye open for rear-ward shelves and odd corners; for often the most important books are shy, and do not press forward to the front counters.

Of course reading is of many kinds; there is reading for stimulus, there is reading for anaesthetic. No one would be silly enough to confuse those two functions. The narcotic value of the detective story is not less to be esteemed than the intellectual voltage of—say—Paul Valéry. The wise amateur recognizes all potations in their due service, just as the acolyte of Silenus may suggest Old Fashioned Cocktails to numb a pain and Musigny 1915 to promote a delicately heightened perception of earth's loveliness. But one of the truisms about books is this: that the things you have heard since childhood were great, really *are* great. They do not, like a cheap champagne, go dead after ten or fifteen years. One of my happiest adventures lately was lending Francis Thompson's essay on Shelley to a young stenographer. When she brought it back her eyes were brilliant. "I didn't know that people could write like that!" she cried. "Tell me something else that's as good." A young business man, a Harvard graduate, admitted privily that

reading was something that had always been
rather a disappointment to him: he wanted a book
that would really give him "a kick." Greatly daring I tried *Dreamthorp* on him; the result was iden-
tical. They both now cry for another dose of the
same sort of medicine; not so easy to provide, but
I now waver between *The Opium Eater* and
Sirenica.

One has to struggle hard against one's impulse
to make out lists of suggestions for our modern
Leonora. But that, after all, is not our purpose. We
want Leonora to go pioneering on her own hook.
Gonzalo, in *The Tempest*, is said to have made a
quick choice of favorite books for Duke Prospero
to read on the desert island—probably the beginning of the old gag of what books one would choose
to be marooned with in the South Seas—but no list
is given nor are we told whether there were any
selected for Miranda. I got as far as sitting down
on the floor beside a favorite bookcase and began
jotting down a few titles at random but balancing
such things as *Marius the Epicurean* against the
poems of Emily Dickinson I gave up. After all I
don't know Leonora, even by glimpse; I have no
notion what private o'ergrowth of complexion—so
did Shakespeare first christen what we nowadays
call a complex—may condition her lively mind.
But when one is weary of writing about books—
for they are only of import in so far as they help us

to live life itself more boldly and generously—then one thinks of the moment when some young high school girl, some eager college boy, some fashionable young matron, find their ways for the first time into some book of genuine truth and beauty, see the world momentarily anew and feel the glow of that immortal heat when we know ourselves collaborators with Destiny in the endless fashioning of life. What does it matter in what particular volume they first encounter that moment of millennium? It may be some little Everyman copy of *Walden*, some play like Ibsen's *Wild Duck*, some liberalizing essayist like Matthew Arnold, or some marvellous old-timer like Thomas Fuller—hard to find, but worth search. I myself believe that Leonora should certainly have on her private shelf one of those rich and suggestive little anthologies about books and reading that give one a start down so many rewarding trails. There are many such: Broadus's *Books and Ideals*, published for a few cents by the Oxford Press is one; Ludwig Lewisohn's *A Modern Book of Criticism*, in the Modern Library, is another, of which a very modern young woman said to me that it was the first thing she ever read that showed her that literature was not just something on paper, but the very tissue of life itself. Hugh Walpole's charming little book on Reading is still another; but they are endless.

291

In the unalterable selfishness of life, concerned with my own affairs, you see I don't really much care what Leonora reads, or whether at all. But it might mean a huge deal to her whether or not she ever experiences those millennial moments. I know a man who turned a corner in life when, with the Warden's permission, he brought away with him after a jail sentence two or three books from the prison library that had meant much to him during a dark time. These books, still marked with the prison rubber stamp, hold a place of pride on his shelves. He is not at all ashamed of them, and I honor him for it.

The truth probably is that in the matter of stumbling upon the books we most need, and very often don't know we need, we all require help. And better than all the help the mandarins of letters can give us is what a great and well-stocked store does in simply having the books there. So the best I could do for Leonora—and for Leonardo too—is to try to inoculate them with the bookstore habit, dropping in and browsing and asking questions. And when I hear that Leonora has bought a book not because she had heard of it—or seen the author—but because she had *never* heard of it and it looked interesting, I shall know how she's grown since 1711. She must be getting a Big Girl now, bless her heart!

For after all, bookstores are places of magic, and

And writing about Amy Lowell's life of Keats he says:

> It is a good book in every sense of the word. Not since P. P. Howe's work on Hazlitt have I read anything so rugged and nugatory.

These excellent comments are somewhat marred for me by the painful suspense as to whether this vigorous critic, whom I justly admire, knows the meaning of *nugatory*. Or another instance—equally nugatory: a cheerful compiler of biographical data about current novelists, in a memoir of William McFee, remarks:

> He was born, without mishap, about the time "Copperfield," a fat and fascinating volume, first issued from the press.

The sprightliness of this sentence is corrupted for me by the fact that "David Copperfield" was published in 1850, and Mr. McFee was born more than thirty years later.

Some of the worst writing ever seen appeared lately in evening newspapers that undertook, before the event, to describe a total eclipse of the sun. Reporters who had not time to view the actual scene, compiled imaginary descriptions of green and orange flames shooting across the sky. These violent attempts to describe what was not, naturally missed the pale and serene beauty of the genuine spectacle. This was bad writing because it was absurd and insincere. Where behavior is incommensurate with the true significance of the event, absurdity always begins to appear. At the same time there appeared—in the New York *World*—an editorial on the eclipse that showed true meditation:

Once all men would have tried by magic and sacrifice to alter the inexorable course of the shadow. Today they are going outdoors to enjoy the spectacle and to understand it more accurately. In the record of that change of attitude toward the universe lies the story of the emancipation of the human mind.

A free mind is an understanding mind, a mind that has found its place, judged its power and made its peace with the natural order of which it is a part. . . .

There, I venture to say, is good writing: good because it is honest, thoughtful, and not inflated beyond its intellectual coefficient.

Obviously it is a parlous task to teach literature, because literature is merely bouillon cubes of life; and those who are "studying" literature have, for the most part, not encountered life very closely. It is the problem of intimating to a child in a porcelain tub the cruel insignificance of the sea. The meaning of the tub is so plain, the meaning of the sea so obscure.

Near the room where I write this there is a tablet on a street-corner which tells how Poe read "The Raven" aloud to his luncheon-cronies and sold it simultaneously to three journals in the neighborhood. Just that little inscription helps to make "The Raven" a greater thing to me: for I see it not just as something I pattered at school but as sheets of charmingly graceful script (have you ever seen Poe's handwriting?) fluttering over a malt-stained table in an Ann Street tavern. I see it as the expression of some wild, ecstatic, impoverished dream that fretted that hot pale forehead. And what a sense of the dreadful reality of literature one had in the Morgan collection of manuscripts shown at the Public Library. The little stained scrawl of Shelley's "Indian Serenade," taken from the yacht after two months under water; Keats's will—those few poor lines: "All my estate consists in the hopes of the sale of books publish'd or unpublish'd," and the added wish that "my Taylor" (his generous publisher) be paid his few pounds; or Jane Austen writing to her sister some ingenious speculations on the planning of a new dress ("As I find the Muslin is not so wide as it used to be, some contrivance may be necessary.") Harry Fielding's receipt for £600 for "Tom Jones," Bozzy's letter to Temple confessing that he writes while "suffering severely for immorality," Swift rhyming for Stella on her birth-

297

day, Burns alluding to one of his prettiest verses as "this random clink"—could one not hear, from every glassed-in case in the great room, the whisper and beating of these troubled hearts? It was intolerable: one could not linger too long. "Oh I *adore* Sterne" said a lady with a lorgnette, gazing into the case where the MS. of one of Laurence's sermons lay side by side with his letter to "Bramine" . . . "I have some time foreboded I should think of you too much; and behold it is come to pass."

"Oh, *look* at his *handwriting!*" cried the lady over the Addison case. "Isn't it *fascinating!*" Somehow it seems as though textbooks have a way of obscuring the truth that literature is just that—handwriting; that there was an actual fist behind it, and that these poor shreds of scribble were leaves from a growing tree. There was a poet who died the other day, T. W. H. Crosland, whose angry and fiery heart pushed real blood into the veins of his work. In his book on "The English Sonnet" he wrote (of Michael Drayton):

Here we have no mewling, honey-lipped, sugared "sonneteer," but a gentleman with a temper of his own and something of a fist in which to hold the quill. The notion that poetry, and sonnets in particular, are written only by the mild-mannered, and persons in precarious health, requires to be dispelled. As a fact, great poets are not only the sanest people in the world, but physically and temperamentally the toughest.

Now he is dead: as dead as Milton; but when he was alive, he wrote exciting things. He sat down and brooded on his topic, thinking how wrong everyone else was: he brooded until he bubbled with rage, and then in a superb and delightful anger he began to write, with knitted lips, flailing about with his pen, distributing largesse of jeers and jewels. His work suffered, as the work of an angry man must; but he was real. When our correspondent can convince her pupils that literature is a human voice, expressed from actual hearts by the form and weight of life, she has accomplished as much as can be done for those young skeptics. Even then her most skilful insinuations will never startle them as much as what they find out for themselves.

There is a young man of twenty-two or so whose letters I am privileged to look over from time to time. Perhaps a man so much older shouldn't be allowed to read these letters; yet though they are so gorgeously young they are also very wise and shrewd, and sometimes nippingly humorous. As young men should be, he is proud and sensitive; when he feels lonely or has a swimming in his head he gets out Shakespeare and rereads him; occasionally, in a burst of enthusiasm he slips into his letters a sonnet or lyric of his own. But even without that you would know him a poet by chance phrases. "If a sparrow comes before my window, I take part in its existence and pick about the gravel." Or this comment he makes on Shakespeare's sonnets—"they seem to be full of fine things said unintentionally." Yes, there he hit upon a big truth; and again: "The excellence of every art is its intensity, capable of making all disagreeables evaporate from their being in close relationship with Beauty and Truth."

Some of his letters that I have seen are addressed to a publisher; occasionally, and with most engaging humor, appealing for an advance payment; occasionally discussing less tangible matters. He remarks, for instance, that poetry should surprise the reader "not by singularity but by a fine excess." This is a nourishing thought to ponder; though he himself, with his clear honesty, would not care for any casual dicta to be too fiercely solidified. "My dear fellow," he writes, "I must once for all tell you I have not one idea of the truth of any of my speculations—I shall never be a reasoner." And he speaks of "the innumerable compositions and decompositions which take place between the intellect and its thousand materials" before it reaches any particular perception of beauty.

Specially young are his rather cavalier deposi-

300

tions as to the irrelevance of women in any rational scheme of life. They are mere children, he remarks, to whom he would rather give a box of candy than his precious time. When you hear him saying that, you tremble a little for him. It was not much later he was writing that to express his devotion he needs "a brighter word than bright, a fairer word than fair." And concludes with the world's oldest cry—"I know before night I shall curse myself for having sent you so cold a letter."

For the kind of people who are worthy of such infinitely precious confidences, and won't blab about them, these letters might be a surprise. The name of the man who wrote them was John Keats.

32

TO-DAY, for the first time this year, has the color and sound of winter. That empty lacework of nude twigs, which will be so familiar a sight in months to come, still seems a bit strange. Except for the little Y-shaped birch tree, which always holds its leaves longer than any other, Satisfaction Piece is under bare poles. Satisfaction Piece, I should explain, is the little wood-lot next door, cynosure of these windows where I sit. (What an agreeable history the word *cynosure* has. First it meant a dog's tail; then, the constellation that looks like a dog's tail, viz. the Little Bear, containing the Pole Star; then, the Pole Star itself; and hence, something that everyone looks at and admires.) I call that small tract of jungle Satisfaction Piece because, after years of hankering and doubtfulness we bought it not long ago. And always, when you buy property, during those mystifying but enjoyable transactions in Phil Clarke's office at *The Thrift*, Brooklyn, I find some notation about a Satisfaction Piece. This particular plot of ground (don't magnify it in your imagination, it is only 46/100 of an acre) is well named. For over eight years I have lived alongside it, trespassed upon it, gazed at it from the bathtub every morning, and suffered anxiety when the rumor ran that Somebody Else had bought it. Now I repeat it is ours (subject, of course, to a mortgage held by the genial old Thrift, my father confessor in all such matters). Satisfaction Piece!

I first heard of The Thrift (which is a bank in Brooklyn; its emblem is a bee-hive with some busy bees flying about it; its assets, I once read in a leaflet, are $7,182,853.91, which always gives me a thrill because somewhere toward the right hand end of that train of digits my small *peculium* is evidently included) long before I ever knew I would be one of its clients. In the early times at Doubleday's those of us who were cubs in the Sales Department grew accustomed to hearing

302

our boss, D. N., the Sales Manager, calling up
The Thrift repeatedly. D. N., I believe, was
chambering his nautilus: in other words, building
a mansion in Kew Gardens; and undoubtedly The
Thrift had some hand in the affair, as it has with
most of us in Nassau County. But D. N., by some
particular charm of Cape Cod accent, could not
possibly pronounce THR. *Hullo, Frift?* he used to
ejaculate over the phone; so often that we all
grew familiar with the word, believing it the name
of some mysterious customer, like the Syndicate
Trading Company, to whom large jobs of over-
stock could be sold. When Mistletoe was sent out
to pound the pavements himself, to try to sell certain laggard titles in bulk to Liggett's and Charles
Broadway Rouss and McCrory and any who would
take them, he sought vainly in the telephone book
for the benevolent Mr. Frift.

But what I started to say was that this, the
first wintry afternoon of the year, is one of those
off-days (less frequent lately than I like them to
be) when one shuts himself in here alongside
Satisfaction Piece, occludes thoughts of other
business however fascinating, and lies low. The
strong November wind hums in the trees, and you
are (was it Hazlitt's phrase?) "happy thinking."
On such an afternoon, following several strenuous
days and nights, you might even, secretly, repose

yourself a while with a detective story. For a man in solitude has no shame; and behind that closed door none can see what you are about. I can think of many things more deplorable to look back on than an hour's innocent siesta induced by the charms of police romance.

But not less pleasant, on these afternoons of slack, to turn over some of the accumulated catalogues. Most of them go into the paper-basket at the Roslyn Heights P. O., unopened. I bought that paper-basket myself, and gave it to the U. S. Government, so that I should not feel responsible for embarrassing our kind postmistress by overloading the inadequate little tin toy provided by Washington. (Let me add that I deducted the cost of the basket from my Income Tax, justly I think.) But there is a pang in consigning any book catalogue at all to the rubbish heap. You never know what bird of strange plumage will twitter on an unexpected branch. Some catalogues I always am wise enough to bring home for scrutiny. Frank Hollings, for instance, of 7 Great Turnstile, High Holborn (Telegraphic Address: Opuscule, London). Here, rummaging Mr. Hollings, we observe J. M. Barrie's humorous remarks at a dinner in honor of Frederick Greenwood, the famous editor, in 1905. (You remember the story that it was Greenwood who did much to start Thomas Hardy's reputation. Going on a railway journey in

1872 he happened to see *Under the Greenwood Tree*, lately published, on the platform bookstall. His own name caught his eye, he read the book and wrote enthusiastically about it.) Anyhow it appears that Mr. Greenwood was a great smoker of cigars. Barrie says:

"I did not smoke in those days. I abominated it, but my game was to get round him and study his weaknesses. So I took to writing in the paper about smoking, and wrote so many articles about it that we ultimately made them into a book, and long afterwards I read the book, and was so fascinated by its pictures of the delights of tobacco that I took to smoking myself."

It is sad to reflect that the opportunities for self-education so far outrun one's capacity. Why, I often wonder, should anyone worry about not being able to go to college, or subscribe to correspondence courses, when he may have gratis whole carloads of auctioneers' and booksellers' catalogues? The rudiments of literature and history, for example, which I was sent to college to study, I was too green to grasp; but I have picked up an honest smattering since, mostly by suggestions in catalogues. As Melville said of the whaling ships, so I can truly say of the Anderson Galleries and the American Art Association, they have been "my Yale College and my Harvard." Such intuitions of taste as I may have formed in the matter of furniture or pictures, such sprinklings of information in history or bibliography, are due largely to faithful study of those unending series of catalogues. Unknown benefactors, the stockholders of those gallant athenea, those dioscuri of culture, have spent a great deal to keep me supplied with catalogues, the textbooks of my illumination. It is decent that I should mention my gratitude, and sometimes report what looks to me like progress.

Particularly I enjoy a catalogue where the identity of the seller is not divulged. Then, brooding over the contents of his collection, to speculate on his character and tastes is as pleasant as reading a detective story. The catalogue before me is that of the "Superb Library of A Prominent New York Theatrical Man." Perhaps the disasters of the current season on Broadway account for the sale. Or perhaps he concluded, as many a Theatrical Man has had to, that he had no time for Standard Authors as he ought to be spending all his time reading scripts. What a theme for an essayist, by the way, would be the mysterious fate of play-scripts. What becomes of them, and what dark magic is it that makes them so dilatory in getting read? Why are they never by any chance returned, and why are almost all of them the fifth or sixth carbon copy? One day I was having breakfast with a famous stage director in his hotel bedroom, and some argument arose about an old play which we vaguely remembered. In the zeal of the moment he leaped out of bed and went to open a large trunk which accompanies him everywhere. I watched with interest, expecting in my Bœotian way to see layer on layer of the lively dressing gowns and well pressed morning coats which keep artists happy. The trunk was full to the brim of scripts. There, in the various colored cardboard bindings affected by the different agencies, the yellow, the red, the blue so familiar to all producers, there they were in hundreds. Now I know what happens to scripts. Directors keep them and travel round with them.

But we were speaking of Prominent T. M. whose library was sold. He must have had plenty of houseroom for there were the most incredible number of complete sets, which always looks very suspicious to the student. The Navarre Society, and the enterprising George Barrie in Philadelphia, and other lively brokers of vellum certainly got into him in fine style. Few of the items traditional in such libraries were missing. Paul de Kock was there in blue and ochre morocco, and Robert Ingersoll in crushed levant; Victor Hugo in 41 volumes with "doublures of marbled calf, white watered silk fly-leaves, gilt tops." Horrible! The only thing I can't understand is how T. M. escaped having a set of Casanova unloaded on him.

These endless sets of solid morocco give one much to meditate. I rather envy T. M. his 50 volumes of the Yale Press's "Chronicles of America" because I suspect there's a lot of good reading in them; but such a perspective of yards and yards of Britannica and Carlyle and Dumas and John Fiske and Eugene Field and Flaubert and Gibbon and Grote begin to appal. The "Astral" edition of Wilde with "floriated gilt backs, crimson morocco doublures, fly-leaves of white moiré," would undoubtedly have pleased Oscar; but what does Walt Whitman think of himself in "old-rose morocco, fillet and dentelle borders in gilt, old-rose watered silk fly-leaves?" Among these Winter Garden trimmings occasionally a human voice is heard. In a set of Mark Twain we find a letter of Mark's tipped in, which says: "I can't do no literary work the rest of this year because I'm meditating another lawsuit and looking around for a defendant." Always in these catalogues I ponder the inevitable set of Burton's Arabian Nights, printed in Benares by the Kamashastra Society for Private Subscribers Only. The innocent old Arabian Nights I frequented in youth had been briskly surgeoned, and I always pause upon the cataloguer's discreet allusions to Explanatory Notes on the Manners and Customs of Moslem Men, and "anthropological data of the most strange and private nature." I used to wonder how much wages were paid to proofreaders in Benares, and thought it might be amusing to get into correspondence with the editorial staff of the Kamashastra Society. But I became discouraged, because years ago I wandered by chance into a second-storey bookshop that specializes in curiosa, and found it a very tedious place. Besides I am not entirely ignorant of the Moslem view of life for I once visited a night club in Weehawken.

In T. M.'s catalogue I also came across an author we don't often hear of, George M. W. Reynolds. There are twenty volumes of him, in "midnight-blue morocco." He was "privately printed for Members of the Oxford Society," whose headquarters however were not anywhere near the Isis but in Boston. Some of George M. W. Reynolds's frontispieces, the catalogue says, were COLORED BY HAND. One of his books is "Lady Saxondale's Crimes," in 5 volumes; I should love to hear from anyone who has read it or will tell me about Reynolds. What has he done to deserve midnight-blue morocco?

T. M.'s library was not all of this proterve tinge by any means: there were some very fine things in it, though one can't help feeling they got there rather haphazard; and to murder rare old first editions by rebinding them in these morocco monkey tricks is happily a craze gone by. I forgive him everything for having a set of Thoreau. But there is much in the annotation of his collection that makes one realize what has been wrong with the Broadway theatre.

There are many surprising stories and human eavesdroppings to be found in these catalogues. My eye fell upon this little note signed by Judge Mountain, executor of the late Mayor Raymond of Newark:—

I give you the books of a man who drove the administrative forces of a large city by day and who sought the solitude of his library with weary, drooping shoulders at eventide. Into that library came only his friends. To enter his house was to enter another world, to dine amidst exquisite crystal and silver, to examine dainty etchings, to pore over first editions or examples of fine printing. Many of these books have been read aloud, many have been tenderly caressed. They were chosen with a fine discrimination.

The owner of these books was an astute politician and an executive of wide vision, yet for almost forty years at spare moments he patiently designed and painted miniature church models, accurate in the most minute particulars.

And there is something that always catches the mind off guard in that phrase I find in the Conditions of Sale:—"Title passes upon the fall of the auctioneer's hammer."

33

AUTUMN, if ever, is the time to try to speak the truth. To *write* truth would be more accurate; truth is rarely spoken. Even one listener is an embarrassment.

There are a few weeks in autumn when more subtly than at any other season human beings become exquisitely aware of their tender predicament. The year, the year we loved, passes through the colors of Spain and the Indies. She is lovely on her death-bed. There are afternoons filtered through sleepy gold when one dare not think, so acute is that sense of passage. Even Keats left his ode to Autumn unconcluded by any definite sentiment, probably because the "moral" of autumn is mortally unbearable. We see it in every wrinkled brown leaf, in every log we burn. The last stanza of Keats's ode was never put on paper, but you can taste it in every mug of cider.

Of all human follies, the collecting of autographs is probably the most exasperating. Of course the seasoned observer of this humor knows that the only autograph worth having is one that was never intended as such. In spite of the insistent claims of competing prophets, from Moses down, it is not yet proved that the greatest Author of all anywhere autographed his work—

not legibly at any rate. But the sweet sobriety of autumn, even more than the lewd merriment of spring, always seems to me the closest we come to his signature on the dotted line. It is his unpromissory note. And it always suggests the central doctrine that the whole of life, everything, all we can ever observe or suspect, is one huge analogy. The explanation, if ever attained, will be of unspeakable simpleness; it will be the infinity at which all parallels meet.

Man, not less than the chipmunk, is attentive to the small silver threat of autumn evenings. It is then that Mistletoe, rodent larger and less picturesque, is impelled to lay away his little provender of nuts. Aware of the long dark winter he also would like, poor soul, to put down some storage of notions, some kernels of beechnut prose or verse, to remind imagined survivors that he too was once alive and aware of comedy. And it is then that the reader, happier than the writer, can turn to those nuts that chipmunks of the past have harvested for him. What a chipmunk, for example, was Wordsworth, for an autumn evening.

If one could put down adequately the thoughts and fancies of one day only, what a nut that would be for posterity. And what a love we (who are, for all previous chipmunks, Posterity: an important thing to be)—what a love we hold for those who in honest autumnal mood have uttered

312

the beautiful misgivings of the heart. It is often said that mankind reserves its deepest affection for those who can make it laugh. I wonder. Surely our greatest love is for those who can make us reputably sad, for we always suspect that they may be telling the truth.

Of all the lifelong adventures of one day, I can only take space here to record one: as a proof of sincerity I choose Today itself, the day I know best. Dean Swift, an elderly Studebaker, was not behaving well: it was obvious, even to a slovenly mechanician, that one or two spark plugs were not firing. She was, as we call her when in trouble, the Gloomy Dean. While Pete, our excellent technologist at the local smithy was (in the words of the immortal Anatomy) rectifying her perturbations, I heard a vigorous harangue proceeding from a loud-speaker within the garage. A parson of nation-loud repute was putting his Sunday afternoon certainties on the air. It was the first time I had heard his voice, and I was amused to note that like many of the propheteers and parvenus for whom America is reproached he was audibly of alien origin. But what struck me was the terrific haste and vehemence of his discourse; as though in imminent danger of interruption. His remarks were harmless in themselves; as far as intellectual ether was concerned their wave length was modest enough; but the noise and hurry of their emergence

from the trumpet was appalling. I repeated to myself the familiar thought that if you're talking to
a great many people you've got to be very
Positive.

By this time, Pete (a great admirer of this parson, I must add; Pete gets genuine virtue from the
jets of homily that come yelling out at him as he
tinkers the Sunday afternoon traffic) had fixed the
spark plugs. Incautiously, the engine running, I
laid my hand on one of them, and got a shock
that tingled me notably. It wasn't painful, it was
merely thrilling. I felt it pass, a miracle of sprightliness, through the cords of both arms. Obviously
there was something there that was in a mighty
big hurry to get somewhere. For the instant I
happened to be part of the circuit. There again,
I said to myself, as the Dean went on her way,
was an example of something that had a message
to deliver to a large public, and was very positive
about it. Analogy once more!

Everybody, this is the real riddle of the universe, always seems so certain about everything,
except you yourself; and only You Yourself know
how devilish uncertain and anxious you are about
a lot of things. "There are many voices," says the
old wisdom, "and none, it may be, without significance." That damnable dubiety seems to run
through the whole tissue of existence; and yet,
odd paradox, we are equally convinced, in mo-

314

ments of sanity, that some supreme unifying simplicity underlies the whole riddle. What's the answer? What is it of which Wordsworth said

Thou dost preserve the stars from wrong
And the most ancient heavens through thee are fresh
and strong.

The name that Wordsworth gave it is an unpopular and uncomfortable one, so I don't mention it. It isn't quite the right word anyhow.

Even in a bookshop, God help us, we can't avoid these discomforts of decision. Prosperous citizens to looard of Central Park in New York have lately learned to their horror that some of the smartest speakeasies have been selling poisoned liquor; some of the very nicest bookshops unavoidably sell books that have a high content of wood alcohol. The Bookseller, like the pharmacist, deals in dangerous drugs; many a young intellect, fevered with some too Circean syrup, has uttered Romeo's *O true apothecary!* and expired.

Autumn, to return to our theme (if there was one) is the season of humility; for in these months, brilliant with decay, Nature suggests to us her most disquieting analogies. Decadent literatures have always been witty; earth itself in autumn is at her most epigrammatic. We need feel no shame that you and I cannot solve the questions that Lucretius and Wordsworth have agreed not to answer. Since we don't have to talk over the radio on Sunday afternoons we can afford to be undogmatic, and smile to each other over our very human anxieties. When the leaves are off the trees we can see the stars better, and we follow the enchanted grievance of autumn with the lovely fairytale of Christmas. We are nothing if not fanciful: we celebrate the legend of divine humility by a roaring largesse of luxury. For one month in the year, Literature almost enters the category of Big Business.

34

HERE and there, leavened in among masses of populace, are those few to whom the name of the late Thomas Bird Mosher still carries a special vibration. Mr. Mosher spent more than thirty years in betrothing books and readers to one another; like the zooming bumble-bee and with a similar hum of ecstasy he sped from one mind to the next, setting the whole garden in a lively state of cross-fertilization.

The famous twenty volumes of the *Bibelot* are Mosher's testament, both the greater and the less as his friend Villon would have said. These are twenty books—yes, and duly stamped in black and red—that any clerk of Oxford would be glad to have at the head of his couch.

"The resurrectionist Mosher" his kinsprit Billy
Reedy called him. Aye, how many exquisite things
he disinterred, and how far ahead of the thunder-
ing herd to see the good things coming. In one of
his crisp little prefaces he spoke of "that saving
remnant who when they see a good thing know
it for a fact at first sight." As early as 1900 he
was hailing the Irish literary renaissance in Yeats,
Lionel Johnson, Moira O'Neill and others; and
coming to the defence of *vers libre*. It was in those
little grey-blue *Bibelots*, chance-encountered in
college days, that Mistletoe first met Fiona
Macleod, Francis Thompson, Synge, Baudelaire,
H. W. Nevinson, William Watson, Arthur Upson,
Richard Jeffries, Arthur Symons, Alexander Smith
. . . . one could carry on the list *ad lib*. What was
there in this hardy sea-bred uncolleged downeaster
that made him open so many magic portholes? He
had the pure genius of book-fancy; an uneducated
man, as uneducated as Chaucer and Lamb and
Conrad; and I like to think that when he took Aldus's device for himself there was some memory
of the time when an anchor meant more to him
than an emblem printed on a title-page.

I like to think of the good luck of the people
who had the fun of learning in the *Bibelot* something of the extraordinary thrills that literature
can give. I think it is not extravagant to say that
as a collection of a certain kind of delicacies, this

cargo of Mosher's is unrivalled. I suppose it is the most sentimental omnibus that ever creaked through the cypress groves of Helicon. Like all men of robust, gamesome, and carnal taste, Mosher had a special taste for the divine melancholies of ink. Gently tweaked by subscribers for his penseroso strain, he replied "We shall prove that a humorous *Bibelot* is not, as we have been informed, out of our power to produce." But, speaking from memory, I believe he exhumed only the somewhat Scollay Squareish hilarities of James Russell Lowell's operetta about the fish-ball. Its title, *Il Pesceballo*, is the best of it.

I think indeed that a too skittish and sprightly *Bibelot* would have been out of the picture. Mosher's sentiment was of the high and fiery kind, the surplus of some inward biology that made him the rare Elizabethan he is said to have been. He was by no means the indiscriminating allswallower; his critical gusto was nipping and choice; in those brief prefaces you will find many a live irony, many a graceful and memorable phrase. The particular task that he set himself in the *Bibelot* was, moreover, not prone to casual mirth. He was the seeker among "spent fames and fallen lights," the executor of unfulfilled renowns. The poets he loved were those who were "torches waved with fitful splendor over the gulfs of our blackness."

Take it in beam and sheer, the *Bibelot* is an anatomy of melancholy. It has been called an encyclopædia of the literature of rapture, but it is that kind of rapture which is so charmingly indistinguishable from despair. Mosher loved the dark-robed Muse: he emprisoned her soft hand and let her rave; he fed deep upon her peerless eyes. He was the prince of editors: he did not come to his task until he had tried other ways of life and found them dusty. He was almost forty when he began publishing, and what did he begin with? Meredith's "Modern Love!" Think of it, gentles. Would not that have looked like a lee shore to most bookmen in Portland, *arida nutrix* of publishers? But it was what he called the "precious minims" that interested him. There was in him more than the legal $\frac{1}{2}$ of one per cent of Hippocrene. In 1895 he began his *Bibelot* and carried it through monthly numbers for twenty years. As editor he never obtruded himself. When he died I don't think there was a newspaper in America that had a photo of him available in its files. He was the potential author of one of the most fascinating autobiographies that were never written.

So it was that there came to us, from what has been called the stern and hidebound coast, this most personal and luxurious of anthologies. These twenty little grey briquettes pile up into a monument. He was always, in the phrase he loved to apply to his favorite writers, "touched to finest issues." He knew lapidary work when he saw it. Once he spotted a poem written by a contributor to the old Bowling Green. At once he wrote for permission to reprint it in his catalogue. "It is one of the few things," he said, "that to me seem almost absolutely perfect." May I tell you, without breach of manners, what it was? Life is very short anyhow for paying one's respect to the things that need admiration. The poem was "Night" by William Rose Benét.

In these twenty volumes there is enough material even for those of us who never knew him to guess fairly closely into Mosher's own tastes. He was all for "songs gotten of the immediate soul, instant from the vital fount of things." And however sharp his taste for the fragile and lovely, there was surely a rich pulse of masculine blood in his choices. He was often accused of piracy. If it be piracy to take home a ragged waif of literature found lonely by the highway, to clothe her in the best you have and find her rich and generous friends—if this be piracy, then let any other publisher who has never ploitered a little in the Public Domain cast the first Stone and Kimball. The little upstairs fireside on Exchange Street, Portland, is one of the most honorable shrines that New England can offer to the beadsman of beauty.

They pile up, I repeat, into a monument that

any man might envy, these twenty little fat books.
No one reader will agree with all Mosher's choices,
but surely never did any editor of genius ramble
with so happy an eye among the hedgeflowers of
literature. A Scottish critic has said there is only
one enduring test of a book: is it aromatic? These
beautiful books, from beginning to end, are fresh
with strange aroma and feed more senses than the
eye. Words of Arthur Upson's, printed here by
Mosher, describe them:

> Wine that was spilt in haste
>   Arising in fumes more precious;
> Garlands that fell forgot
>   Rooting to wondrous bloom;
> Youth that would flow to waste
>   Pausing in pool-green valleys—
> And passion that lasted not
>   Surviving the voiceless tomb!

The *Bibelot* began and ended with selections
from William Blake. And like Blake, Mosher gave
us the end of a golden string.

35

THE happiest form of publishing, and one that
will always appeal to a few exploring tempera-
ments, is the small business which exists as the

personal expression of some single genius of taste. Publishing as a one-man joy may eventually be superseded by vaster congeries of editing and manufacture; yet it is not likely, for in that field distinction is plainly a function of *x*—*x* being the rare and individual gift of sensibility.

From the evening in February 1914 when he went to Brooklyn for the first time, to see a book exhibit at the *Eagle* office, Mistletoe was curious about the remarkable work done under the imprint of Mitchell Kennerley. I doubt if there has been in our time any publisher with more sensitized development of the special publisher's instinct for Knowing It First. What comfortable taste he always had for the sobrieties of fine bookmaking. That one of the most beautiful of modern type-fonts is named for him is well known. From the appearance of his rare little anthology *Modern Love*, in 1906, down to the catalogues of the Anderson Galleries under his regime, Kennerley's magic with paper, type and ink was manifest in everything that bore his name. He was trained in the lively schoolroom of old John Lane where he began as an office-boy; the humorous and tragic decadents of the Nineties surrounded his boyhood at the Bodley Head—

> When every hair upon the Bodley Head
> Harbored a separate poet.

His anecdotes of those days remain the most entertaining inside panorama of the Sunflower Decade. He came to New York in 1896 as Lane's envoy, to establish an American branch.

Now that it exists no longer, it cannot be unseemly to say that Mistletoe found Mitchell Kennerley's carefully guarded sanctum in the former Anderson Galleries building the most interesting chamber in New York. The first port of call for visiting collectors and connoisseurs of all the arts, an attentive listener heard there the shrewdest backstage talk about books and life. There is a delicious spice of boyish mischief in the great financiers who are the top-rank collectors, and the boy learned to carry many assorted secrecies without flinching. It was always his intention to attempt a catalogue raisonné of the books on the shelves of that room. He never got round to it, and it must now be done by the able librarians of Vassar College, to whom (on his retirement from the Anderson Galleries) Mr. Kennerley gave that extraordinary collection of Firsts of the Nineties and Early Hundreds. Such a catalogue, done with the proper inside information, would imply the richest part of a history of our own times.

Such a history would have to record that Kennerley, probably more than any other editor, was first to remark and put between covers (either in *The Forum* or in books) much of the finest stuff of our day. His Lyric Year competition in 1912 was admittedly the mouthpiece for the newer voice in American poetry. It was he who first started Edward Carpenter, Leonard Merrick, D. H. Lawrence, Frank Harris (quantum mutatus) on this side of the inkwell: who issued the first really portable *Leaves of Grass*, who introduced Hergesheimer, Vachel Lindsay, Arthur Ficke, Edna Millay; who initiated the Modern Drama Series of great European plays. I mention only such items as occur to me offhand; reference to his publishing lists would afford surprising reminders. Kennerley was unquestionably the first Modern publisher in this country, in the particular sense in which the word is used nowadays. In matters of literary sensitiveness few others have ever caught up with him.

I always think his most characteristic editorial touch was what he did in *The Forum* when the Great War began. He ripped open the September, 1914, issue of the magazine, already on its way to press, and inserted, as the leading feature of that number, a reprint of The Sermon on the Mount.

At one end of that hospitable room, behind a tall barrier of filing cases, was a little basin with running water where hands might be laved. From that sheltered corner occasionally arose the gratifying clatter of oscillated ice, as M. K. mingled some specially aromatic cocktail, or withdrew from his long rows of pigeon-holes a crusted bottle of sherry from the officers' mess of the frigate *Constitution* (the irony here used to please his visitors), or rum from the India Docks, or a bottle of *fine* that had been in Napoleon's own cellar at the Palais des Tuilleries, or some of Francis Joseph's 18th century Tokay. Those filing cases contained every conceivable precaution of civilized emergency, from ingenious corkscrews and pipe reamers and fly swatters to spare shirts and clean napkins and shaving cream. Once by some chance Mistletoe found himself on the way to an evening dress engagement but had forgotten to bring black socks. Time was pressing, haberdashers in that part of town were closed. In an inspiration of despair he directed the taxi to the Anderson Galleries. Yes, M. K. was there as usual. "Have you got any black socks?" he cried anxiously. M. K. went calmly to the famous filing cases and drew out a sheaf of beautiful silk hosiery. They fitted perfectly.

One never knew whom he might meet in that magic place. Once J. M. was in the hidden washstand corner, cleansing his hands. He heard someone enter the room, and a voice which he knew instantly was unlike any other in the world. Deep, vibrant, with far-away bells of loneliness and passion; melancholy and humorous at once, and a noble spacious timbre like someone speaking in a cathedral—what forgotten rumors of childhood did it recall, when he had been told about that voice? There had never been more than one—but surely it couldn't be——

He came out from behind the partition. It was. Mitchell said "I want you to meet Mrs. Patrick Campbell."

Sometimes, instead of going out for lunch, two little shiny buckets of chicken salad and sandwiches would be sent over from the Plaza. Over a glass of the *Constitution* sherry a narrative mood might come upon the host, and Mistletoe sat entranced by unexpurgated memoirs of the Nineties. Not to have known that room would have been to miss the finest flavor of publishing aesthetics.

Another individual imprint to commemorate was that of B. W. Huebsch. It disappeared from title-pages in 1925, when Mr. Huebsch merged his business with the young Viking Press. His emblem of the seven-branched candlestick almost always marked a book that had some genuine reason for existence. A publisher always active in the general interest of the trade, he was also never reluctant to concern himself with what looked like Literature. Sometimes he was too high-minded an idealist for Mistletoe's terrene taste. The Thorstein Veblen sort of thing was, I dare say, too intellectual for J. M., and the political austerity of the old *Freeman* too severe. These, I grant, were Mistletoe's demerits, not Mr. Huebsch's. But it was when Huebsch came out with things like the Notebooks of Chekhov, or H. W. Nevinson's *Farewell to America*, or Sherwood Anderson's *Winesburg, Ohio*, or poets like Winifred Welles, that Mistletoe said to himself Here is a publisher with instinct. One tactic of both Kennerley and Huebsch that might have been imitated by other houses was their reticence in the matter of jacket-blurbs. When Anderson's *Horses and Men* appeared, it bore on its wrapper only six words of publisher's comment. "The mature artist at his best," said Huebsch tersely.

Huebsch was, I think, the first American publisher to recognize the strange talent of James Joyce. It used to be waggishly said that any Irish, Hindu, or German artist could find a home in Mr. Huebsch's list when no other publisher would take a chance on him. This generosity of his brought him some great names as well as, I daresay, many tedious hours with wandering Swamis. No document would be more valuable to my own brand of sociology than a list of the rambling libertads for whom Ben Huebsch must have bought lunches in those years. As an American encourager there is one specially shining matter that must be mentioned. I don't know how long Sherwood Anderson's MSS may have been on the street before any publisher retrieved them and made honest books of them. But when Anderson's first publisher jibbed at a volume of short stories it was Huebsch who came to the rescue. He saw what required a genius of sympathy and shrewdness to see, Anderson's great stature as a troubled, fumbling, but completely sincere artist. This, if he had never done anything else, makes us all Huebsch's long-time debtors.

The matter of Sherwood Anderson may perhaps be enlarged upon briefly, for it is important and suggests some of the better parts of publishing. In the life of Vincent Van Gogh by Pierard we read of the strange tormented adventures of the Dutch painter before he came to at least some partial mastery of his own gift and was followed by the slow and heavy feet of critics. One of Van Gogh's masters at The Hague wanted him to draw from plaster casts, and gave him a head of Apollo to copy. Van Gogh, whose mind was full of the tragic faces of Flemish coal-miners, flushed with inarticulate fury, shivered the Apollo on the studio floor, and "rushed away, never to return." I seem to see, in many of Anderson's stories, something that I find also in the strange and thrilling pictures of Van Gogh. I see the classic plaster lying in bits on the floor; I see the fiercely courageous attempt to give life to the strong, unapprehended contours of human trouble. The lavish pigment drips from the canvas, as it did in the studio where Van

328

Gogh's master cried out in horror and sent him away to learn drawing. There are sometimes great sprawling clumsinesses of phrase, burdensome reiteration of a few elemental situations, a queer and hampering technique; but there is also magnificent fertility and heat and fine suspicionings into truth. And occasionally that savage lust of the actual that again reminds me of Van Gogh's great words—"One must create quickly, quickly, in haste, like the reaper who in the blaze of the sun is silent and thinks of nothing but his work." If you had not been hospitable enough to realize what curious felicities Anderson can achieve, consider the fine, pitiful conclusion of that deliciously-named story "The Sad Horn Blowers" (in *Horses and Men*); for his nipping humor "The Triumph of a Modern" in the same volume. This latter must have been a sore grievance to some contemporary faddists who culted Anderson rather hard.

It was these qualities in Anderson that Mr. Huebsch saw: the qualities of the man who, even in his most disastrous book (which a publisher of less artistic repute would have been pinched for) could write such lines as "It was only by lying to the limit he could come at truth;" the man who wrote so wryly humorous a bucolic as *The Triumph of the Egg*. So Huebsch became a Sad Horn Blower for Anderson, and for many other fine unestablished artists unlikely to become cornu-

329

copious for a publisher. I see in a New York paper
an advertisement to the effect that golf "shorts"
are to replace plus fours because they have been
"sanctioned by the Prince of Wales." This kind of
thinking is occasionally discernible in the publishing business too, where tendencies also run in
undulations of fashion. But I don't believe Ben
Huebsch ever waited for some favorable gust of
"sanction." His taste was so broad that I don't
think he would even have objected to a book
that might sell in large quantities, if he liked it.

36

WHAT was there in the damned old place that
made us love her so, beyond reason or sense? Was
it her incorrigible shabbiness? There's a queer
eddy of wind on Hudson Street, which so operated
that all the jetsam of the highway was drawn in
airy suction to twirl and nestle on our front pavement. A lively scour of breeze, from whatever
quarter, funneled into a vacuum beside our steps:
all the papers, loose trash, cabbage leaves, dis-
jected rubbish, deposited humorously in the path
of the arriving patron. I used to imagine this some
deliberate jocularity of neighbors until I studied
the meteorology of Hoboken. There is actually a
spiral of atmosphere that gathers every casual leaf

of paper on Hudson Street and spins it to that door. It availed not how often our burly and diligent McBride went out with his broom. The explorer from Manhattan, delicately choosing his way, doubtless smiled to read the legend "America's Most Famous Theatre" blazoned on so proletarian a façade.

What was it indeed that made us love her? Was it the queer diversity of her fortunes? She began life as a beer-garden; she has played burlesque and vaudeville and stock and movies; has known every vicissitude; and the certainties too, both death and taxes. There is a scrubwomen's cupboard upstairs, formerly used to store mops and pails and aprons; we turned it into our little business office; there was just room for Mistletoe, a typewriter, one of those skewers you spear bills on, and a telephone conversation with prospective customers. On the wall of that humble closet were some historic numerals scrawled in pencil. They date from the days when Marty Johnson was manager and playing burlicue, fourteen performances a week. The figures record the house's old High Water Mark for weekly Take. Marty remembers that it was the Stone and Pillard burlesque company that hung up that record. I shan't quote the digits, but we nearly doubled them once during the run of *After Dark*.

"My Old Lady, London," cries Eddie Newton

in his tender and charming tributes to the world's
greatest town. In somewhat the same spirit I give
you my mistress, that jocund and preposterous
old theatre. The Old Rialto, she's toasted!

There must have been some subtle and instinctive affinity between us, for from the time Throck
first showed her to me I had no other god but her.
I endured plentiful reproach on her behalf: the
warnings of friends, the groans of old kinsprits.
When are you going to get back to your writing,
they said—as if sitting in a room and writing were
life complete. Well, there's plenty to write about;
but in the joy and annoyance and perplexity of
the theatre there is something that moves deeper
than mere writing (which, as an exclusive occupa-
tion, is a lonely and morbid job). I see that wistful
mystery peeping out sometimes in the casual remarks of such champion old showmen as Mr.
Belasco—in whom the stage is not just an exhilarating gamble but (as the famous collar would seem
to imply) a form of naïve theology. In the miracle
of the theatre you see a form of art in actual impact upon its ultimate consumer. Faulty, clumsy,
imperfect as your intuitions may be, you see (and
feel) an intangible and radiant thing struggling for
communication. Occasionally you see that same
thing at the mercy of an audience insensitive to its
conventions. The old melodramas, for instance,
which afford the audience so many heart-easing

332

opportunities for collaboration, also tacitly assume that those who "assist" (admirable French word for the spectators) do not chime in at the wrong moment, simply because by doing so they lose the niceties which are necessary to their complete pleasure. So long as the things one loves are worth fighting for, so long it is worth the labor, day after day, to return to the hazardous and hopeful task. Raising a play is as patient and continuous a job as raising a child. And though there are times when one is too proud to speak for things one loves, there are also times perhaps when one must be too proud to be silent.

I sat down after a certain performance to let my mind move over some meanings and memories that the Old Rialto has for me. It was the kind of performance that means perhaps most of all: a matinee when the house was meagre, when the Public showed its large and inalienable capacity for Staying Away. (What a genius for Not Coming the public can sometimes have, every showman knows.) And by one of those happy chances it proved one of the finest performances I have seen anywhere. The company gave their best: one had the divine pleasure of seeing some of them actually achieve what one had known was latent but had not quite come through before in the way of feeling and (as directors love to say) "projection." The

audience, at first frightened by its own smallness
(people have always a delicious instinct of inferiority when they find themselves fewer than
they expect) then warmed into genuine and affectionate enthusiasm. Sincerity on the stage came
across the footlights and created real union. Old
and poor and unfashionable as the theatre was
that afternoon, by God I was proud of her; and
I said to myself that even the humblest of her
lovers might speak out for her. For such moments
men live, when they see their fellows giving all
they have, without assurance of gain or glory.
And I felt honorably sorry for those who were not
there, for they had missed something beautiful
and merry.

How many extraordinary memories of companionship in mirth or anxiety the show business
affords. I know something of the problems of the
author; even, if I must be candid, of the trouper;
but for the close pressure of reality I bespeak your
sympathy for the "Front of the House" and the
Manager, that seldom romanticized figure. I look
back upon some notably unsuccessful ventures,
and I perceive how enormously important it is in
this Divine Comedy to learn how to Take a Lick-
ing. Perhaps you have never stood in the box office
of a dying show, when there is plenty of time to
smoke and meditate between customers, and considered how charmingly pretty the tickets are,

piled up in the rack for Advance Sales. White, yellow, fawn, green, pink, red, lilac—such attractive colors and all equally unsalable. Yes, to have lived through some of those afternoons is a necessary part of one's education in Show Business. I can hear Mistletoe muttering to himself over the checkbook as he figured out how Saturday afternoon was to be met; hear the depressing thump as Kathryn rubber-stamped a thick wad of tickets to be given away to paper the house, marking them as "duckets." (Or should it be "ducats"? I rather suspect that that term for free tickets is as old as Shakespeare. Many a manager, at such times, has echoed old Shylock's cry of anguish—"Thou stick'st a dagger in me: four-score ducats at a sitting!" Perhaps that was even a little showman joke that Shakespeare put in to amuse himself.) What delightful flurries of hopefulness—the promptness with which one answers the tiny buzz of the telephone. (Box office phones do not ring, they purr softly in a confidential annunciator.) I hear Tom saying: "When an agency orders eleven tickets on you it ain't a bad sign." Nor shall I forget the time when a tall powerful person appeared at the window and I was all ready to assure him that I could give him two in the tenth, yes, and right on the aisle. He hesitated, seemed singularly anxious to speak as intimately and discreetly as possible, and finally, inserting a large

335

and mobile mouth right into the round aperture in the glass, remarked "I represent the Sheriff."

Fortunately, just across the street from the Lyric stage door there was an excellent lunch-wagon, where one could get a very filling meal for about twenty-five cents. There is no old trouper anywhere who does not look back with affection on many such interludes.

Perhaps our costly experience at the Lyric made us love the Old Rialto all the more. There is an air of unbelievableness about her that still persists even when we know her so well. She is so gorgeously unaesthetic! When the house was built they quite forgot to put in any dressing-rooms, which had to be supplied afterward in a lean-to addition leased from the adjoining property. They are approached through a tunnel under the theatre, a stony old passage-way as romantically satisfying as any crypt in Westminster Abbey. To our great pleasure this dressing-room wing had a legal easement upon it permitting the maintenance of clothes-masts, from which the linen of Hudson Street flutters bravely over the rear alley. That alley served as Green Room on summer evenings. Nothing could be pleasanter than to see the company taking their ease out there on benches in the warm night; and Old Tom, the crapulous sandwich man in *After Dark*, whose rags nothing could

336

further tarnish, stretched on the cobbles. Good beer is not far to seek. May I make a managerial confession? I was substituting in the rôle of Old Tom while Arthur Morris was on vacation. During that week there was a member of the company who missed a critical cue at matinee by dallying overlong with the clam broth cup in our favorite clam brothel. I was much outraged by this breach of professional rigor, and prepared a Notice for him which I was going to hand him that evening. That very night, so is human frailty chastised, I committed the same error myself, in the same tavern. I destroyed that Notice undelivered.

There were a few minutes in the second act of *After Dark* while Old Tom waited offstage in his boat, before Eliza jumped off the dock. It was then that they sang "The Little Old Log Cabin in the Lane," and the substitute Old Tom used to lie there, gazing up at a border of blue lights overhead and speculating on the complete improbability of the whole affair.

I suppose it is the intimate sense of companionship in effort which is part of the theatre's magic. You surrender much of the complete egotistic control which a writer has over his own job; in return you receive the curious joys and pangs inseparable from a parliamentary affair proceeding by chancy human compromise. And the collaborated efforts of the theatre, however arduous, are by necessity

337

undertaken in a social spirit more intensely grotesque and emotional than any other work can suggest. It is a commonplace of experience that sometimes in rehearsals you attain effects you never touch again. In that elastic, casual, farcical and nerve-strained period, marked by endless hours, irregular meals, weariness, despair, cauldrons of midnight coffee and screams of laughter, certain vibrations of human comedy are most strongly plucked. Particularly, I admit, in our Hoboken rehearsals, many of which were held in haphazard places. Most of the rehearsing of *The Blue and The Gray* was done in the parlor of the Continental Hotel; it used to be special fun to see Joe Samperi, the hospitable little proprietor, gravely watching in a corner; the fortune of the play meant as much to him as to us. I often wondered what his guests may have thought, when they came into the lobby to register and heard the outcry of Northerners and Confederates practising their romantic bitterness in the parlor. And the mythical Philadelphian of the old postman story, if he dropped into Bill's grill-room across the back alley one of those evenings, was surely disturbed to see officers in correct C.S.A. uniform lined up at the bar for hot clam broth and liverwurst.

Any theatre, anywhere, is always an appeal to the imagination; but very specially, in this death-

day of the oldtimers, a house that has had so long
and checkered a career. A place like that arouses
loyalties that sound almost too sentimental for
print. I do not forget how little Eleanor, then our
box-office cashier, used to call me up at home in
the evenings when *After Dark* was beginning to
go over the top. One night she said "It's over six
hundred, isn't it wonderful!" There was a pause,
and I heard a queer gargling sound. "Excuse me,"
she continued, "but I couldn't help it. I'm crying." Nor do I forget how Mildred stood by in
the box office in the bitterly cold weeks when
After Dark had closed and the house was lifeless
until we got *The Blue and The Gray* ready. The
furnace was not on, and in spite of electric heaters
arranged in a formidable battery we could not keep
Mildred's extremities warm. But she sat on a stool,
on a pile of telephone books, and pattered away
on a typewriter; and anyone who telephoned was
sure to get an earful about what a grand show the
new one would be. There was the memorable time
when we closed two shows the same evening.
Something like $7000 in cash had to be paid out
that day to meet all salaries. It's a lot of money,
and it took some brisk shuttling of funds between
one box office and the other to meet all requirements at the imperative moment. I was tied to
my post, for I was trouping that night, but Tom
came back during the show, drew me behind a

339

drop, and said with the true Irish in his eye "Well, we may be closing, but anyhow it's with flying colors." After it was all over he repaired to the clam brothel I have already mentioned, had half a dozen of what he needed most, and fell into a peaceful nescience; for which I honor him. Scribbled on the wall of a telephone booth in Cleon Throckmorton's studio is a note jotted there by a fevered manager in the bedevilment of business collapse. It says *Singing Ushers $150*, referring to a debit item of that fatal evening. Those were the Singing Ushers who pursued Tom up Hudson Street with madrigals of controversy. In its mixture of absurdity and grievance that pencil scrawl serves as epitaph of the Hoboken Theatrical Company.

Let none take these intimacies amiss; they are of the blood and heartbeat of Show Business; as much a part of its immortal pulse as the proudest gala performance.

So can you wonder that we loved her? That she took on in our minds a meaning somewhat beyond what you may actually see in her rather dingy fabric? Over the window of that miniature box office we put up a tablet in honor of Dion Boucicault, to the effect that his play had "brought an old theatre back to life and restored a fine tradition of the stage." I hear a good deal said and argued about the Death of the Theatre. There isn't much wrong with the theatre when a forgotten old playhouse could arouse such devotion as she had from her servants, and give such Elizabethan hilarities to her audience. She catered Pure Fun—rarest and divinest commodity of all. It can easily be marred by the ignorant, who will never know that Fun also has its sensibilities. But for those who were capable of Fun she offered an experience.

Let no man be fool enough to try to explain too fully what or why he loves. My mistress gave me what I never knew I would have; what indeed no man ever foresaw having—several gray hairs.

37

I SAID to myself, I will make a certain date an epoch, after which I will try to be more continuously alert to the things I feel to be so.

Also I will get my hair cut oftener, and really try to improve my finger-nails. I will consider getting my hat cleaned, and answering letters. Perhaps I will even learn the names of birds and flowers, and not let the tenderest tissues of my silence be torn open by telephone bells.

But there are no epochs in Time; it flows and flows and is not divisible by deliberation. Even when we write A.D. 1930 that is purely for convenience. It means nothing.

And now my new epoch is here. I am happy about it, but still the blessed moment wriggles from under my finger. It flows and flows; whether it passes through me or I through it, is hardly worth arguing if only Time and I keep even pace together. I am done with working against Time.

Time sifts into everything, like dust; even the cups and saucers on the table change their look when Time is in the mind.

To float easily in Time, to move concurrently with it, without anxiety, lie on your back. Nothing except the tip of your consciousness should be above the stream. Lying so, I bathe myself in Time. People are often alarmed to see anyone in that horizontal posture. He is suspected of thinking.

If I give you my Time, I give you all I have.

Give us this day our daily Time; forgive us our wastages.

Time, like nakedness, is holy: it is the bare body of life. Prudent people have made fetishes of it. Clocks are the figleaves of Time. How few dare face Time unveiled.

I was ashamed because I had heard myself say I was tired; and lying down to think it over, to equal myself with the living hour, I heard the warm zigzag hum of a bluebottle fly who had cruised in at the open window. He even drowned out the birds whistling in their high green gallery outdoors, applauding the simple melodrama of a hot May afternoon. He whined like a dynamo: he seemed a symbol of Time itself, and changed his gears as it does. I did not see him, I only heard him go. Now he sang in even career, droning on straight levels of elapse; then there was a sudden confused mumble of rotation (I suppose he blundered into the pane)—an indignant twirling flurry, a somersaulting spin. Exactly so, with variation strange, Time reckons in the bluebottle human wit. All know the steady buzz along main highways of duration. But I almost think we have the best of it in those whirling seizures when (as Sir Philip said) the helmet makes a hive for bees. When we cannot wait, no, not an instant, to crowd thought on thought, mirth on mirth, yet never have to apologize to the preceding moment for treading on its heel. For we never quite catch up: even though, as the devout physician said, Time is only five days older than ourselves. But ah what glamoured drunkenness is that full being: even the sad citizen of Dreadful Night knew it—

> Sits long and ariseth drunken
> But not with the feast and the wine;
> He reeleth with his own heart,
> That great rich Vine.

343

Lying so (supine, the grammarian would call it) and with one foot crossed over the other (like a marble Crusader) I float in Time, a passive participle; a mere adjective, yet still retaining some properties of a verb. I feel that exquisite completeness of the body touching support all along its full stretch. Women, I think, do not feel it so entirely: more callipygian than ourselves, more gibbous in the sedentaries, they arch slightly above the horizontal at waist and hams. (Will someone please lie down on the floor so I can verify this?) Thereby did Mrs. Lydia Pinkham make fortune, trading on fatigues in that tender valley of Eve's back. Perhaps they also suspend a little more than we above the flat norm of Time. But I fear the old one with the scythe is no discriminator of sexes.

I was getting dangerously near writing for my own amusement; which was not the intention. (Did you ever stop to think what fun De Quincey must have had?) There are ways of taking a very small idea and toying with it and writing round about it; not bad fun, and sometimes profitable to a journalist; but as a journalist I am dead. (I am sorry to be dead in any respect, but it is good practice.) Here we deal with other stuff, most precious, most volatile; though alleviating it where possible. For it would be a pity not to be aware of the richest source of ridicule in the world —myself.

Stretched out so, the feel of the legs is important. At first perhaps there is a little drowsiness gently distributed: you may pass into a small but not regretted stupor. Then Psyche, not less efficient than Mrs. Pinkham, reasserts herself. There is the purest sensational pleasure in tightening the cords and muscles of the legs, to know their strongness. You are utterly at ease. You have joined the drift of Time: it flows in soft metronome with every artery. All channels of life are filled with it, and you feel strength coming in, the endless energy that Buddha was so dubious about. But not just mere energy for doing: an energy also of receptiveness, of understanding. It is this brightness of wisdom that every common day seems so well planned to tarnish. You know strange things, and are not ashamed.

I get up and sit at my table. It is like turning the hour-glass end for end. A different balance, a different rhythm; a different quality of thought.

Things that are beautiful and unquestionable in that pose of death or dream, sound a little solemnified when we sit upright. I have not forgotten them, but am shy. It is a pity that one has to write for publication.

Remember, then, not to be more afraid of being absurd than William Blake was.

It is a great thing, even if not mad oneself, to be a sympathizer with madness in others. We do

not know nearly as much as we need to about
Charles Lamb.

I have an enormous pleasure in smoothing with
my hand the brown wood of this table; this plain
honest table which I bought ten years ago from
the Russian relic-merchant in the village and have
worked on ever since.

It is good satisfaction to wipe the dust and
tobacco-crumbs from this grainy wood, to regard
old stains of ink, old burns and scratches, to feel the
honor of service rubbed and darkened in the board.

I have been happy at this table, where my hand
has traveled far. Many ominous words have passed
across it. Frogs and crickets have kept me company, and one by one have put away their music—
all save that one sole cricket that none can out-
watch. He keeps liaison with the birds of dawn.

Your hand too would love this smooth brown
wood.

Donny looks out at me from under the rose-bush
Where he lies heavily, flattening the pansies—
He made himself comfortable for a hot morning,
Sprawled as luxurious as Omar Khayyam.
But he looks a little anxious: he is wondering
Will I turn the hose on him, as sometimes happens?
Donny is aged, obese and indolent,
And much disrelishes a cold hose-shower.
With relief he sees me go indoors.

346

Yet how many times, I reflect rather sadly,
We are in such a hurry to spray cold water
On some harmless and thoughtful philosopher
Who has slipped away from the glare of sunshine.

One of the things I shall miss most when I am dead
Will be walking with naked feet on bare floors
In summer nights, when the hardwood boards
Are deliciously tepid to the palms of the feet.
For if you love life you should love it all over
And even feet have their privileges.

38

I SUPPOSE it is valuable, for intellectual reasons, that a man's life should be as much of a paradox as possible. It has always amused me to observe that though all my best instincts are for lethargy, quietism, postponement and concentration, I usually find myself in a hurry. What an accurate word is *distracted*, for if I pause to examine my mind I can usually find it subject to various diverse tensions. Perhaps that is well: like the outer ligatures of a spider's web these help to keep the central gossamers of the spirit from collapsing into a silky tangle. And though theoretically I abhor the business of being in a hurry, yet I must be honest enough to confess that often it is in that condition I find myself happiest. And how, otherwise, would the occasional interludes of exquisite indolence be so perfect? Evidently there is some deep necessity for life to be as full of opposites as possible.

During an autumn of exceptional hurry his mind often turned back to an afternoon of amazing peace. It was in early September, on a beach on Long Island Sound. First let me explain that there is some notable virtue in owning a small frontage on actual tide-water, because to feel some proprietory right in the perpetual movement of the tides seems to put one in relation with huge things. The whole turn and tension of the cosmos is apparent there on your own shore; and that of itself is enough to keep you aware of enormity. On this drowsy afternoon, while the family sprawled on the sand or capered among boulders, he was thigh-deep in warm golden water, pulling up masses of seaweed. Air and water were so exactly the same temperature that it was almost impossible to say how much of him was in and how much out. In the clarity of those green and tawny shallows thick clumps of weed wavered softly, and when, after strong pulling, they came up from their rocky fixture, they crackled and seethed in the hands. The water, running out through all that tangle of rubbery cells and fibres, makes a most curious spongy hissing. Those masses of seaweed were full of innumerable small five-pointed stars. September, it appears, is kindergarten time among the echinoderms, and every tress of seaweed carries in it dozens of baby starfish, perhaps a quarter of an inch across. He could not help believing that there was some considerable meaning in this—they were like tiny pentameter epigrams. But on such wise afternoons one does not explore too fiercely for meanings. One observes and is content.

The chief danger in being so busy, and consequently so absorbed in one's own notions, is that one forgets that others are equally under pressure, equally absorbed. And in making liberal allowance for one's own preoccupation he forgets to make adequate obeisance to other people's. At this very moment, trying to get on with these paragraphs, I was interrupted by the telephone, and was indignant to find it a call for Stella, a cheerful Polish maid; and then I remembered that Stella also means a star and has her own necessities to twinkle. So I suppose that in the thickest tangles of daily seaweed these youthful starfish are lurking. Abbé Dimnet, in his charming book, *The Art of Thinking*, retells the familiar old story of the Spanish sailors becalmed off the mouth of the Amazon and dying of thirst. "They could not believe the natives signalling that the water all round their ship was good to drink and they had only to throw down their buckets."

349

I was amused the other day, re-reading Leonard Merrick's *Conrad in Quest of His Youth* which I had not read for some fourteen years, to find that his hero who thought himself so elderly and went wistfully to try to revive early romances, was actually 37. The comedy was that when I first read that book I supposed it quite natural that a man of 37 should consider himself pretty elderly; whereas I know now that 37 is only the beginning of the real fun. No one reckons age by years anyhow, but by receptiveness to new ideas. Even if one always marks the end of a calendar by making apologies for one's errors, it is not in any ignorance of the unlikelihood that those errors can be mended. Abbé Dimnet very wisely counsels us to try to cultivate and intensify those of our moods which we know to be most essentially *us:*

There is in us a stratum more sensitive than the rest, which we know and where we can go at will. A behaviorist would say that the inevitability of the response from that stratum in our consciousness proves that it is biological, but all I want to say is that we know from experience that the response is sure. If we live a great deal with ourselves we increase our personality, and if we revive certain facts or periods, or phases of feeling in our lives, we heighten our receptivity.

Our life with its peaks—which we know—of sentiment, effort, nobility, or increased intelligence, is a veritable mine of evocative moods. A few minutes' leisure is enough to replace ourselves in such moods, and no sooner are we conscious of them than the phosphorescence of intuitiveness begins. Poets know it well. Their own experience, sometimes woefully restricted in appearance, is the constant support of their inspiration. They, as well as artists, are remarkably like children, and have never broken the thread binding the various periods of their lives together, as men living in the world, and for the world, will do.

But alas, as every student of *moeurs* is aware, it is usually just after visiting those upper slopes of the spirit, and resolving to build a bungalow there, that our worst landslides of conduct go roaring down into a crevasse.

So wise and winning and unpretentious a little book as Abbé Dimnet's does not clench its brows in contortion like the Penseur of the august Rodin (that old faker). One reason, incidentally, why I now suspect that Rodin wasn't really so very much of an artist is because when I was twenty-two I thought him so tremendous. I suspect that if at 37 you still feel about things as you did at 22, something is wrong.

So he ended the year's notebook as usual, with the Apologies of the Season—apology for occasional eruption from duty, for slips of temper and imperfect cadences in prose. But remember that a pen is not a jade in harness. It is a feather, lifted on the wind.

351

THE FUEL AND THE FIRE

39

THE ship sailed at midnight. There are queer intimations of mortality in those midnight sailings; allegory sometimes slips in as a stowaway. They could only happen just so in New York, the divinely insane town that Shakespeare would have relished. Bunyan, hardly so much. The semi-hysterical leave-taking parties in state-rooms, the hallooing crowd on the pier, the scuffle round the gangway when the last visitors are being firmly pushed off by patient British quarter-masters. All ashore that's going ashore. The proud and rending cry of the whistle as she begins to slip sternward into open river. A sudden silence falls along her laundered decks as she turns in the dark stream and heads toward longitudes. How tall and black are those downtown buildings.

All ashore that's going ashore; this is no picturesque narrative of oceanic humors; we're going to talk about literature. And the well-wishing adventurer setting forth, somewhat lonely and tired and incredulous, now observed that the friends who came to see him off had finished the Scotch. Methodical as usual, he did a little sedative unpacking. He put out on the reading shelf his fat one-volume Complete Shakespeare. But he went to bed with a chance E. Phillips Oppenheim. Never once in the whole six weeks did he open that other. It was queer, for surely the Plays offer us the most mysterious of all detective stories, and the avowed purpose of the expedition (he told me gravely) was "to think about Shakespeare." He did, a great deal, and I shall transmit, as far as I think prudent, what he has confided. He went, in love and humility and foreboding, to recapture what he could of Shakespeare and England and gin-and-ginger-beer. I am content to let him do it in his own way.

Oh Shakespeare, whoever you were (does it much matter?) how the mind of the artist runs out to greet you. Dull, vulgar, cruel, you often were; and then burst upon us with such glorious stuff: life become pure rhetoric, life made worthwhile for us animals of posture. How they have tried to bury you in owl-droppings and cinders; made you a discipline for the young and green in judgment. "How the man must have suffered," cried the solemn Nietzsche, "to be so much in need of playing the clown." Perhaps you played the clown because you enjoyed it. In joy and horror and thanksgiving the mind flies to meet you. You have become more than just yourself.

You have become symbol of the creative passion and instinct. To think about you, to camp and picnic on the fringes of your Forest of Arden, is not to look cowardly backward but to dream forward for achievement to come. You are our lost Atlantis and also our tomorrow morning.

He had long suspected, he told me, that Shakespeare was important; but he wanted to begin again at the bottom (the only place to look for Atlantis) and find out whether Shakespeare was important for John Mistletoe. Whether he might be important for anyone else was secondary. The study of Shakespeare requires thinking about the whole problem of artist-temperament, which is always disconcerting to good people who are Fond of Literature. Further, Shakespeare comes to us involved in all the human association of those who have read and ranted and muddled over him so long. How can we dig him out of that? or do we want to? His total impact on our present minds is greater than the sum of everything he wrote. It is an accumulation of innumerable awarenesses. Lively writers scoff at the haggling devotion of scholiasts who have argle-bargled over minutiæ. But why not let them be happy with what they understand. May not each man dig in the garden as him pleases best? What will he find anyhow but himself? The mere survival of the text, from a litter of hen-tracks, is miracle enough. That was no mean triumph for much-abused humanity. It had its Shakespeare and recognized him. He wasn't even censored. There was a star danced and under that was he born.

And what happiness can compare with that of the man who has some maggot in his head about Shakespeare. The ciphers, the theories, all the notionable conjectures, what fun they are. Read Frank Harris's two books on him if you want to see a man having a good time. They are worth reading, too; they deal with Shakespeare as though he were human, with blood current in him, acting on motives a masculine creature can understand. But they are not likely to be approved by professional scholars.

So Mistletoe tried for a few weeks, on highway and heather, on bowling greens and on London streets, in public houses or under English sky, in the smell of air and the voices of people, to distinguish what might still be identifiable of the essence that created Shakespeare. He did not look in the British Museum, nor even in the Birthplace itself. (There is a pub just opposite the birthplace which would be better covert to trail so runnable a stag.) Even on shipboard—"huge bottoms through the furrow'd sea"—there are many glimpses that bring the mind subconsciously back to its theme. In the precise slant of those tall funnels, in the greasy spinning silver of a propeller shaft, in an engine-room worker wearing a monkish conical hood of sacking beneath the oily throw of huge cranks, were the finalities of art. A ship is the high cathedral of artifice, an anthology of paradox; every line of her is both theology and epigram. How much did Shakespeare really know about ships? He did very well with the smattering he had: books have even been written on his use of sea lingo—as they have on his knowledge of flowers and birds and fishing and deer-stalking. (The only thing that ever seriously troubled the English about him was the legend that he had been a poacher. They are a nation that believes in game being killed according to strict etiquette.) He was careful at least to distinguish (e. g. *Comedy of Errors* I, 1, 76–77) between *ship* and *boat*, which few landsmen do; though the famous passage about the drowsy ship-boy asleep on the high and giddy mast always seemed to me unseamanlike. There's not much sleeping done in the crow's nest.[1] But at any rate I'm sure Shakespeare would have loved deck tennis.

[1]In comment on this, Mr. Robert Boissevain writes:

"Shakespeare is right again. I cruised for several years in the nineties on Dutch men-of-war—full-rigged ships. We used to have a lookout in the fore-top, which on men-of-war is a platform with railing; coils of rope invite sleep and rest and many an hour of my watch below have I passed in the fore-top—the horizon wider than on deck; no sound but the sighing

There were days of sunshine, when the Gulf
Stream water pumped clean into the canvas swimming tank was as warm as 80°; and even that mid-
Atlantic water seemed emblematic: it was as
much saltier than coastal water as Will himself is
more vital than Ben. There were also days of fog,
and then the Lizard and Eddystone and Plymouth. And as though the age of Elizabeth were
coming out to meet him, in that green harbor was
the tender *Sir Francis Drake*. At the North River
piers it is usually the helpful Barrett family
that nuzzles one in—the tugs *Grace A. Barrett,
Geo. N. Barrett, Edw. E. Barrett*. But at Plymouth it is *Sir Francis Drake* or *Sir Richard
Grenville*—symbols of England's sense of romantic
continuity.

and groaning of the rigging—most lovely sound never again
to be recaptured.

"The lookout in the fore-top during the night watches would
have to call out "All's well' after each bell. However, we found
that this countersign would be sung out once in a while between
bells—sure sign of a fitful slumber. We then decided on giving
a new countersign at the beginning of each watch. On my
watch I had to name the countersign and I preferably chose a
girl's name—a name sweet and dear to me, and in those days
I had no lack of choice either. It was a great thrill to hear the
beloved name bellowed forth over the wide waters in the stillness of the night or accompanied by the sound of the wind in
the rigging and the swish of the waves.

"And it kept the shipboy on the high and giddy mast from
drowsing."

There also he noted the increasing divergence of
our two languages. An American girl and an Englishman had most happily understood one another
all the way across. But now, as the Briton saw
his good earth again, he suddenly began to talk
English. "How curious," he remarked to her,
"this lovely view and those ga*sóm*eters." (Put a
very strong accent on that second syllable.) The
Philadelphia damsel stared with wild surmise
round the Devonshire littoral, thinking perhaps
that the ga*som*eters were some rare foliage, some
rich sepulchral ruin. Puzzled she begged his par-
don; he repeated the mystic phrase. Mistletoe,
standing near, saw the perplexity in her entreating
eyes. "Gas tanks," he whispered. It was her first
introduction to the strangeness of her own tongue.

It is queer that people try to "teach" literature
without attempting to give any suggestion of the
color and shape of the country it comes from. And
passengers get off the ship at Plymouth and hurry
up to London by special train to be in time for the
theatre on Saturday night. Yet they might stay
aboard thirty-six hours longer, smell French wood-
smoke in the dark at Havre and see the gray-white
scarps of Dover next afternoon. Almost opalescent
they lift out of mixed sun and vapor. Seeing that
chalky bourn, that forehead of Albion, you remember it is the dread summit of Lear. Not for
nothing is that symbol of her hard island story

known as the Shakespeare Cliff. Round the North
Foreland in pale blue evening and up the Thames
Estuary. And as the train takes you from Tilbury
next morning, in just the midsummer drizzle one
would hope for, it loiters among dockyards and
sidings where small English daisies, a little sooty,
grow beside the rails. The best textbook of literature, we remarked before, is an atlas. Next best,
perhaps, to get a feeling of the lie of English land,
is C. E. Montague's book *The Right Place*—our
well loved Montague who fed on Shakespeare as
few men have done. And like all zealots of living,
he feasted on maps. Where will you find places
where more may be learned than at the Map Shop
in St. James's Street, or our own Hammond's on
Church Street in New York.

In his amateurish investigations Mistletoe admits his indebtedness to a rakish low-backed car
christened Lagonda. The name was new to him,
and her sprightly demeanor (she was bound in
leather, like a book) suggested the nickname
Gioconda; which her young owner, whom we will
speak of as Kinsman, at first thought a trifle
familiar. She is described as the "Two-Litre Speed
Model," and lives up to it. She is the kind of
vehicle that is unhappy unless moving close to
fifty miles an hour. At anything less than forty
she actually groans with suppressed desire. The
highest Mistletoe saw her speedometer record was

seventy-two, but he believes she went faster than that while he was in the back seat holding on and not sheltered by the windshield. The roots of his hair ached for several days. The inscription on Shakespeare's monument at Stratford might well have occurred to him: "Stay passenger, why goest thou by so fast?"

Lagonda is the best commentator on Shakespeare, Mistletoe told me. She would not do anything so crude as rush off to Stratford straightaway. No: she began with casual marginalia—the meadows of Runnymede, seen in blended shine and shower; the old pink almshouses at Bray, founded by a Tudor fishmonger. Yes, Bray of the Vicar and of the Hind's Head inn where they have treacle tart on the menu and a parrot reputed to grow profane on hard liquor. So young Kinsman offered the bird neat brandy, but oaths were slow in coming. They even dribbled it on his poll, hoping the fumes might penetrate. It did not seem to prick him in his corage, but the fowl may have cursed heartily later in the afternoon. Then Burnham Beeches, the most Midsummer Night's Dreamish place imaginable: a forest of huge gray boles, wrinkled and crippled and velvetted with moss. Shakespeare pretended it was "a wood near Athens" where Titania and Oberon held court, but Burnham Beeches was the kind of thing he

363

was thinking of. Not so old as those beeches, but now nearing its 300th birthday, is the walnut tree under which Edmund Waller was buried at Beaconsfield—the Waller of the adorable verses "On a Girdle." How graceful is his epitaph:

EDMUNDI WALLER
hic jacet id quantum morti cessit
Qui inter poetas sui temporis facile princeps
Huic debet patria lingua, quod credas,
Si Graece Latineque intermitterent Musae
Loqui amarent Anglice.

But as Milton was Waller's contemporary, the *facile princeps* is a transgression. The thoroughfare to Oxford (and thence to Stratford) runs past Beaconsfield Church: when Shakespeare went by, as he must have done many times, he passed close to the green hollow where William Penn was to be buried, and only a few miles from the cottage where his greatest successor later worked on *Paradise Lost*. Mistletoe was much pleased with the imperial clematis growing over the door of that cottage at Chalfont St. Giles, by the first edition of *Paradise Lost* generously deposited there by Senator David Reed of Pennsylvania, and by the extraordinary likeness of the curator to Thomas Hardy. But equally he emphasized to me the neighboring house of call known as Merlin's Cave and a fine old ratting print he saw there.

Lagonda stood patiently outside that pub in a long summer sunset.

These matters are not irrelevant to his vision of Shakespeare. He reminds me of the lively choruses in Henry V. "Let us, ciphers to this great accompt, On your imaginary forces work."

40

AND little Essex Street, which runs off the Strand just below St. Clement Dane's, is also a logical footpath toward the Elizabethan age. I am no antiquarian, but I suppose in my vague way that little or nothing remains of Essex Street as the Queen's young sandy-haired Robin Devereux knew it. Even the old water-gate at the foot of the way, round which buzzed poor Essex's foolish and fatal treason, has probably been rebuilt since the Fire of 1666. But perhaps not; perhaps down those very stairs, Mistletoe liked to imagine, passed the Earl's messenger crossing over to Southwark to ask the players at the Globe to revive *Richard II* for one performance only, for political reasons. They did so; it was the one time Shakespeare might well have got into serious trouble. The bells of St. Clement's—the most famous in the world, for it was they that young Falstaff and Shallow heard at midnight—are also of later tuning. And Essex Street's antique air has been broken by some rather insistently modern architecture. The great house of the Essexes is gone, of course, and I remember no token of the Essex Head tavern where Dr. Johnson's last club used to gather. ("Every member present shall spend at least sixpence; one penny shall be left by each member for the waiter.") Towards lunch time it is Essex Street's fancy to pass through the little side alley into Devereux Court. The Devereux Arms is still there, with the bust of the first Earl over the door. It was once known as the Grecian; the learned items in the *Tatler* were dated thence, and I hope it was from that same little pewter bar that Dick Steele wrote some of those ingratiating notes to Prue explaining why he could not get home for dinner.

There is magic yet on Essex Street. Mistletoe was startled as he went down the slope. From the alley that runs off on the right sped a moving flash of gray, darting in silent flicker close past his face. For one surprised instant he thought it was an arrow, or even a ghost from the sixteenth century. Then the shadowy missile teetered pecking on the roadway and showed itself pigeon. One of Essex Street's burly cats, lounging against the wall, shrugged its elbows.

At the very bottom of the street you can sometimes see Lagonda herself, waiting. Where is she going this long sunset? Perhaps to B. Pollock's in Hoxton, "Juvenile Theatrical Print Publisher," where good old Mr. Pollock is still there in the famous home of Penny Plain and Twopence Coloured and remembers his visit from Robert Louis Stevenson. Perhaps Lagonda is bound for the highwaymen's pub at Putney—passing on the way that laundry with the name that gives the American visitor a twinge: Loud and Western, Inc. That is the inn where the footpads had their drink while waiting for wealthy travelers crossing Putney Heath; it is also where the elderly Swinburne was allowed his one daily beer when he lived under tutelage at Number 2, The Pines. Or perhaps it is Streatham this evening, with a notion to see the grave of Mr. Thrale the brewer. But by stopping at Streatham's excellent White Lion for a "gin-and-French" (London's sadly tepid substitute for a Martini) she was too late and the churchyard was locked. But Mr. Thrale would forgive her. Or it might be old Temple Bar, sequestered these fifty years in the woods of Theobalds in Hertfordshire. The most thrilling way to find that massive relic is to come upon it at night in the dark avenue of trees. Lagonda turns to face it, switches on her searchlight, and like a spectre London of the 18th century is evoked before you. A dead world comes pouring through those pale arches.

367

Still once more, it might be Clerkenwell, to see Sekforde Street, named for Sir Thomas Sekforde, a Tudor stalwart to whose memory Mistletoe owes piety. At the corner of Woodbridge and Sekforde Streets is the Sekforde Arms, a modest pub, which belies its name by not showing the escutcheon. Sir Thomas was an energetic spirit. He engaged (we are told) in smuggling, piracy and miscellaneous frauds, condoned because he advanced much money to the great Queen. He was high in her justiciary, this Suffolk squire, but uncourtly in habit; when Elizabeth complained that his boots smelled of the byre he retorted "Madam, it is the smell of the parchment of unpaid bills." She understood perfectly and did not take it amiss. The almshouses and grammar school Sekforde endowed in Woodbridge, just before the Armada, were typical Tudor foundations; at just such another country school Shakespeare got his hornbook in Stratford. One of the shrewd old fellow's ordinances for his almshouse showed his lively cunning in human nature. The inmates were to be fined twopence for swearing—but only after three months' residence. Old people naturally take their transfer to a house of charity with some crotchets and quavers; so he allowed them ninety days of cursing to get used to it.

A little further down Sekforde Street is the "Crippleage," a home for crippled girls. The name sounds a little cruel somehow, but the girls themselves seem in happy spirits. A group of them came laughing out of the building, one stumping gaily on a wooden leg. They smiled cheerily at Lagonda. One very small damsel of the neighborhood, whose cockney was too strong to be readily understood, explained the surprising silvery fabric of her garment. It was cut down from her sister's wedding dress. Across the street was the Watercress and Flower-Girls' Christian Mission. It needs long training in Englishry to appreciate the importance of watercress. When Lord Bacon's old house at St. Albans was put on sale lately, one of the advantages urged by the "estate agent" was "Magnificent beds of watercress." The English used to munch watercress for breakfast before they learned about grapefruit. Certainly Bacon's essays are flavored with its clean sharpness. They are the mustard-and-cress sandwiches of prose.

Mistletoe harped a good deal on Sir Thomas Sekforde. I try to abbreviate him on this topic, but he insisted that it was all germane to his purview of Shakespeare. Woodbridge in Suffolk, where Sekforde had his country home and where he is buried, might just as well have been another Stratford, he said, "but thank God it isn't. It hasn't been spoiled. That's the kind of place Stratford was before the rotary clubs got at it. And think of the difference in the bathing." He made me look over a reprint of the Woodbridge church-wardens' accounts which gives an inkling of some social problems of the Tudors and Stuarts. I found he had marked these items:

	s.	d.
1595—Paid for a Common Prayer Book.....	6	0
Goodinge the smith for scouring the town corselets..................	2	8
1596—Making a place upon the Pillarie for the witches to stand on.............		3
1 gal. of wine when the Attorney came to Town......................	2	0
1600—Paid for an hour glass for pulpit......	1	2
For wine and sugar when Mr. Grunndie preached	3	4
Paid to Grosse woman that came, to depart the town..................	5	0
1606—Mending of the stocks...............		2
To a Thatcher for a day's work.......	1	10
A poor man that had great losses by sea		6
1607—For the keeping of the Potsworker's daughter's bastard..............	2	4
1612—Paid to the constables for digging up of Leicester's wife..................	10	0
Sheet for Widow Clarke, and laying her forth.........................	9	6
For bringing of the poor body to church		6
To two Grecians brought to my house.	1	0
1625—16 Leathern Fire Buckets..........£2	0	6
1626—To Ffosdicke for taking him out of his grave..................		6

1627—My diet when I went to London
   for 18 days................ £1 16 0
  Given to the Irish soldiers to send
   them out of the Town...... £2 0 0
1633—Meeting at the *Crowne* about the
   almshouses, for beer and sugar 3 8

The Crown inn is still there, and it is a pleasure
to Mistletoe to remember that his grandfather
used to play bowls on its quiet bowling green, as
also on the rival turf of the Sun.

But we come back to Essex Street. There was
one specially vivid morning, a blue but uncertain
weather with great rafts of cloud steering above
from W. to E. The papers were full of the news
that a princess had been born in the night, and at
Glamis too—another reminder of Shakespeare.
How else would one ever have learned the right
Scottish pronunciation of that castle, which apparently is a monosyllable—GLAMS, GLAAMS, or
GLAUMS. Highbrow London editors were inclined to be a bit superior about the homely Scots
phrase of the attending physicians' dispatch, that
the royal baby was "doing fine." But surely it was
too humane a morning to haggle over niceties of
diction. In one of those rare advantages of idling
he was carried along in the great flow of London's
living. On Essex Street the little tricycle of Henry
J. Glaisher, bookseller, with its box-front for trans-

port of goods, was waiting outside Methuen's while the messenger was inside collecting his orders. It was a day for aspiration: one hoped that Henry J. Glaisher, of Wigmore Street, was buying good books—perhaps some of those steady sellers of Mr. Lucas—and disposing of them rapidly. Wigmore Street . . . yes; that was where the Young Man with the Cream Tarts settled down and became ("says our Arabian author") a comfortable householder. So do the phantoms of fiction nudge one. In the noonday sunshine two musicians with a piano on wheels and a fiddle had taken their pitch at the top of Essex Street, which still glistened underfoot from a sudden sprinkle. The pianist, an elderly fellow with alert hands, was busy upon some current madrigal. The gay and yet subtly grievous tune tinkled and yammered down the bright little roadway. AN OLD PRO, said a card on the piano. Across the street stood a man in a raincoat, with waxed and pointed mustaches, smoking a pipe and pensively watching a pigeon on the pavement. Apparently he was paying no heed to the music, but you could see it working in him, sensibility germinating towards act. Sure enough, soon he came over and dropped some coppers in the box. We shall all be Old Pros presently. Just above this eddy of tune and pause the great mellay of the Strand was pouring by. In those moments of intuition London's very stones

372

and mortar seem sentient, stained with the pathos of life; her smile-and-weeping weather a necessity of her truth.

41

I DON'T want to be misconceived. The Empire State Building means as much to me as any number of old London pubs and churches. That high consummation of unbelief, modestly underdescribed by its artificers as "An office building of character," makes a day in New York seem all morning. It holds the sunlight later than it ever stayed before. You come out of the Penn Station and pass along 32nd Street, and then, even if your thoughts were on the ground, you are aware of a new presence. Your eyes are lifted up by that amazing crag. Pale and sharp-cut, Euclidean paradise of solids, veined with parallels of silver, it stands against clear heaven; a mountain made by hands. It seems impossible. The chalky summit of Lear is a molehill to it. Edgar was dizzy to observe the dreadful trader who gathered samphire on the cliff; what would he think of that scaffold, some eight hundred feet aloft, where men work daily. "Ten masts at each make not the altitude." This is indeed New York's own Shakespeare Cliff. I wish Bill could have seen it. It would be fun to quote Cleopatra to him—"My country's high pyramides," giving the word the four syllables he would expect. Perhaps he would answer by a very different heroine: "O brave New World that has such people in't."

Across the street from that office-building of character, Mr. I. Miller allures the customer known as Milady with slippers of Greekish shape. "The glory that was Greece comes to shoedom," his poster says. Which delights me also. Every man in his humor, and this affiche is as native to I. Miller as the Spartan understatement to Colonel Starrett. But because the huge sparkling upwards of Starrett make me fear to die and miss so much future, I am not less happy with St. Bride's small turreted spire off Fleet Street.

Thinking of the vanished Waldorf, I wonder whether the new leviathan construction has spared the old letter-box that stood on Fifth Avenue just outside the hotel. It was there that Mistletoe used to mail his manuscripts in the exciting days when he and J. D. K. and I lived together at 149 Madison Avenue. The first poem he ever sold to a New York editor was mailed in that box, and gave him a hopeful notion that envelopes dropped there might be lucky. What became, I wonder, of Will Low's painted ceiling of Cupids in the old Marie Antoinette room of the Waldorf, the usual rendezvous of two young people in the noble winter of 1913–14—the last winter of the pre-War world.

374

Is it needful to remind ourselves that this, now, is perhaps also pre-War? I hear occasional rumor among thoughtful men that the world's fightings are not over. It will be a while yet before people forget; I do not suppose anything ecumenically serious is likely to emerge for—well, what shall we say? a decade? a generation? But now is the time to be thinking against it. I read that Mr. Pabst of Milwaukee is spending nearly a million dollars on a new factory for genuine beer, so as to be ready if and when the brew begins. Similarly the League of Nations is patiently installing its machinery for distilling a little international good sense against emergencies. Both deserve encouragement. Neither War nor wood-alcohol help very much.

Shakespeare's *Measure for Measure*, by the way, seems to be partly a satire against the attempt to enforce impossible laws. (It has been said that Prohibition's only achievement has been to move the corner saloon to the middle of the block.) In spite of the Duke's disclaimer in his opening speech, "Of government the properties to unfold" is exactly the theme of the play, which can well be examined as a grammar of political science. What platinum shrewdnesses:

> We must not make a scarecrow of the law,
> Setting it up to fear [frighten] the birds of prey
> And let it keep one shape, till custom make it
> Their perch and not their terror.

375

The law having been scarecrowed, "athwart goes all decorum." That sounds contemporary enough. And the counsel of Pompey the bootlegger to Madam Overdone (the racketeer of a love-easy) is just what every bootlegger of today knows true: "Though you change your place you need not change your trade." C. E. Montague's witty story *My Friend the Swan* (in "Fiery Particles") describes how profitable Shakespearean quotations can be to an advertising agency. Just so I hope yet to persuade a friend of mine, an illegitimate vintner in the Forties, to rubricate over his bar the martial line from *Antony and Cleopatra*, "I have yet room for six scotches more."

One of the pleasantest things about Shakespeare (and about ourselves) is how often, going ahead with our notions in our own secret way, we find presently that he had done it all before. Once Mistletoe wrote a scene which used for comedy that poor creature the stewed prune. That, he thought, was surely his very own. And then, long later, reading *Measure for Measure* for the first time, he found (Act II, Scene 1) that apparently the prune was cue for a laugh even in 1600. There are always new sadnesses, but how few new jokes. How many of those who saw the play *After Dark* as revived in Hoboken, and were pleased by its subtitle *Neither Maid, Wife, Nor Widow*, realized that the latter phrase was a quotation from Shakespeare. Mistletoe didn't; he thought he had made it up himself. But see *Measure for Measure*, V, 1. So you can take the commonest most diurnal experiences known to all—the sight of someone fainted on the street and the samaritan attempt to push back the curious and give the victim breathing-space; or the pricking qualm of one who has crushed a fly or beetle; or a toothache, or a grain of dust in the eye; or—go humbler yet—the economical salvage of broken meats after supper; you will find that our Friend the Swan has noted the form and pressure of them all. Even the Long Island commuter, when he takes that horribly overpassengered 5:33, may have found himself wishing to petition the railroad, as Goneril did Lear, "a little to disquantity your train." But Mistletoe's happiest adventure in *sortes Shakespearianae* was when he was fired from a newspaper and was able, just before it was too late, to find *The Taming of the Shrew*, Act IV, Scene 1, line 37. He once said to himself, when caught soliloquizing, that he had had every experience that is possible in the world of words, for he had been writer, publisher, lecturer, editor, bookseller, reporter, columnist, librarian, dramatist, manager; even (in a manner of speaking and God save the mark) actor, parson, and professor. But the greatest of these was to have the newspaper presses stopped to take out an allusion to Shake-speare.

If you begin reading Shakespeare at the begin-ning—that is, in the play he is credibly supposed to have written first, *Love's Labor's Lost*—you need travel no further than ten lines to find a phrase leaping out to show the imperial color of his ink. "The huge army of the world's desires." He seems to have expressed them all. How good it is to re-member that he had his moments when he groaned for "this man's art and that man's scope."

Yet any student in his senses remains far enough this side idolatry. Up to the present time there still remain a number of the plays I have never been able to read through, probably never shall. Once, led on by the raving of the frolic madman Swinburne, I tried to read *Cymbeline*, "the play of plays" that honeyed extravaganzist called it. If you want to see an aesthetic bachelor in a fine frenzy, hear Swinburne on Imogen—"the im-mortal godhead of womanhood, the woman best beloved in all the world of song and all the tide of time." In the earlier acts I found much that was pleasing; I approved even goodfornothing Cloten for his fondness of bowling; the bedroom scene kept me alert; Cymbeline's defiance of Rome was good groundling stuff, and the luring of Imogen into Wild Wales, though sheer nonsense, is Good Theatre. But the business of the exchanged clothes

378

and the headless body was too much for me. When I found Imogen (immortal godhead of womanhood) burying the body of her supposed husband "to keep it from the flies," I was finished. Anyone who can read beyond that, save for purposes of mere pedantry, is a better soldier than I. Of *Two Gentlemen of Verona* I confess I shall never remember much but the enchanting scene of the letter, and the clown and his dog. It amused me to note that it was a comedian and his dog who most disturbed the critics in the Hoboken revival of *The Black Crook*, that faithfully Shakespearean pantomime. But probably nothing that has happened since 1603 was ever so gorgeously, grotesquely and merrily Elizabethan in spirit as the whole Hoboken rumpus. There were people there who, without ever having read a line of Shakespeare, were closer to him than whole universities of dons. Even the food and drink in Hoboken were Elizabethan. It used to be odd to see marinierte herring and Moselblümchen on the board together. It was that very combination—"pickled herrings and Rhenish"—that killed poor Bob Greene in 1592. The polite comment would be that we must all win our groatsworth of wit with a million of repentance. But sometimes the figures are reversed.

Any play with twins in it is likely to annoy me. Twins are often very charming, but Shakespeare, who fled from Stratford after the birth of his own, need not have made a hobby of them for plot purposes. Even *Twelfth Night*, most reputable of the Gemini plays, scarcely deserves all its renown. Its contemptuous subtitle suggests what the author thought of the wearisome 5th act. Throughout the plays there are plenty of reservations to be made; there are many scenes when one shares the mood of Sly the tinker: "'Tis a very excellent piece of work, madam lady; would 'twere done." Ben said it first and best: there were times when Shakespeare should have been stopped. "Sufflaminandus erat"—he needed someone to put on the brakes. We like him all the better for it.

I think it was Beverley Nichols who used to tell the story of a tedious woman who insisted on boring a modern Elizabeth (Lady Russell) with excessive details of some military hero. "And can you imagine, he was wounded in sixteen places." Lady Russell's reply was final. "I didn't know men had so many places." Shakespeare had all the places there are. That is why, in a queer stupid way, one feels that almost any man's life, intuitively written, would serve as the biography of Shakespeare of whom we know nothing. We know him as we know none but the gods—only by their works. The fashionable comment is that he was always a great poet but only occasionally a great dramatist. The best way it has ever been said is by Don Marquis, quoting the reminiscence of the

Mermaid Tavern parrot via archy the lower-case
roach—

> oh says bill to think i am
> debasing my talents with junk
> oh god what i wanted
> was to be a poet
> and write sonnet serials
> like a gentleman should

Because England is a small country, very beautiful, and an island, poets have had special tenderness for her; her own pens have always been able
to idealize her as the Elizabethans did the Queen.
That loving sense of limit, of boundary, of circuit,
is a great pleasure to the imagination. I can feel it
in Manhattan, where zealots never forget her
rivers. I know it well on Long Island. It is strange
to consider that probably millions of people have
never experienced that geographical luxury.
(Walter de la Mare's fine book *Desert Islands* suggests it with great skill.) Shakespeare was notably
sensitive to the islandishness of England. He could
carry the feeling both inward and outward in the
physical scale. He could perceive it in the circular
microcosm of his theatre—"this wooden O" as he
called it—and then expand the same metaphor to
the whole planet, "the little O, the earth." Perhaps it was not mere chance that the last and
deepest of his plays, deeper than plummet's

sounding, was laid on a desert island, and suggested by the Virginian voyages. It is true that the only American in his works—Caliban—was not a promising specimen.

But we left Lagonda waiting for us at the bottom of Essex Street.

42

IN THIS Halloween weather the eye goes deeper and deeper into the woods. Veil after veil is lifted away, like those successive scrims in the transformation scene at the end of *The Black Crook*. Vision goes farther, clearer in; color changes daily; form distinguishes; more and more sky sifts through. The year has reached its Age of Reason; the dimpled infant of last January's magazine covers now begins to show the wrinkles of Voltaire. The coal dealer, or a broken boiler in the cellar, feelingly persuades us what we are.

About 8:25 of such mornings, once a week, an amateur instructor both happy and frightened, and very likely having missed his breakfast coffee by oversleep, takes anxious cover in the washroom of a certain college lecture-hall. The window of that Ajax commands the approach of students coming at 8.30 from morning "collection" in another building. The old bell repeats its familiar soft note: a specially Quakerish tone which says

thee rather than *you:* even when rung to celebrate
a football victory that pacific old bronze cannot
sound strident. Foreboding from the lavatory
window the instructor sees his pupils coming.
They look agreeably carefree. A group of some
sixty sophomores to be lectured on Shakespeare.
Happy task, yet offering many a doubtful pang.
He remembers that that building, now dedicated
to the literæ humaniores, was for many years the
engineering shop, and still shows a queer sort of
ventilating chimney, intended to carry away
fumes and exhaust vapors. May it still so operate,
he hopes privately. For a too sincere desire to transmit the fire and folly of that Elizabethan age very
likely combusts sometimes into gaseous jocularity.

But Shakespeare at 8:30 A. M. . . . In the lucid
brightness of an autumn morning (and perhaps
without even a cup of coffee to infuse the vitals)
to face the level rationality of youth with his uncertain surmisings on such enormous topic . . .
to the cool Voltairean stomach of early day,
Fancy's child might well seem the barbarian de-
bauched with frenzy . . . even Lamb, luxurious connoisseur, demanded for his Shakespeare thoughts
an evening candlelight and the world shut out.

Stand and deliver, however. Sometimes in pen-
ultimate attempt to order his thought he uses
those few crisp minutes to look on some favorite
local talismans. There is the sunken garden just

beyond the library, where the ribbed iron bench hides beneath the yew tree just as it did twenty years ago. There is the old milestone—8 Miles to P, it says, meaning to Philadelphia—against the side of Chase Hall, to remind one that when the college was founded it lay along the most famous highway in America, the Lancaster Pike—which romantics remember as the Conestoga Road. (It is a pity to know so little of one's native State. Why is not Conestoga as well worth pilgrimage as Stratford?) I suppose that milestone must have been lifted from the nearby turnpike in some student frolic of many years ago; it has been where it is now for as long as anyone has memory. How many of the blue Conestoga wagons must have rolled past it in pre-railroad days. It is pleasant to remember that symbol of pilgrims and pioneers leaning against the classroom wall where Gummere gave us our first echo of the pilgrimage to Canterbury. That same stone, I think, is alluded to in the college's first land titles dated 1830. Kipling has suggested in the Stalky saga (so oddly mixed of brutality and sentiment) how quickly tradition grows up in a school or college. Is there any alumnus whose heart has not been moved by the story "A Little Prep" which describes the return of the Old Boys. Perhaps also there are a few teachers of "English" who have been twinged by that later Stalky item "The Propagation of

Knowledge," in the volume *Debits and Credits*. It should be made required study for entrance into the Modern Language Association.

Another stonework near for pious thought is the old arch, all that remains of the ancient greenhouse and grape arbor, destroyed by fire in 1855. The rumor was that some of the students had been busy with forbidden cards and tobacco in that fragrant humid retreat; but it might also have been spontaneous ignition due to the appearance of the most inflammatory book ever written by an attender at Quaker meeting—*Leaves of Grass*. Once a mulberry tree grew by the old arch, but it has vanished. Perhaps it was that tree which begat the mulberry cordial a long-ago matron of the college used to prepare to hearten the boys for Midyear Examinations. Mistletoe was sorry to see that tree disappear, for a mulberry is always a link with Shakespeare. There has even been a rumor that when the next addition is made to the Library the old greenhouse arch might be demolished. Indeed I hope not. It is one of our pleasantest relics of simplicity, and like the Conestoga Road it faces toward the West and the sunset. A pensive stroller might even let it remind him of *Ulysses*—

All experience is an arch wherethrough
Gleams that untraveled world whose margin fades
Forever and forever.

Surrounded by trees and stones so thick with memory, the unskilled amateur may well feel John-a-dreams, unpregnant of his cause. But a glimpse of these fragments of humble association confirms him in his instinct. It is not so much a question of "teaching Shakespeare" as of trying to guess the temperament that lies behind such colossal creative gust. A relish for it cannot be prematurely enforced. The slow grief and laughter of life must savor it to our need. We can only use Shakespeare as a symbol of a certain kind of spirit, of the artist's infuriated gaze at life. It is not Shakespeare himself who is important now, but ourselves. What can he do to make us more aware? We are not here to second the significances of others but to discover significances of our own, in the nearest and dearest things. We need a grammar of Feeling. We have to try to keep alive the dying Shakespeare that struggles in every heart, and soon perishes in most. To help that impish Ariel live his full span is the job. It has not necessarily anything to do with literature. No one was ever less "literary." He tried to write a conventional polite sonnet-sequence and see how his own anguish burst it open; so much so that a man can hardly leap through any of the emotional hoops of life without finding Shakespeare's words usurping his own thought. If he were alive today he would find in Manhattan or in Hollywood material

386

as exquisitely bitter and fantastic as on Prospero's enchanted island.

No one less gorgeously imperfect than he would serve as symbol of our wayward hearts. Like religion or any fever, he drives men mad; he comes too close to home. He cannot be studied, he must be lived. You meet the very men and women he knew. People invent codes to explain him when everything he says is merest plain sense, familiar to any man of blood. He grows with us and in us by mutual relativity. Twenty years ago I ticked off the twenty sonnets of his that spoke plainest to my then condition. My present choice of twenty —if I had to choose—only includes nine of that earlier selection. By what gay or sullen seizures I have made that shift is no one's concern but mine. But what may have sounded like balderdash at twenty may be the very tissue of truth when forty winters besiege the brow. That famous and terrible outcry (Number 129) which some have called the greatest sonnet ever written means utterly nothing unless it has been lived. The well-loved Dr. Schelling used to make a point of quoting Heming and Condell's preface to the Folio— "If you doe not like him, surely you are in some manifest danger not to understand him."

There is some paradox lurking; it darts in and out like a lizard in a hot stone-pile, I see just the flicker of its tail. At the very outset of our education, when we are being drilled in all sorts of well-proven doctrine and well-behaviored manners, we are given this loveliest and rowdiest, tenderest and obscenest, carnallest and most spiritual of poets and bidden to make of him what we can. There seems to be a queer kind of tacit bargain too that we are not to take unfair advantage of the gift by really using it. Our magistrates would be prompt to say we were wasting our time on *Flaming Youth* and *Bad Girl*, yet to our amazement we find *Venus and Adonis* Recommended Reading. Is then Shakespeare the chink in Authority's armor? Are they gently suggesting to us that even Philosophy 4 does not answer all questions, that Mirth and Beauty and Despair have their maddening claims, that even to chief magistrates life is often perplexing and points arise not covered in the rules? Perhaps encouraging us to read anything so dangerous as Shakespeare is Authority's oblique way of hinting at truths it would be unseemly to admit.

For Authority (whose job is not easy) knows it is very unlikely that many people will read Shakespeare carefully. Moreover the people who support "literature" have mostly been bred and tamed by years of prudent comfortable living to put out of their thought the wild, savage, laughing and despairing world of a mind like his. Authority is always cautious. Consider the case of two Presidents of the United States who long hesitated to speak a dedication at the tomb of a former President because that tragic fellow had been shown warmly and regrettably human. What a speech Jesus or Abraham Lincoln would have made if invited to Marion, Ohio. America is a comic country. The only native books that sold largely in the depressed traffic of 1930 were one on how to build a backhouse and one on the sorrows of President Harding. Readers of *The Specialist* would have been surprised to learn that Sir John Harington had written much the same thing in 1596 (*The Metamorphosis of Ajax, With a Plaine Plot of a Privie in Perfection*). The book trade was much alarmed lately at the new idea of books being sold in drugstores; but Ben Jonson suggested that merchandising idea in his epigram *To My Bookseller*. The study of Elizabethan literature will always be one agreeable way of keeping ahead of the times. And the most appealing argument a Shakespeare attorney can advance to his jury is that in earlier days Authority tried to keep him out of the hands of the young. There's a passage in a book of 1641 (Jo. Johnson, *The Academy of Love*) deploring the fact that unless their grandmothers intervened "young sparkish Girles would read in Shakespeere day and night."

Windows were bright in the mild autumn dusk

when he came back to that good place where this book began. Dry leaves, rattling underfoot, were drifted in heaps about the darkening lawn, discarded notes of Summer's long lecture course. Men were singing in the dining hall. To hear their enormous high spirits made him feel, for the first time, almost grown up. It is a queer sensation.

43

THERE is a man from Fleet Street staying at a hotel in New York; it is his first visit to America and as he is both shrewd and sensitive he feels heavily the impact of our vast, genial but terrifying pandemonium. He is the most valuable kind of visitor we have: the trained journalist who has deliberately erased his mind of all hearsay; who makes himself clean receptiveness on which New York can write her own memoranda. He is saving all the queer little notes that New York writes him. He ordered a bottle of White Rock, for instance, and was startled to find on its neck a caveat to this effect, "This bottle is sold on the understanding that it will not be used with any alcoholic beverage." Not to embarrass him, therefore, I took mine straight. Before we left the room he was careful to wash out the tumblers; for, he remarked, "I believe in obeying the law of the land." So does New York make hypocrites of us all. He happens to be a Scot, and was as amazed as only such can be at the purposeful benzine we administer as "Scotch." He is delighted by all the minor *affiches* which are so happy a feature of American hotel civilization. The bright "Good Morning—and here is your copy of the New York *Times*. Breakfast is waiting for you in the Rosebud Lounge." A little card *Please Do Not Disturb the Occupant of This Room* warmed his philosophic cockles. He gazed out at terrible eyries of edifice and tried to promise himself not to be disturbed. But when he found that the hotel, anticipating the mortality of trouser buttons, had forethinkingly threaded a needle for him, he was strangely touched. Now he divines in America a more than maternal tenderness.

Like a wise man he will cherish as many as possible of those little scraps of announcement that come his way. They are clues dropped in the great paper-chase or treasure hunt for a nation's soul. By them one can sometimes suspect the etiquette of a strange civilization. To prove to him that the English element in America is only a small tithe of our racial amalgam I showed him this from that same day's *World:*

With Frank Bartos at quarterback, the racial distribution of Fordham's varsity eleven presents a perfectly balanced diagram of Irish, Poles, and Italians. On the right of the line are Elcewicz, end; Miskinis, tackle, and Wisniewski, guard; all Polish. To the left, in the same order, are Conroy, Foley, and Tracey, sons of Ireland. Between the Polish and Irish contingents stands Capt. Tony Siano, the Italian center. Directly behind him is his Polish quarterback, Bartos, and behind him another Pole, Pieculewicz, at fullback. And finally, balancing the Italian-Polish succession from center to fullback, are two Irishmen on either side, Murphy and McMahon at right and left halfback.

I myself, on visits abroad, save all *petites annonces* with great care. In London one always reads the Agony Column of the *Times* at breakfast; in 1930 one of the first things I discovered was this:

The executors of the late Professor Herbert Hall Turner announce that he left directions that his body should be dissected, or otherwise used for the general advancement of science, and that his death should not be made the occasion of any religious service or other ceremony. Professor Turner also left the following message for his friends: "I venture to hope that there may be some who will care to drink a glass to my memory, and, if so, I beg them to do so at such time and in such company as they may find convenient, and further, that they will choose their own liquor; but if anyone should desire to know my preference, then I say, 'Let it be strong ale.' And I desire these my wishes to be published in 'The Times' Newspaper as soon as possible after my death."

I am glad to report that a little group of us, in the Rainbow on Fleet Street, had the silver mugs filled and drank Professor Turner's memory standing. Godspeed to goodman in the dark. He was an astronomer, so he was not unused to it. That little notice seemed characteristic of an island of individuals. At such a moment one somehow remembers Rudyard Kipling's fine toast at a St. George's Society dinner—"My lords, ladies and gentlemen: for what there is of it—for such as it is—and for what it may be worth—will you drink to England and the English?"

My heart is with that good Scot while he looks at New York and tries to unify her in his clear mind. Here will he see no enemy but steam heat and rude liquor. When he remarked on Fifth Avenue in a drizzling dusk that something about it reminded him of Glasgow I was certainly surprised; but it showed that his mind was at work on private analogies of his own. Physically there would not seem to me much likeness; yet Glasgow is also a city of many disregarded prohibitions. There were some sharp counsels that our much-admired William Bolitho made for himself when he came here on his first journalizing visit and

search. "To avoid allusiveness and the mixing of
themes. To beware in this dangerous mission
women's souls and poor men's drink. To flee the
two enemies of writing, laziness and sickening
industry. Not to seek smartness by hiding enthusiasm."

No one, I think, need hide his troubled passion
in writing about New York. It is one of the few
themes in the world that can only be approached
as Melville dealt with Moby Dick. The day is ripe
and overripe for such a cry of love and anger in
honor of this city of ours. It will come. In due
season we are always granted the artists we require, and they the emotions they need. What is
said will be right without our quite knowing why.

The perfected irony of all human doings and
feelings is eminent in the writing business as in
all others. The beginner yearns hotly to get into
print, whenever and where-ever. Yet a time may
come when he yearns with equal passion to keep
out of print until he has mastered the thought that
bothers him. His only concern comes to be the
expression of those strong intuitions that look
unhandsome if uttered too green. Like poor sentimental Troilus in Chaucer, a writer has his doubts
and timidities. He kneels by Cressida's bedside—
Cressida representing the Muse for the purpose of
our fable—and confesses his tender hopes and
adorations. But grizzled Pandarus (you can sym-

394

bolize him as the cynical boblisher, or just as plain
human Necessity) tears off the young man's shirt
and bundles him naked into bed with her. The
perfect Cressida is not to be wooed in that fashion.
It is hardly surprising that the first time she meets
a handsome Greek she walks out on Troilus.

While my Scot is exploring New York, it pleases
me to be thinking about the Fleet Street he has
just left. Suppose I never saw Fleet Street again,
what would I want to remember? To anyone interested in writing that street must always be
sacred. It was first named for a drain, and much
intellectual rubbish has been shot down that channel, but also it has run for centuries with much of
the bravest ink in the world. Many famous
churches keep an eye on it, and it is bounded at
each end by the journalist's two most dangerous
indulgences—liquor, and libel. I mean of course
Shireff's wine cellars at the foot of Ludgate Hill,
and the Law Courts in the Strand. What strange
irony there was last summer in the wrapped-up
memorial to a famous Newspaper Proprietor
against the wall of St. Dunstan's church. The
shroud, some sort of thin white sail-cloth, was
swathed about the carved head and bust; it remained gruesomely so for many weeks while (so
we were told) there was difficulty in finding the
appropriate Celebrity who would consent to unveil it. The Unknown Journalist, irreverent press-

men called the hooded figure; Fleet Street knows too many inside and unprintable stories to be easily awed. The light wrapping twitched and fluttered strangely in evening breezes; passing there at night it seemed as though the formless shrouded face were writhing to break free, struggling to escape from its smothered sheeting and rejoin the inky life in which it had been a cæsar of caprice. Poor ghost: many a young Hamlet among reporters must have considered that restless white shape in the dim shadow of the church, straining against oblivion. It was grim and added one more sombre memory to a street where men live one day at a time, and peddle their opiate of words.

Fleet Street has plenty of dark rainy days; it is probably drizzling there at this moment. My present thought recalls it in a clear lustre of heat that England knows but rarely. The final cricket match with Australia was just over; afternoon papers, which had thriven on hourly extras to cry progressive details of play, now had only the weather for sensation. As the mercury climbed above 90, one poster read:

THE THERMOMETER
LATEST SCORE

And it really was grilling, for in London one makes no preparation for such warmth. When you

396

asked the handsome bar-lady at the Rainbow please to put some ice in the gin-and-ginger, the small pellet actually was melted before the glass had reached your lips.

Now when I think of going along Fleet Street I think at once of Twining's aromatic merchandise in tea and coffee and spices. The modern newspaper began in coffee houses, and it is only right that the first thing to admire on Fleet Street is a coffee trader. And the next thing is the excellent pipe-merchant Weingott, and thereafter the god of wine himself at the Devereux or the Rainbow or the Cock or the Cheese. I pay my tribute to Messrs Hoare the bankers and the *Manchester Guardian* office and Anderton's Hotel (where I aspire to lodge if I can ever find an empty room) and Bouverie Street famous for *Punch* and Bolt in Tun Court where there has been a booking office ever since Chaucer's time. But as much as anything I think of Corporation of London Dust Cart Number 6. It was standing opposite the new building of the *Daily Telegraph* and one of those Anzac-looking street cleaners with turned-up hat was (I think) collecting sweepings from a bin on the pavement. Or perhaps putting them into the bin; I'm not sure what the man was doing, for I was admiring the horse. He was one of those huge brown English beasts with his forelock braids neatly tied with blue ribbons, brass bosses all over his harness and the arms of the Corporation of London marked on them. How beautiful he was, strong and patient and on the job. If I had been a better journalist I should have asked about him: his name, where he stables, how long his working hours are, and where he and Dust Cart Number 6 take the jetsam of Fleet Street. I didn't ask any of these things, I was so perfectly happy admiring the animal himself, his sleeky mass, the huge barrel of his body, the warm puff from his scrolly nostrils, his strong well-polished gear—

> Thin mane, thick tail, broad buttock, tender hide—
> Look, what a horse should have he did not lack
> Save a proud rider on so proud a back—

and the happy touch of care in those braids and blue tapes. Was it too fanciful to see in his whole honest bearing some symbol of London itself, a nation's beast of burden, slow enduring strength and kindness and sense of order, yet sweating a little. You divine a similar virtue (and I intend no comic comparison) in some of London's magnificent policemen. See them standing, planted with feet well apart, holding back a press of traffic. The white capes for gray weather, the ruddy close-shaven cheeks, the fine helmets—always I want to mate an American girl and a London bobby and start a really perfect race. A quite different notion of a great city's tragedies was suggested by a scrawny little white bitch running lost on Cannon Street, her fawn-colored nose miserably smelling trouser legs in search of some imagined god. Just opposite her were handsome boxes of purple flowers on the cornice of a building, emphasizing the gilded lion and unicorn where Messrs Colman make Mustard, Starch and Blue for the King. The Cannon Street Hotel, it occurred to me in that region, would be an amusing place to stay. Why do all visitors insist on the West End? I don't suppose any American pilgrim has ever stopped in that roomy place; how agreeable it looks, and what mysterious trains go from Cannon Street Station. And for wives there would be the pert little boutique of ELFIN, Ladies' Outfitter, on Railway Approach, Cannon Street.

But we are mixing themes, contrary to Bolitho's advice. I didn't mean to go as far as Cannon Street, but I wanted you to look at St. Paul's from behind. What is this rumor I hear about the St. Paul's pigeons being done away with? Surely they are as much a part of St. Paul's as the sea shells you can see edged in the stone of the south parapet, to remind us (as the London Perambulator has said) that the stone glories of London are stamped with the signet of the sea. What is a cathedral without pigeons? It cannot be. And across the open space behind St. Paul's comes another fine horse, a big dapple-gray pulling a lorry of Gaymer's Attleboro Cyder, "the champagne of England," a slogan truer than you perhaps think. Yes, I hold that hot noontime clearly in mind: the brown horse on Fleet Street, the dapple pulling casks of sparkling Eden past Wren's great dome, and three pretty girls reading in an arbored archway in the cathedral gardens. As far as I am concerned they are there still. Miraculous sunlight burned upon all that clumsy swarm of traffic, which does not thrust in fierce criss-cross as in New York, but loops and eddies in rounder more puzzling patterns. Lyons' windows were ornate with Bath buns, jam and treacle tartlets, sausage rolls, veal ham and egg pies, Cornish patties, Dundee cakes, scones, 1/- lunch boxes, and glass facsimiles of very gaudy ice cream sodas. And now the pubs were open. It was time to get back to Fleet Street.

In that hot meridian, sun and shadow are mixed on the stone, as they were in the heart beneath it. It is under a quiet tree where the filigree of flickering leaves hovers gently; there is a tall lamp-post near (I imagine he was not fond of the dark?) and a lucky black cat asleep. From open windows comes a drowsy occasional click of typewriters. The stone says HERE LIES OLIVER GOLDSMITH. Much more explicit is an adjoining monument, the reclining figure of Iohannes

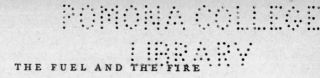

Hiccocks. He was Magister in Cancellario, and Inter severiores Iurisprudentiæ litteras Urbanitate Morum Conspicuus, Cives Bonus et Inconcussus. Obit 1726. So the unshaken Hiccocks was there even before Oliver was born. Some urchin has diminished his urbanity by pencilling a moustache on the stone face. But Goldsmith rests better under the plain four words. Like a true Irishman he would have been fidgety beneath the Doctor's heavy Latin in the Abbey.

44

A COLD singing Northwest—the breath of Autumn's being—thrashes the copper shreds of Satisfaction Piece. On "the blue surface of his airy surge" the dogwood tree tosses and looks lean. Shelley's cheeks would be flushed in such a scouring air. How did he keep his fingers warm to write the Ode? And I think also of another windy passage that has its urgent magic, Chaucer's

> Out of these blakë wawës for to saile,
> O wind, O wind, the weder ginneth clere.

A very different weather from those hot calm London noons of which I was writing. And it is queer: this very morning I learn of the death of Tommy Pope—"Mr. Pope of Twickenham" as he was affectionately nicknamed, known and loved in every bar on Fleet Street. Little Tommy Pope, endeared by his sudden murmured wisdoms and his shy pathos, needs no stone bust at St. Dunstan's. On Fleet Street the only real memorials are words in print. The great parson of that church, John Donne, would have known how to say tribute to that troubled, witty, lovable and kindly-meaning apparition. The real Fleet Street, which like all newspaper coteries is jealously selective, knew Tommy Pope and took him to its heart. If there were a memorial to him at St. Dunstan's it would not have to wait long for someone to unveil it. Like our own long-vanished Steve O'Grady, Pope was of the long line of God's chilluns. The first marching song of that noble army of the unprovided was Chaucer's Compleynt to His Purse. Tommy Pope died on the very eve of publication of a book his Fleet Street brothers had generously put together in his honor, *Journalists at Play*. He was one of the little group I mentioned that stood up in the Rainbow that hot day to drink the memory of Professor Turner; how little we thought to be so soon drinking his own. Many colleagues much younger than himself had a quaintly paternal tenderness toward this gentle spirit that had been seasoned, but never hardened, by difficulty. Brave little man, picking up crumbs of journalism, he was the sparrow that fell. I take leave to reprint Earle Welby's tribute to him in the *Week-End Review;* it shows the spirit of ink at its best:

It is a desolating thought that we may range through the taverns of Fleet Street now without hope of seeing in any a little, gray-haired man engaged in the unhopeful business of balancing six review copies under his left arm against a mysterious and presumably manuscriptful case depending from his right, while he needs a third arm for the acquisition of refreshment. Strange and desolating that never again shall we hear his swift-working wit crackle across our talk, an interruption that never destroyed any desirable continuity of conversation but deftly sidetracked bores without hurting their vanity.

The gods, capricious in their distribution of gifts, had decreed that he should not mean to those who read his journalistic work one-hundredth of what he meant to those who heard him talk. But he attained easily to this, that there was no day of his life in which he did not say a dozen good things and do a dozen kind things. He had a profound religious faith, with an unrivalled knowledge of the character and location of the past, present, and future leaders of the Anglican Church; he had also, what one of his friends may perhaps be allowed to think more, that natural piety which enables its possessor to respect every genuine human impulse. No man can ever have been half an hour in his company without being beholden to him not only for laughter but for a little more confidence in human nature, for a comforting demonstration that man is an amiable animal in his declensions no less than in his aspirations.

He brightened, sweetened, made more naughty, made more wholesome, every place in which he stood.

Lagonda was still waiting at the foot of Essex Street. I had been trying to seduce young M. K. into a green escapade from town; yet it was only Wednesday, early in the week for an ambitious publisher to leave his desk. But the heat came to my aid. Officially 90°, it was certainly much more than that in the little book-lined office at Number 22. It was the weather, rather than any special curiosity about Shakespeare, that persuaded him. Lagonda, always ready for anything, was prepared.

I try to tell this plainly, not making too much of small things; nor yet (what is worse) belittling things that to me were great. The enormous web of that city spreads out in endless circuit; at the heart of it you are aware of the domed nubbin of St. Paul's like the round belly of the spider itself, fed on human toil, anxiety, and hope. A golden misery of heat, effort, noise and fume lay upon that wide stony network. We shot outward toward sunset. I don't remember much but speed. Was it then, weaving through the alarming swiftness of London traffic (Lagonda actually seems sinuous, to flex her lean low flanks and ripple herself through like a darting otter) we caught a glimpse of Punch and Judy playing in a side street? That was good to see, old make-believe still going on.

The greatest Punch and Judyist of all was subtly behind this sunset project, who could make less-than-human puppets say more-than-human things. It was part of the picture too—it "made sense," as our current argot has it—that the last person we saw in Russell Square when we set spark for Arden chanced to be that deep-musicked poet who has entered so magically into the minds of Shakespeare's characters. Hear him (Walter de la Mare) on Falstaff:

'Twas in a tavern that with old age stooped
And leaned rheumatic rafters o'er his head—
A blowzed, prodigious man, which talked, and stared,
And rolled, as if with purpose, a small eye
Like a sweet Cupid in a cask of wine.
I could not view his fatness for his soul,
Which peeped like harmless lightnings and was gone. . . .
He puffed that paunch, and wagged that huge, Greek
    head,
Nosed like a Punchinello—

(But *was* Falstaff hook-nosed? I see a long fleshy neb, well founded on bone and widely pudged about the nostril, but straight; suggesting on that deathbed the sharpened pen to Mrs. Quickly.)

Yes, it all Made Sense. It made good Elizabethan sense that the poet, telling how his house was to be found, localized it by a pub. "Go to the Dumb-bell and turn up," he said. And his telephone number was Maidenhead soandso. "I

405

should be far too bashful," said Mistletoe, "to ask the telephone girl for a number like that."

Like a swallow Lagonda skimmed into the sunset. She stopped, reluctantly, long enough for us to see Windsor Castle far off in the warm glow; and a new moon farther still. It was eight o'clock dusk when we reached the Red Lion at Henley. Riverside inns were well filled that thirsty evening, and we had to wait for a table. It was worth it, for in the twilight I saw four swans come through four arches of the bridge at the same instant, like four lines of a perfect quatrain. They did so with almost an air of conscious calculation. They are the right birds to typify the Muse, so beautiful and bad-tempered. Speaking of quatrains, was it the Red Lion where Shenstone devised his "Written at an Inn at Henley," which the Doctor repeated to Boswell "with great emotion"? The bar lady serving us our aperitif explained that the ice machine had crocked under the strain of so hot a day, and also with great emotion we paraphrased Shenstone—

> Whoe'er has travelled life's dull round,
>   Where'er his stages may have been,
> May sigh to think he still has found
>   His warmest cocktail, at an inn.

Now Oxford lay at the end of our thoughts. It was not Elizabethan, but we telephoned thither to be sure of beds. The cheerful voice of the prima donna of Cornmarket Street replied reassuringly. I wondered if Shakespeare took occasion to notify his Oxford hostess, Mrs. Davenant of the Crown, in advance.

It was strange to come there so swiftly through warm darkness. I remembered the smell of that road but not the details. Lagonda's lights shone on villages I could not identify; while I thought we were hardly past Dorchester we were already on Iffley Road, where (as I explained to Lagonda) Kathleen used to play hockey. Lagonda has a little movable searchlight; like a lorgnette she can gaze with it wherever she chooses. She flung a beam upon Number 19 where long ago some young men, quite unintentionally, first stumbled upon Modern American Literature. It looks quite unchanged; I mean Number 19 does.

I do not mention the name of the noblest Oxford inn, of which a connoisseur has said "every line and curve of the old building is a 17th century lyric." It is not known to the general run of tourists and should not be; it is so demurely hidden that many men have lived their whole college career and never entered that courtyard. Only a few yards away is Woolworth, yet you turn in at that gateway and find a Jacobite innyard hung with flowers and vines. Floors and ceilings have sagged under centuries of service; you go along the slanting passages upstairs with shoulder against the wall, as in the alleys of a rolling ship; the warming pans hung there seem like pendulums to measure the angle of list. By Lagonda's keen instinct we arrived just before the bar closed, and sat out in the warm dark yard with a cool gin-and-ginger. In that courtyard you are as carnally close to Shakespeare as you are likely to get. The Crown, Davenant's grog-shop where Shakespeare used to tarry going to and from Stratford, was next door. The Davenant house, rebuilt, still exists (it pleases me that it was the property of New College; that seems to have been his first academic association) and if Mrs. Davenant was as hospitable as legend loves to believe, Will may have spent his Oxford nights there. But it was a pub, not an inn, and there is better likelihood that he actually slept in the hotel I refrain from naming. The worthy house has taken the tradition in its stride and never tried to capitalize it.

But the romantics from Aubrey down have had a good time erecting jubilant romanza out of the Davenant affair. It is not surprising, for the color of the tale is irresistible. Shakespeare passing through Oxford, interested not in colleges but in the amiable handsome landlady; the husband, afterwards Mayor, who was "seldom or never seen to laugh"; the godson who himself grew up to be a witty poet and did not discourage the rumor of his left-handed parentage. There are good stories about the younger Davenant, but the best of them is his apology (during illness) for not having finished *Gondibert:* "I shall ask leave to desist, when I am interrupted by so great an experiment as dying." A man who could die with such Caroline insouciance might also have been begotten informally. Anyhow, even though the dates didn't fit, it was agreeable for Oxonians to imagine that Mrs. Davenant might have been the Dark Lady. It was a hard blow to this genial fable when her bedroom in the old Crown was repaired a few years ago and wall-paintings came to light which showed the chamber decorated with pious mottoes, of which *Feare God above all thynge* was the most legible.

Those who tinted the bust of Shakespeare would not hesitate to tint his biography; and perhaps the more legends the better. Sometimes the legend is truer than the truth. Pursued by posterity as never man has been hunted, he evades them still, and they fall to scuffling among themselves. I like to take the famous stanzas about the hunted hare (in *Venus and Adonis*) as representing Shakespeare and his sapient trouble-tombs:

For there his smell with others being mingled
The hot scent-snuffing hounds are driven to doubt,
Ceasing their clamorous cry till they have singled
With much ado the cold fault cleanly out;

409

Then do they spend their mouths: Echo replies,
As if another chase were in the skies.

Meanwhile the poet himself, "far off upon a hill,
stands on his hinder legs with listening ear." What
is pleasanter than the anguish of magistrates because in the Latin hexameter of the Stratford
monument there is a false quantity. Above this
bogus Latin and beneath the bogus escutcheon he
sits with cheerful but rigid stolidity in his niche,
looking rather like an old Kentucky colonel in a
club window. The hands, holding quill and paper,
rest on a tasseled pillow—those hands that had
earned a pillow to rest on. That bust has been the
subject of heavy fighting among the clans, but I
enjoy believing it adequately suggests what he
finally did look like. He did not necessarily think
the way it looks, for who ever had more wary pro-
tective coloration?

But one who arrives at an inn at night doesn't
spend time brooding about Shakespeare. Happy is
that godlike secrecy of reaching anywhere in the
dark; and coming to Oxford makes one feel as a
young poem does when it first gets printed in an
anthology. I liked a saying in a fine little book of
proud stomach, *The Poet's Progress* by Walter
D'Arcy Cresswell, a New Zealand poet. "I left
Oxford that morning," he says, "but first I paid a
visit to Shelley's tomb (for so it appears), and this

is the holiest place on earth." Earth is full of holy places, but I know what he meant. Those who have seen the naked marble locked in its blue crypt, the drowned body of dead music flung ashore, know how Oxford can do penance. The heaviest heart is moved by that white cenotaph, which seems the prophetic soul of the wide world, dreaming on things to come. Shelley is not dead; he is so alive that the other day when November came blowing from crystal space one man telephoned to another to reread the West Wind. The printed pages, torn from a book for closer study, were on his mantelpiece the next day in the tower of Sherry-Netherland, where that pinnacle hums like harp-guts in the gale. "I read it eleven times," he said. Shelley was not dead that afternoon, when we crossed the river in the ferry *Hopatcong* and saw the Downtown Dolomites glazed with tinsel sheen.

We sat quietly in the innyard, drinking gin-and-ginger and listening to a cool trickle of water dripping somewhere in the dark. We went out and strolled as far as Carfax. Once I caught just the beginning of Big Tom's booming bell-metal, but it was drowned by the motor traffic in the High. Oxford, as we noted some years ago, may eventually be the British Detroit. The motor works are growing bravely in that suburb which used to be famous only for a monastery; already the wits speak of the

411

varsity as the Latin Quarter of Cowley. Our talk that evening was not sentimental. Mistletoe was seized with a sudden idea of what fun it would be to build a typically modern New York hotel in Oxford; austerely futurist in design, with really cold cocktails in summer and really warm bedrooms in winter; with ice water and radio and all the American ingenuities. How the Oxford boys (great dabblers in Modernity) would love it and what tremendous business we would do in Eights Week. Then the American tourists could go to the antique inns and the English trade would come to us. What should we call it? The Cecil Rhodes? The Parson's Pleasure? The As You Like It? We rather fancied ourselves as hotel managers; it would be a notably profitable exploit, and it is bound to happen sooner or later. We thought of asking Mr. Selfridge to join us in such an enterprise. It might teach Oxford architecture a lesson, too, which it needs. My heart sank when I saw one of its recent errors, the School of Pathology (1926), a factory of lewd red brick and trimmings. Any Long Island village has done itself better in its modern High School.

Anyhow there was no difficulty that night about warm bedrooms. Those little single rooms up under the roof had been generously baked by the all-day blaze. We went to sleep not with Shakespeare but with Dr. Austin Freeman.

45

PERHAPS they had been a little disappointed to find themselves in those small hot attics, instead of in one of the big double chambers that overlook the yard. But Mistletoe will not forget the next morning's surprise. At six o'clock sunlight was flooding into the room, yellow as candle-flame; it was a morning blaze "like gold to airy thinness beat," and there across the low roofs were the Radcliffe dome and St. Mary's spire. They were a tender pigeon-throat color, as in Turner's painting of Brasenose quad (where Pater condoned undergraduate bonfires because they lit up the spire so beautifully). That dome, that spire, Mistletoe always associated with *Marius the Epicurean*. He loved their stone charms with pure detachment; he had rarely used either the one for reading or the other for worship, but they were part of his permanent picture of the world. In the level burning of an August morning all those silver-scurfy stones shift and turn in opal colors. Like an old gray hen, Oxford seems to sprawl and spread her feathers to the sun.

Yes; suddenly, unexpectedly, in the first issue of a new day's likelihood, was a fresh vista of Oxford, never seen before. Something rich in the mind, both proud and humble, felt renewed. There

has always been such fat premium put on easy im-
age-breaking, quiet minds sometimes keep their
surest loyalties too secret. In such morning honesty one was proud to love what was so beautiful;
and he wondered if that old home of Humanities
ever entered into a bandar-log uproar about Hu-
manism. Would anyone, who had really tasted the
nourishing comedy and tragedy of mature life? In
the clean tranquil temper of Marius himself they
climbed to the queer little attic bathroom of the
inn, where after the tub you may stand on a raised
platform and dry yourself while looking from a
skylight across Mrs. Davenant's own roof.

So advantageous a summit, and the pleasing riddle of Mrs. Davenant herself, might have provided
good occasion for homage to Woman and her necessary dominion over the artist. Strange that
Marius (so far as I recall) said little of her; her exquisite rationality, her humorous willingness to be
civilized. (Perhaps Marius, whatever he called
himself, was still more Oxford don than Epicurean.) Surely Woman is instinctive artist in every
gland; the rest of us only so, stupidly and by dull
persistence, between interruptions. Shakespeare,
with the wild wisdom of a man carrying a whole
unborn world in his brainpan, allied with the
Town, not the Gown. In that monkish city, carefully fortified against the more urgent anguishes of
art, Woman's enormous wisdom seems diluted and

remote. Gladly, because she has no real power on them, they have conceded her all sorts of equal privileges. But in a university sex must remain an interesting binomial theorem; capable of intelligible demonstration, but nicely weighed and set apart. It is not so in the full intermingle of life. It is something different in the Shakespeares and Marlowes and John Donnes.

He would have liked to go on thinking about John Donne (a poet women of blood adore at sight, whereas innocent men have to be laboriously taught to relish him) and even about Brantôme (he always said that there were not nearly enough writers with a circumflex accent). But it would seem to the shallow that these thoughts were tainted with literature. As a matter of fact he was not thinking about them at all, but about himself in their moods. The only way to learn anything about poetry is to live through all the emotions the poets have recorded. His experience of literature had been entirely unsystematic, picked up by chance excerpts and encounters; in bookshops, drug stores, and human hearts. His only ambition had been to bear witness that might be, for a few generous or patient readers, a true report on a certain not negligible generation. A generation that had its first brightness of boyhood in a world now utterly dead, but which many hard-working people toil anxiously to revive. A generation which reaches its full efficiency in the most curious situation; being, as Matthew Arnold or someone said, between two worlds, one dead, and the other powerless to be born.

Skilful in elusion, he could always conveniently label with a deceptive literary affiche, matters he deemed too gloriously direct for general utterance. I remember that when he was running a newspaper column, and desired to ventilate a somewhat subversive sentiment, he sometimes used to enjoy printing it as a quotation from Thoreau or Emerson. Only once, in many such experiments, did any reader question the authenticity.

We sat down to bacon and eggs in the little coffee-room that looks out over the cobbled and flower-hung inn-yard. I hope it was true about Mrs. Davenant. I should like to think that Oxford meant something more to Shakespeare than just a place where they lock up at 9:05 p. m. I hope his stomach shook a little with love's own terrors as he came riding over Magdalen Bridge. But all that Mistletoe remarked was, "This isn't the old original Cooper's Oxford marmalade."

Some day it would be worth looking up again George Moore's great tribute to *Marius* in *Confessions of a Young Man*. "A constant and careful invocation of meaning that was a little aside of the common comprehension, and also a sweet depravity of ear for unexpected falls of phrase. . . ."

Looking back over these small adventures, and inserting the appropriate thoughts we might have had, is unfair to ourselves. Neither Mistletoe nor I is likely to have the right thought at the right time. We were out to attempt something more fruitful than thinking; to get the feelings of things and try to let intuition be alive and aware. "Pictures in our eyes to get, was all our propagation."

One can afford to love things one does not have to live with. Santayana fled back to Oxford when he found Harvard crude, but probably the rising tide of busses and filling stations soon moved him on. The sacred edifice of Balliol is now marked with a big metal sign DANGEROUS CORNER, which gave its own pleasure to a New College man bred impatient of the old Balliol disdain. The precocious child of the street-walker said, quoting Sir Thomas Browne, "Mummy is become merchandise." So one might think of Alma Mater, seeing Carfax and Cornmarket terrible with traffic. But then, rounding into the Broad, you meet one of those excellent old parsons with white beard and black straw hat and know that some of the good Lost Causes are still solid. And in Blackwell's noble bookshop they are offering Clement Shorter's copy of Defoe's *Jure Divino*, dedicated "To the Most Illustrious Lady REASON, First Monarch of the World." But Blackwell's is a dangerous place: you can wander and wander, penetrating always

417

deeper in posterior passages of print, until drugged and stupefied. And we had only a few hours.

Mistletoe wanted us to revisit New College garden. He told me that a few years ago he brought home to Long Island a bay horse-chestnut he had picked up there. He planted it and watered with care, but long time went past without result. Finally, trowelling about, he dug it up by chance and found it shrivelled and full of small curlicue maggots. A cynic would have found sombre allegory in this; would have said that many Oxford seeds parch or go wormy in the sandy loam of Afterwards. Mistletoe only said that he was disappointed; a chestnut tree from New College would have been good for spiritual rheumatisms. He insisted on our seeing Long Room, a medieval Ajax, and recited its famous motto, "O Cloacina, goddess of this place . . ." but more quotable is one of the memorial tablets in the cloister, an inscription in honor of a famous oarsman—*Princeps arte remigandi*, a prince in the art of rowing. The view from the bell-tower was as lovely as ever. Thence you look aslant on Oxford's gray pattern, the many squares of stone each brimmed with forenoon light and a wedge of black shadow on the southern side. At the Turf tavern, secret in the elbow of Hell Passage, the shiny shove-ha'penny board was still in use. In that alley, or in the New College cloister, the clash of bells drifts overhead

418

like heavy plumes, or falls downward with unseen weight into the white pool of silence. There many a young Caliban has been pricked by the impossible loveliness of his own age and time. Oxford's bells are like the strange airy noises of the tawny island—

> Sometimes a thousand twangling instruments
> Will hum about mine ears; and sometime voices,
> That, if I then had waked after long sleep,
> Will make me sleep again: and then, in dreaming,
> The clouds methought would open and show riches
> Ready to drop upon me; that, when I waked
> I cried to dream again.

Were Caliban and the two pickled Italians left behind on the island, like Stevenson's three mutineers? The parallel with *Treasure Island* is too close not to notice.

But on such a day the right place for vacation was Parsons Pleasure, the old bathing pool. On the way we had a chance to see Rhodes House, the new headquarters of that most romantic and purposeful of all generosities. It is an extraordinary building with magnificent oak timbers and multitudinous symbolisms, chief of which the zimbabwe bird of Rhodesia. Finding Shakespeare everywhere, as one does if one looks, it was exciting to learn that the fire-dogs in the great hall are embossed with emblems of "Shakespeare's poem *The*

Phoenix and the Turtle, which suggests the mingled ruthless energy and tender generosity of Cecil Rhodes." Certainly there is the gusto of Rhodes's Crœsus fancy in that house, a kind of imperial anthology of materials. The southern front says: DOMUS HAEC NOMEN ET EXEMPLUM CECILI IOHANNIS RHODES OXONIÆ QUAM DILEXIT IN PERPETUUM COMMENDAT.

To young K., Parsons Pleasure was new; his Oxford experience did not include a Summer Term. He saw it at its best that ardent August noon. The cold Cherwell stream comes down a long aisle of trees among unspoiled meadows; it tastes and smells rich of Oxford earth. It is a clean country creek, and with the Shakespearean instinct of getting to London; that same water flows by Westminster and Southwark a few days later. It might by easy chance have been the river of Stratford: on the ridge of Edgehill only half a mile separates springs that flow into Avon from those running into Cher.

Parsons Pleasure itself is a bracket in the stream; a by-path detours picknickers around it so that the naked simplicity of the bathers is not disturbed. Occasionally an ignorant freshman or visitor poles his puntload of ladies round the wrong corner and blunders into this monad retreat, then awkwardly pushes out again with much feminine squeaking. The voices of boating parties are heard beyond the trees; the rush of water down the weir is a sleepy overtone. There, on the small grassy mead, men and boys of every size and shape lay browning in absolute sunshine. A naked cleric, a nice tanned one in a Panama hat, trudged steadily to and fro studying his breviary. Of him K. remarked, "It's the first time I ever saw a parson stripped. He looks just like a regular human being." Books and towels were scattered about, blue wisps of pipe-smoke shredded in the air. Lying on the warm turf one could hear the heavy hissing plunge of bodies diving; I can taste and feel again that inland water with its earthy chill and its light but steady push of current. Down green meanders of its shallow valley the Cher curves loitering, past the old churches and tea arbors of a dozen rarely discovered villages. They are only names now— Wood Eaton, Water Eaton, Islip, Hampton Poyle, Hampton Gay, Shipton, Nethercott, Steeple Aston—but we knew them once. That cold water, gently dividing the burning hours, brings with it some fertile secret of the old midland shires; but it comes also from further away than that; from a fairy-tale we will never re-explore. There, by those dingy dressing-hutches and under the willows, you seem very far inside something. The humorous and maddening world is palisaded away by strong protections. Green fields and gray walls and enormous widenesses of peace lie between you and life. Those naked boys throwing a medicine ball, the older men stretched basking in the sun, somehow make one want to read Aristotle and Plato (in translation, of course). And truly one of the subtlest of the dialogues was talked out by Socrates and Phaedrus in just such a place: sitting by the Ilissus with their feet in the water.

Mistletoe said "I would reread the *Phaedrus* if I thought it would really help me, but I'm wondering. I honestly believe I can get more from Walt Whitman. As a matter of fact, Plato is one of the few authors who have ever come somewhere near shocking me. Perhaps it's because they made such a fetich of him at Balliol." He took a plunge in the stream as though to shake off the topic.

"Walt Whitman would have enjoyed Parsons Pleasure," I suggested as he came out, rubbing his thighs in the sun. I was thinking how Walt, after his paralytic stroke, used to go down to lonely Timber Creek, hang his clothes on a fence rail, wallow in the brook and wrestle with an oak sapling for exercise.

Mistletoe was doubtful. "I'm not so sure. He'd find a little too much smell of tradition in this old greenery. He'd much prefer the lonely beaches of Long Island. Remember how he used to run on the sand at Coney shouting Shakespeare at the

surf? Did you ever get that desperate shut-up feeling, indoors at night, and bust out naked into a
warm rain-storm? There's no shower bath like it.
Think of living in a city, where you couldn't do
that."

"It's curious that almost all philosophers worth
while have been associated intimately with rivers
and seas or water of some sort."

"Yes," said young K., "they've done almost
everything to it but drink it."

46

IT WAS comic in such a place to be still tweaked by
awareness of Time. But we had promised Shakespeare to be in Stratford that afternoon; so in the
usual perversity of humans we left one of the few
truly Shakespearean scenes in England to go and
dig the dust at Stratford. Good friend for Jesus
sake forbear, was his last word to this world. They
have observed the letter of the prayer, but not, for
anyone's sake, the spirit. The last thing we saw
in Oxford was the swans in Worcester garden,
the quadrangle where De Quincey lived. I wish we
had gone into the hall where he was sconced
for appearing at dinner without a waistcoat, "from
indisposition to bestow on a tailor what I had destined for a bookseller." True spirit of Chaucer's

Clerk! Can I not see his small face at the window, pale master of the purple word. The modern lover of Oxford sometimes whispers to himself Quiller-Couch's lines—

> Know you her secret none can utter?
> Hers of the Book, the tripled Crown?
> Still on the spire the pigeons flutter;
> Still by the gateway haunts the gown;
> Still on the street from corbel and gutter
> Faces of stone look down.
>
> Faces of stone, and other faces—
> Some from library windows wan
> Forth on her gardens, her green spaces,
> Peer and turn to their books anon.
> Hence, my Muse, from the green oases
> Gather the tent, begone!

We gathered, and went. As the wench Lagonda turned toward the White Hart at Wytham for our bread-and-cheese lunch I wondered what De Quincey would have thought of her metal miracles of passion—he who was in ecstasy when the mail coach ran at thirteen miles an hour. Would he not have found in her, as he did on the box of the Manchester Mail, the Glory of Motion and the Vision of Sudden Death? Yes, and a Dream Fugue also.

We went too fast. It was hard to shoot over Swinford Bridge pausing only long enough to pay toll; the bridge where bicyclists used to sit idly swinging legs over the river. There one usually remembered the near manor of Stanton Harcourt where Pope saw the two lovers killed together by lightning in the hayfield and wrote some sprightly epitaphs for them, which were considered too so-phisticated for the village church. This afternoon a storm would have been welcome; the heat was in-credible. With coats off, Lagonda's maroon leather scorched the shoulders. The upland way we chose, bearing off from Witney through Charlbury and Chipping Norton, was a clear blaze of burning stupor. Furnace air pressed hard upon us. Lagonda yelled and threw miles beneath her.

Far away to the left were the Cotswolds he once knew: lucid Colne and Windrush, and the heights of Chedworth where some old Roman thought good times had come and settled down to be a country gentleman. Bibury in its green wimpled valley where a boy went one cold spring vacation to live for a month in the cottage of the postman and study for examinations. Such solitary pleasure as only the student knows; mornings and long evenings over books, the back warmed by a small coal fire. The prolonged annotation of Louis Blanc's *Organisation du Travail* for a special thesis on the French Republic of 1848. Oh laborious in-formation, where are you now? How can he organ-ize his own travail to give some miniature of that pleasant bumpkin time? The afternoons on bicycle, pedalling with or against the March gales on those open slopes; the cry of newborn Cotswold lambs, strange sound so few have heard. What boy-instinct took him to unmarred Bibury where life was as anciently simple as the sheep-shearing interlude of *The Winter's Tale?* It is something to have spent weeks of equinox alone with Cotswold gales. Examinations hung heavy on the horizon, the bittersweet anticipation of the last Summer Term, the anxiety of the child soon to be shoveled out to discover a living. Then, for once in life, he tasted the placid relish of unbroken application. There was only one parenthesis: to bicycle back to Oxford with the MS of a deeply-felt but pedestrian poem to be typed and submitted in time for that year's Newdigate competition. It was (very rightly) unsuccessful, but the subject set that year was "Oxford," and had to be attempted. How could a boy be happier than bicycling in from a Cotswold trout-village with the rough draft of a poem on Oxford in his pocket? Let greasy roads skidder under his wheels and the cold small rain sting his face. The almond blossoms were budding by Magdalen Bridge. There was another important reason also for this return. Inquiry into the life of Louis Blanc revealed the fact that Viscount Morley had once known him. A letter had been written in the hope of learning some personal memories of the French liberal. To which Lord Morley had very kindly replied that he would shortly be visiting All Souls (of which he was honorary fellow) and the inquirer might call and ask questions. In that frail, knowing and admirable old profile he suddenly saw what austere greatness might look like. The old man was dressing for dinner, assisted by a valet, and the boy remembers how the latter came to the door and said "His Lordship will see you now." He was profoundly impressed by the thought that age and worth might rise so high as to be attended by a personal man-servant. As for Louis Blanc, he was only a phantom excuse for a reverent glimpse of one of the great rationalists of the Victorian age.

Perhaps you have forgotten the pure dream of excellence that burns in the thoughts of youth? "Let fame that all hunt after in their lives," bursts out our Shakespeare in one of his very earliest bravuras. I would give little for the boy who is not troubled by that passion. It is only later that he may learn how shabbily it can transform into "Rumour, painted full of tongues." The student was thrilled about that time to discover the good epitaph of Lionel Johnson, a New College poet not now much remembered:

Bonarum Omnium Litterarum Peritus Aestimator Inter Poetas Wiccamicos Haud Minimus Habebitur.

427

That, he said to himself, is the kind of epitaph worth dying for. You could not possibly tear such thoughts from any boy himself, but he can admit them later if they happen to encourage others not to be afraid of their equal ingenuousness.

Many Cotswold thoughts lay on the left as Lagonda raged across the lonely Chipping Norton highland. Rollright is the name on the map, and she did. Far behind them somewhere was an old Cotswold church. I think, from the description he gave, it must have been Cirencester; or possibly Winchcombe. He remembered only a tall square tower overlooking a market place, and wide sweeps of brown country. On one of those windy March days a boy climbing the tower groped up the dark spiral stair and heard the gusts boom round the old stone shell. At the top he stood long under tall pinnacles and looked abroad, lonely and happy and uneasy. Four Roman roads ran off like a cross, to the ends of empire. Wind flapped and hummed in sudden diapasons.

He was going down the stair again, feeling his way in the black middle of the tower, when he heard voices coming up from below. Feminine voices, just such treble squeals as you would expect of two girls climbing a blind passage in freakish mood and suspecting no stranger. One voice was fulsomely flapperish, but the other had what the youths of his coterie used to call the Kathleen quality; Kathleen being a name symbolizing for them some special charm of coquetting virginity. It was a blithe voice, with the clear birdlike chirping that makes English feminine prattle irresistibly quaint to the American; it was a timbre allegro and mischievous, not (as was the other) merely silly and banal. He heard these two voices rising up the narrow twist of the stairs. If it were only *that* one, he thought; for much of life's meaning and magic can pass hastily through a boy's mind if you put him alone in the dark and let him hear, suddenly, the right kind of voice.

Undoubtedly the proper gallantry would have been to retreat on tiptoe to the top of the tower, and let them discover him there, then modestly remove without frightening them. On the other hand it would be excellent mischief to groan reverberantly and start a ghost legend; but in that case they would scream and retreat. He waited in the complete darkness until their ascending chatter was quite near and offered a pause. He spoke as gently and Englishly as possible. "So sorry! 'squite all right. I'm just coming down. Beastly dark. Rather a stumor. Frightfully jolly old place," or whatever the current jargon was.

Outcry of frightened amazement; screeches from voice number 1 in hysteric falsetto; but in voice number 2 a sense of venturesome comedy prevailed. Her accent really was delicious. *Aiow,* the

429

other one kept exclaiming (who can put into pho-
netic a certain English way of saying "Oh"?) but
number 2 insisted "Don't be silly. I want to see
the view."

"Keep over to your right," he said. (The stair
was very narrow.) They came along, groping the
outer curve. Number 1 sounded uppermost, evidently being prodded from behind. They were
laughing now, a bit anxiously. Voice number 1
bumped past with a provocative screech. "Go
ahead, you're all right," he said, urging her on.
Perhaps Voice number 2 would pause a moment.

She was on the same step. He could feel her
brush delicately close. He put out a hand and
touched her elbow. It was a nice elbow in rough
tweed; there was a faint mingled breath of tweed
and hair. Blood pushes fast at such a moment.
How pleasant to invent a little fable; mystic communication impulsive in the darkness; an arm
about her soft body; lips joining; a few tremulous
words, available in memory for pretty allegory,
Alas that truth must be so humble. "Careful,
don't slip." "Thanks, very decent of you."

A lovely voice. Of course he might have lit a
match—but he didn't *want* to see her.

"Cheerio!" They went on into the darkness. The
damp old stones smelled of death. He trembled
as he felt his way down. It was difficult, when he
stood in the churchyard, not to look up at the

high turret, swimming against dizzy blue, but he didn't. He got on his bicycle and rode back to the Republic of 1848. He wondered that evening if the gallant Lamartine would have been so bashful. There seemed to be no consolation at all in the incident. It was—what is the legal tag—"irrelevant, incompetent, immaterial." Perhaps that was why he had completely forgotten it until Lagonda showed him those far slopes of Cotswold over his left shoulder. Goodbye and good luck.

47

STRATFORD's bathing place on the Avon was crowded that afternoon. The meadow was parked with bicycles and Baby Austins; the river plentiful with banana skins and orange peel; the launch *George Washington* churned up and down with merry tourists; the muddy shore of the stream was trodden to a treacle; the dressing kennels stank. Just so the banks of the great river of Shakespeare have been trampled into mire by the hooves of commentators. It was a thoroughly human sight, but not alluring, and we fled away to Warwick for dinner. A brilliant cottage garden by the roadside at Longridge did much to cheer us, and we stopped to chat with the ancient who was placidly editing his flowers. Even in Warwick disappointment

waited, for the gay Miss Absolom of the Old Bowling Green Inn turned down our application for dinner. They were only serving meals for guests
sleeping in the house, she explained. Mistletoe
pleaded that he had stayed there (with Mifflin Mc-
Gill) in 1911, but the old guest books had not been
kept so he could not prove it. However Miss
Absolom relented far enough to accept a gin-and-
ginger, which we drank by the bowling green, and
then at her advice went on to the Crown for meat.
Coming back to Stratford in the cooler evening the
moon was lifting over curious level sheets of mist.
Sturdy artisans of Stratford were just being put
out of the pub opposite the Birthplace; it was
"Time, gentlemen, time." They showed a refreshing skepticism, when asked, as to whether that
was where Shakespeare was born. The pilgrims,
in a mood of irony, saw the closing shadows of a
movie, and studied the George W. Childs fountain
in the dark.

It needs a strong idealizing stomach not to be
dismayed by Stratford in the tourists' rutting
season. The Shakespeare Hotel ("American
Bar"), the little china busts, the Hathaway Tea
Rooms ("Genuine antiques for sale"), the Hathaway Farm at Shottery ("Mixed Holiday Camp,
Army Tents, Town Water, Gas and Sanitation,
Paved Dancing Area, Exclusive Postcards"),
the commutation tickets admitting to all the

association-places at reduced rate, all these seem to take one very far away from that urbane evasive ghost. Even the *Shakespeare Pictorial,* a lively monthly of advertisement, feels the prick of comedy; it observes of itself "This publication is used in the studies of the English classes at the University of Denver. It is a steadying fact." The enthusiastic Garrick, when he wrote (in 1769) his "Ode upon Dedicating a Building, and Erecting a Statue, to Shakespeare, at Stratford upon Avon," hardly knew what he was starting. That was the festival which Boswell (always alert for any kind of hullabaloo) greatly enjoyed, and reproached Dr. Johnson for staying away. Boswell records the "whimsical haberdasher" of Stratford who improved the occasion by selling "Shakespearean ribbands" in bright colors; this was the first of the long line of Stratford tradesmen who have prospered on Prospero. Outside the graveyard the big motor charabancs are lined up. A clear American voice just emerging from the church pleased us with the freakish irrelevance of chance overhearing. "I like her feet, they're so nice and small," he was saying. Perhaps they seemed especially small in comparison with the footprints the visitors had been investigating.

But in the church itself one lays away cheap and easy satirics. There on a bright morning the chancel paving is splashed blue and pink from the colored windows. It was still early and for a while we were alone. I am sorry if you do not in that place feel frost on the spine. There you need not fret over collation of minutiæ. You remember only the great dreamer who, as every artist must, fought for us each; who in his hour carried on undefended heart the burden of all earth. There, if anywhere we can judge of, words became flesh and walked among us. You have to go to Stratford to feel that special twinge, and only the thin-blooded snob will be frightened away by the banana skins and the little china effigies. On the grave was a bundle of heather "from the Shakespeare Club of Leonia, N. J." and a bunch of purple asters with a little paper slip. The stone is inside the chancel rail and has to be read upside-down; we were alone so we stepped softly over the barrier and stood beside the slab itself to verify the inscription. On the paper with the asters was written in strongly Teuton characters "*From a German Shakespeare admirer.*" It seemed to me so important a scrap of paper that I took it with me. If I leave it here, I said to myself, it will presently be cleared away by the sexton. If I take it, I can use it as a permanent memorandum that books are stronger than bayonets.

Perhaps I shall never see Stratford again. I shall think of it in the colors of that forenoon of hypnotic heat, remembering the bench in the churchyard overlooking the river, the trimly revised garden of New Place grilling in the glow, Cass Gilbert's sundial (keeping excellent time) and the rich juice of the mulberries which so prettily symbolize those luscious purple-oozing plays. But I think of Stratford also, as one must, in connection with *The Tempest* into which men have always read allusion to the poet's retirement. Shakespeare himself is the last person I should dream of asking what he meant by that sad and tender fantasy. What we read into it is what makes it important for us, and to the artist it has always offered innumerable suggestions. Probably it came from something deeper than the author's conscious intent, and as D. H. Lawrence magnificently said (in his half-crazed and half-intuitive *Studies in American Literature*) "the proper function of a critic is to save the tale from the artist who created it." We collaborate with Shakespeare in giving *The Tempest* whatever meaning we most need; we save it from being just a masque of "quaint device" for Court amusement, or a footnote on the Virginian voyages. Superb fantasy! as clear as Lake George water; as refreshing as the pool of Siloam.

The island is the solitude of the mind, and Prospero represents Thought, Imaginative Creation of any sort. I like to think of him as a scientist of the Einstein, Jeans or Eddington type; indeed his affection for his mantel reminds me very much of Einstein clinging to the old raincoat which the newspapers have often mentioned. All great scientists instinctively are Shakespeare's kin; Jeans in his noble essay on Cosmogony telling us that the universe "melts away into radiation" is precisely in the Prospero mood. Ariel typifies the magic skill of Art, the stenographer of Thought. Miranda, obviously, symbolizes those tender human ties and weaknesses that prevent the artist from being mere disembodied pensiveness. Caliban, the strong animal impulses—sloth, greed, lust, farce—that the artist must transpose and modulate. The shipload of castaways—who have already annoyed us by their fool behavior during the storm, and become intolerable in their tedious prating once they get on the island—are evidently the necessary but always incomprehending Outside World. Mixed of worthy old counsellors, usurping dukes, treacherous plotters, young lovers, drunken clowns, honest seamen, they offer a fair cross-section of the Audience, the Public.

With these elements and with his Tinker Bell, Ariel, "flaming amazement all over the ship, in every cabin" (have the analogies between *The Tempest* and *Peter Pan* ever occurred to you?) Shakespeare had all that was necessary to portray for us the full cycle of the life of imagination. We begin to perceive that the storm which opens the play was not just a West Indies hurricane. It was a symbolic tempest; a brain-storm if you will. Shakespeare had been through one semi-circle of the hurricane; he was forty-six, his great creative period was over (his mind had accelerated faster than most men's). At the vortex of a hurricane is an area of calm; this he had reached. He was still willing, if necessary, to give the rabble "some vanity of mine art, they expect it from me," but like Professor Jeans's universe he was melting into radiation and knew it. He was abjuring his rough magic, drowning his book, not without bitterness. He was going back to be a Stratford citizen, arguing about the good tangibles of tithes and highway repairs and enclosures. No artist can live forever on the lonely island of his art.

Ariel's taunt to the intruders, "Your swords are now too massy for your strengths," can well be taken, if you wish, as a comment on machine civilization which is overpowered by its own engines, and where our wild play with Nature's forces is our greatest peril. And surely when Prospero says the famous lines

> These our actors,
> As I foretold you, were all spirits and
> Are melted into air, into thin air. . . .
> This insubstantial pageant. . . . We are such stuff
> As dreams are made on, and our little life
> Is rounded with a sleep,

437

he is in the very accent of the intuitive mathematicians who have dissolved all our old rule-of-thumb universe by the transition from Euclidean to non-Euclidean geometry. Even his fits of peevishness are what we might well expect from a philosopher who has spent twelve years in close brooding. But he has taught Miranda chess, which (provided she does not play too much better than Ferdinand) will be a great assistance to the happiness of their marriage. The after-life of Ferdinand and Miranda is an irresistible theme to speculate. Mistletoe touched upon it once in some verses—

> Shall we be happy, King and Queen in Naples?
> This sole sea-rounded life is all I know,
> I fear the buzz and burthen of that world. . . .

but who will do me the larger epilogue I fancy? Prospero would be an indulgent grandfather, pampering the children with stories of Caliban and occasional conjuring tricks. Would Miranda, who had known nothing of women, find the ladies of the court easy to get on with? I think she sometimes sighs for the Bermoothes.

There must have been very human ironies in Shakespeare's last years. He had hardly settled down in Stratford before the town council passed a minute denouncing the drama. "Every third thought shall be my grave," was the magician's retiring resolution, but that still left two-thirds of his thinking for the famous real estate transactions—he who had in fee simple the greatest unreal estate ever created. It is always odd to think of Shakespeare's son-in-law (a Balliol man, Mr. Fripp tells us) as a Puritan church-warden, devilling parishioners for dozing during sermon or drinking after evening prayer. We would not have these legends otherwise. The greater the personality the wider the ripples of paradox it creates around it.

In the fable, Caliban and the powers of mischief are rather easily outwitted. Prospero forgives them all. What else is there to do? It is forgiving one's self that is hard. The epilogue is humble enough. It has been a tough life, my masters. A man does not know the things he has told us without having trodden some queer byways. But he came alive to land. There is an almost unnoticeable character in *The Tempest*, Francisco, who has only one real speech. What he says, speaking of a brave swimmer against troubles, is good parable:

I saw him beat the surges under him,
And ride upon their backs: he trod the water,
Whose enmity he flung aside, and breasted
The surge most swoln that met him: his bold head

439

'Bove the contentious waves he kept, and oar'd
Himself with his good arms in lusty stroke
To the shore, that o'er his wave-worn basis bow'd
As stooping to relieve him. I not doubt
He came alive to land.

It seems, though it is not certain, that he died on his birthday. It would have been like him to do so, thus coming full circle: the roundest circle of human power and paradox that we have known. We have learned that even after a wine has been barrelled it is still en rapport with the vineyard. When next year's flowering comes on the vines, the liquid in the cask stirs and fumes and scintillates in its darkness by some chemical heredity. Those plays and poems have been long in the wood, but they are still sympathetic to their native soil, the old stony vineyard of human yearning. When pure sun or ragged rain beat upon that hillside, the words tremble in their paper storage. How beautifully Virginia Woolf said of him, "thought plunged into a sea of words and came up dripping."

For our own need we borrowed him away from scholars and libraries for a little while, thinking to bring him back to tavern and greenroom where he was most at home. It is time to return him. Much has been said and surmised, little of it that he would recognize. But he would have identified the feeling behind a little casual song written not

440

long after his own time but never printed until
lately:

> So have I seen a silver swan,
>   As in a watery looking-glass,
> Viewing her whiter form, and then
>   Courting herself with lovely grace:
> As now she doth herself herself admire
> Being at once the fuel and the fire.

"At once the fuel and the fire." Is there any better
history of the mind?

48

IT WAS a wet night when Mistletoe said goodbye; it
was hard to let him go. I had known the worst of
him, yet there was something there that might
have been worth encouraging. It was raining
heavily, so I did not long hear the going footsteps.
I am glad it was raining, cold steady downpour,
sweet to taste. It washes a Long Island dogwood
tree, it washes the stone walls of Stratford church.
It would soon sodden to pulp the pages of all these
books. Wash out cheap ink and glue and leave
bare feeling. I never knew about rain until that
night. I saw the blowing storms of the world sweep
into the dusty rooms of literature, whirling aside
our little notes and memoranda, stripping us down
to laughter, pity, and need.

441

Perhaps Mistletoe was reproachful, that last evening we spent together, because there is so much I have not mentioned. Once I came by chance on a 17-cent stamp and found it was a beautiful little engraving, in wistful black and gray, of Woodrow Wilson. I wondered what odd quirk of partisanship had tried to bury Wilson in so little-called-for a denomination. The tragic errors of temperament were plain enough, but who could question the lonely honor of the man. I can see him still as he sat in the house on S Street, one arm paralyzed, the other nervously plucking a handkerchief from his pocket. (It was strange that the man one associates with the end of the War, like that other at the beginning of it, lost the life of one arm.) I can see the almost youthful pinkness of the face, the clear solemn eyes enlarged by glasses, the unbelieved reality of his kindness in welcoming a young stranger who sitting in that room with him felt stir and turn about them all the horror of principalities and powers. I remember the detached bitterness of Wilson's words about the Peace. He spoke grimly, but it was from far away. It was finished. What is so bitter as the disillusionment of a sentimentalist?

The Post Office tried to hide Woodrow Wilson on an obscure 17-cent stamp; likewise, Mistletoe may think, I have said nothing of so many things that meant most. As he went away the straight

rain, sparkling in the street lights, swept and
scoured the night. Just such solid rains in old
nights on Iffley Road, over Magdalen Bridge, bells
rolling in the dark. Queer flashes of memory must
have come over him. Dinner in the Printkeeper's
official residence at the British Museum—"The
Monument" R. L. S. had called it—when Sir
Sidney and Lady Colvin still lived there and that
gracious host and great gentleman told actual
anecdote of those who had been only hearsay
names: Ruskin, Browning, Trelawny, Meredith,
Stevenson, Hardy. As the wine was poured the boy
remembered it was at that very table that the
prudent Colvin warned the butler not to refill
Stephen Phillips's glass too regularly. Colvin was
always, as Stevenson used to say humorously,
somewhat the Stern Parent. There were conscientious austerities, but the generosity and wisdom
were just. Courier extraordinary between Bohemia and Pallas Athene. . . .

Going, in youthful simplicity, all the way down
to the old *Sun* office on Park Row to ask for payment for a poem that paper had published; and
learning that checks for such trivials were not
made out until the end of the week; but the subway had taken his last nickel; he had to walk all
the way back from the City Hall to 32nd Street.
Naiver still, visiting the *Puck* office to try to sell
a poem for cash down. Yes, comic. . . .

443

Driving the old Dodge car, Dame Quickly, in from Long Island: the first time one ever drove down Fifth Avenue in one's own car. Most would think nothing of it, but to him it was a Moment. Reading a Phi Beta Kappa poem at Harvard, for which he had to buy a cutaway coat and march in solemn top-hatted procession, while overseers and elders looked at him just as dubiously as the Barnum and Bailey elephant when he played amateur clown in the circus. They knew by instinct he wasn't pukka Harvard. But he stayed with Professor George Herbert Palmer in the Yard, sat with the dear old man in his book-lined study a hot June night while the philosopher read poetry aloud —he can still hear his kind voice in William Watson's lines:

> Strange the world about me lies,
>   Never yet familiar grown;
> Still disturbs me with surprise,
>   Haunts me like a face half known. . . .

The rose garden of an old house in the Cotswolds where, as a group of people sat sunning, a carrier pigeon with a ring on its leg came teetering among the domestic doves. It was plainly ill at ease, had somehow lost its way or failed of its errand. Its chance host, the great journalist Montague, stood patiently on the gravel trying to coax it to him. His fine white head, his austere weathered face, bent toward the anxious bird which wanted to approach yet watched him uncertainly. Carrier pigeons both, the watcher thought; birds of envoy, commissioned with urgent messages, a talent which is death to hide. . . .

When the children were very young, the intensity of silence in the nursery upstairs while a parent was pretending to telephone to Santa Claus; a creative studying silence that flowed down the steep little stair and sharpened the dull ear. Now they are gone, almost lost already in their own beginning lives, their own assurances. (Must we lose *everything?* he thought to himself.) He sees them, appearing and vanishing among the edges of a thick forest, the brambly forest that youth pushes through before it reaches the open upland—where sometimes it finds Santa Claus again, so strangely altered.

Ironies absolute, but in that purge of rainfall not unbearable. (Perhaps it is the feel of wetness on the face that makes rain so full of humble meaning.) He went once to see a man he loved, one who had carried seas and symbols in his mind, a man who had also moved a whole world with one aching arm. To him that man was reverence. (If you don't worship men, what dare you worship? It is silly to think you can't recognize occasional error in your worshipfuls. Even the wine of the Communion Table is not notable for vintage.) He tried

to tell the old Ulysses, as youth may without of-
fence, that many of whose existence the great
novelist might never dream were glad to know him
on our own soil. The old man said simply, "It helps
me to hear that. It gives me something to stand
on. I seemed to be losing touch with reality."
Mistletoe, for I think the only time in his life, had
taken with him a book he hoped there might be a
chance to get autographed. He is not a collector,
a distributor rather (though he did once hire
a room for the sole purpose of collecting his
thoughts). But this one time he wanted, if it became decently possible, to ask for a signature.
Even then, in the moment of felicity, the radiant
wing of irony brooded over its nursling. He was
clearing his throat to venture the request when
Ulysses began rummaging in a desk. He said to
Mistletoe: "I know this is the sort of thing we
don't do, but —— is very fond of this little book
and made me promise to ask you to sign it for her.
Would you, as a special favor?" With gravity it
was done; so infinitely unimportant a little book;
and of course it was then and forever impossible to
ask for the signature himself coveted. It would
have seemed like suggesting an exchange. There
is good theology in the tiny episode, otherwise it
could not be mentioned. We may have imagined
that if we met God we would ask Him for favors,
but sometimes it is God who is asking them of us.

A night in the theatre. One of the best loved members of the stock company had been taken ill at a rehearsal late that afternoon. No one supposed it serious, but Dennis was obviously too ill to go on. He was taken home, and Mistletoe, who happened to be fairly familiar with that script, volunteered to play the part that evening. Using his friend's clothes and make-up box, in the warm bright squalor of that shabby little dressing room, news came to him privately just before the curtain went up. His friend was dead. No one else was told until later. It was a heavy comedy part, and the obvious clumsiness of the tyro's attempts were good mirth for the company. "Won't Dennis have a good laugh about this" was the burden of their chaffing comment. None but the substitute himself knew that Dennis, who had played that rôle so beautifully with the shadow hanging over him, had taken his last call.

The rain was slanting now; a wind was getting up, rocking the woodland. He remembered the lift and shudder of *Mauretania*'s bow where three college boys, deep down in unsavory steerage, lay on straw mattresses. They were on their way to spend Christmas vacation at home, Christmas 1912. It is always easy to discern an epoch from behind, but there *was* something about that year 1912. Mistletoe liked to imagine that by the chance of that rough voyage and some copies of his own little

447

pamphlet hidden in a steamer trunk he had his minute movement in it. The Best Sellers of that autumn seem of another world altogether. Gene Stratton-Porter, Harold Bell Wright, F. Hopkinson Smith—but queer things were happening offstage. Vachel Lindsay had been peddling Rhymes To Be Traded for Bread. Don Marquis had just begun his Sun Dial column. Henry Mencken was writing a column in the Baltimore *Sun* and those gorgeous reviews in the *Smart Set*. Carl Sandburg was secretary to the Mayor of Milwaukee. John Kerfoot's crisp reviews in *Life* were those most highly esteemed by publishers. McFee came by freight-steamer to Wilmington, N. C., sitting in the saloon all the way over working on his endless MS of *Casuals*. Robert Frost had just sold his farm and gone to live in England. Noyes and Masefield were the reigning importations. The big bookstores were still Down Town. Lots of things seemed still Down Town, but a few zealots were moving out into less frequented suburbs of the mind. Reviewers were getting advance copies of *The Crock of Gold*. And on Christmas Eve 1912 Eugene O'Neill entered a sanitarium in Connecticut and "really thought about things for the first time."

Already how delightfully antique and arcadian all that seems. It always enchanted him to think how much a matter of fashion passing tastes of

literature are, and how hot and unbuttoned the
people get who are always trying to catch up.
How far far ahead Thoreau and Emily Dickinson
got, just by loitering in a pinewood or an Amherst
garden. There was the fable of the Small Hairy
Dog—

There was a small hairy dog that suffered
greatly from heat. So much so that for his comfort
his curators often put a small electric fan on the
floor. This was highly relished by the small hairy
dog, who sat as close to it as possible, turning himself leisurely this way and that to cool. He sat so
close to the whirr, however, that when his custo-
dians left the room they always turned off the
current, for fear he might damage himself.

One very warm afternoon they left the dog indoors while they went abroad on some errands.
The fan was on the floor as usual, but not running.
While they were absent came one of those magically sudden changes of temperature that New York
sometimes enjoys in summer. The wind shifted
to the north, heavy torrid air blew away, a cool
breeze came rippling in over window-sills, sweeping through the apartment. When they returned,
the small hairy dog was sitting alongside the mo-
tionless fan, grinning and turning himself to and
fro to enjoy the draught.

From time to time new winds will blow, but
there will always be some people very like the

small hairy dog. They will believe the fan is doing it.

A boy once stayed in Devonshire in spring, when daisies almost as small as asterisks star the turf. He was on the top floor of the house, and setting out for the morning bath saw he was just too late. Looking down the stairs he saw a ripple of blue robe pass round the corner and a gleam of white ankle. All hope, all dream, all reality, were in that instant flash of April girlhood that turned the shadowy corner. When he went to the bath a little later, on the cork mat was the perfect print of one small damp foot. He kissed the innocent vestige. Perhaps it was like him, perhaps it was like us all—kissing the footprint where life had been, missing life itself.

INDEX

Spectator ~ Addison

The Spring Eater

Evening ?

Marius the

Epicurean / look J. Butterine

a modern book J Butterine